The Culture of Astronomy:

Origin of Number, Geometry, Science, Law, and Religion

THE CULTURE OF ASTRONOMY:

Origin of Number, Geometry, Science, Law, and Religion

THOMAS KARL DIETRICH

Bascom Hill Publishing Group
Minneapolis, MN

Bascom Hill Publishing Group
212 3rd Avenue North, Suite 290
Minneapolis, MN 55401
612.455.2293
www.bascomhillbooks.com

ISBN-13: 978-1-935098-75-1
LCCN: 2011904955

Distributed by Itasca Books

Cover Design by Alan Pranke
Typeset by Sophie Chi

Printed in the United States of America

Dedicated to my wife,
The Guiding Star in my life,
Nuala Mary Dietrich *née* O'Shea

CONTENTS

Part 4. ***Numbers of the Universe and of Man***

Part 5. ***Handbook of Cosmology***

Part 6. ***Concord of Cosmic Myth***

Part 7. ***Mexica-Maya-Andean Culture and Astronomy***

Part 8. ***The Antiquity of the Americas***

INTRODUCTION

The study of ancient astronomy illuminates the spectrum of all human interests and activities. Ancient astronomy stands at the root of the Tree of Knowledge. It is the origin of culture, science, geometry, government, history, law, and religion. It is the premier subject coming even before philosophy as the first institution of culture itself.

Since the stars and the heavenly bodies were the instruments of the first creation, it is logical that the study of their movements and measure should reveal the science behind all things. These are the views of many ancient cultures that have declared that they were taught all knowledge by the angels and the heavens above. There is truth in the observation that numbers and geometry were revealed by observing the sun, moon, planets, and stars. These celestials demonstrated remarkable patterns and synchronic relationships, which inspired human investigation and the inception of all the sciences.

The countless parts of the universe exhibit an unexpected harmony and oneness—a true cosmic interrelationship of all things. Our perception of this great unity inspires our notions of moral balance, law, and religion. Cosmic physics weaves and binds everything together and demonstrates a cosmic worldview to intelligent humans. This worldview not only considers the natural laws in operation upon our Earth but looks at the cosmic laws (the source of natural laws) that have enabled the miracle of life to take place. For, there is nothing alien in the cosmos. Everything is a seed of the universe, a generative particle and supportive member of the whole.

The vast interrelationships of the cosmic world form the foundations of the mechanics, pathways, and formulas that underlie our thoughts. Astronomical knowledge is the first step of human cogitation, from which all logic, reason, and philosophy are born. It stands as the foundation of who we are, how we think, and why we believe what we think is true.

Through the example of the movements, synchronisms, and physics of the heavenly bodies, we have learned to think cosmologically because we truly exist in a cosmic setting. Everything in heaven is related, and everything in the cosmos is harmoniously balanced. When one planet exhibits more eccentricity, the other planets adjust and compensate. Everything in the heavens is bound together—everything affects everything—nothing is independent. These are the laws of cosmic physics, which apply not only in the heavens but upon the Earth. If everything is interrelated in unity, then selfish actions do not just harm another person; they harm the entire system and revert back to the perpetrator. Thus cosmic physics mandates laws, ethics, morals, and finally religion. Vedic karma and Egyptian ideals of *Maat* (divine balance and justice) express these notions of cosmic order.

Astronomy has taught us that the mighty tides of the ocean are moved by the gravitational pull of the sun and the moon and occasionally influenced by the planets. Understanding these phenomena was the beginning of the science of the seasons and weather prediction, which lead directly to the advancement of fishing, tide-pool management, productive agriculture, safe navigation, and trade. Carlos Milla Villena, in *Genesis de La Cultura Andina* (p. 135), says that the study of the cycles of weather and the seasons helps mankind to achieve the optimal production of natural resources in agriculture. This optimization allows others to develop science. As Plato writes, a city cannot rise to the contemplation of philosophy and science until the basic human needs of comfortable shelter and abundance of food are achieved. Advancement and progress of agriculture, fishing, navigation, and trade are a direct corollary to the advancement of cities and society.

The planets teach us about geometry—the triangle, the pentagram, and hexagram. They introduce measurement, numbers, cycles, angles, degrees, time, and refined calendrics. These are the fundamental tools that foster and guide all the sciences. The constellations and star images of the zodiac have been used to record natural history and geological events on the indelible archives of the heavens. The cycles of the Precession of the Vernal Equinoxes, as well as the cycle of the Milky Way, have been used to record natural disasters and above all the great cycles of world creation and destruction.

Archaeological sites like Bru na Boinne (Newgrange) in Ireland mark the sunrise on the day of the winter solstice. This is the shortest day of the year and the death of the sun's light. Some people place a primitive interpretation upon this most important of all festivals. Ancient people regarded the cycle of life as birth-maturity-degeneration-death followed by resurrection and birth once again. For ancient people, the moment of the winter solstice sunrise represented a flashpoint of energy and spirit reentering the material world to ignite the new fire of life once again. Even though nature continually follows a course of cycles, astronomy demonstrates assurance to humankind that resurrection and rebirth will follow death as a unique and miraculous event. Spirit and energy are conserved. Human faith in resurrection is founded upon the cycles of cosmic physics.

In *Genesis de La Cultura Andina* (p. 259), Carlos Milla Villena, says that astronomy is the common language of mankind. From his words, we might amplify to say that this common vehicle creates a universal understanding and culture recognized among people across all ethnic boundaries. Astronomy binds the world together through common thoughts, interests, formulas, numbers, and perceptions.

Galileo wrote, "Philosophy is written in this grand book, the universe… It is written in the language of mathematics, and its characters are triangles, circles, and other geometric figures." The cosmologies from many nations around the world, their calendrics, and cosmic cycles exhibit a unity of experience and common science.

The great common tenet is that the universe dispenses energy and spirit to the galaxy, which transfers it to the solar system and finally to Earth, where a miraculous union of energy and matter creates the human, a dual-natured creature of spirit and matter. This duality creates the drama of life. Evan Hadingham records (p. 247) that the Chinese Emperor's rule was divinely sanctioned by a blending of earthly and cosmic forces: "The king has heaven as his father and earth as his mother..."

Astronomy was the first system of thought that brought order into the confusion of the cosmos. This system made people's lives safer, more prosperous, and more enjoyable. Astronomers expressed the construction of the universe in their holy mandala, showing the structure and placement of demigods, humans, and the earth. In this scheme, the structure of government was often modeled upon the hierarchal structure of the cosmos in the arrangement of their government through kings, supported by their ministers and councils. The Council of Astrologers in China had its chief and 28 members in emulation of the 28 houses of the moon. The Council of Scientists, *Los Camasca Amauta Runa*, in Peru had a membership of 108 governors (derived from the sacred cosmic fractal, 108 + 108 = 216). The time management of labor crews, meetings, councils, and courts were all arranged through astronomy and calendrics.

Susan Milbrath (p. 11) says that all ancient civilizations believed their stars were gods, and their rulers derived power from their connection with the cosmos in life and in the afterlife. Ancient kings—born under certain auspices of the sun, moon, planets, and calendar cycles—used heavenly aspects to confirm their ascension to power. Astronomy and astrology became the foundation and fabric of social organization and the justification for leadership and political power. Hadingham says (p. 247) that Maya astronomy also served as an instrument of social control, a force of immense power and conservatism.

Divine right is not a game that kings will always win. Political astrology presented a dark and pragmatic side of astronomy where scientific knowledge was used to control people and dominate society. The ability to predict events through the knowledge of the measure and movements of the planets and cosmos was a powerful advantage over the uninitiated. This advantage elevated the rulers to the status of demigods as the Masters of Time and the Universe. When the forecasts of his astrologers proved to be correct, the destiny of a king was properly sanctioned and assured. But sacred science used as magic had immediate repercussions—and when predictions failed, then royal families were quickly overturned and replaced. Because of the perfect nature of the science of astronomy, deceptions, falsehoods, and erroneous prophesies were quickly revealed, and the balance of cosmic forces was restored.

Astronomy has also been used as a kabbalah and a mystery of holy numbers and sacred geometry. Why is the creation of Adam only 6,000 years ago? What is the meaning of 666 as the "mark of the beast"? Is the end of the world coming at the conclusion of the Maya Long Count cycle every 5,200 years? And why are only 144,000 souls to be saved at the final judgment according to the Bible? These numbers have always been shrouded in mystery and even associated with evil and the devil to ensure that people preserved these numbers in their holy books and records. Holy numbers, such as 13, 20, 40, 108, 216, and 666, are not to be mystified and feared. They are simple and important primary numbers of astronomy.

History, myth, and natural disasters are written upon the constellations of heaven. Here is a kaleidoscope of reality, an image of the tremendous drama of demigods and epochal ages. The constellations themselves are images of mythological figures. These are the formal background of an extraordinarily developed science. How can anyone say that myth has nothing to do with astronomy?

The heavens have been used by humankind as a giant book upon which to record history and natural events. Myth and history were imprinted upon the zodiac images, constellations, and cycles of heaven, where they were accurately preserved and recorded in a chronological context. The cycle of the Milky Way preserved records of the universal history of our planet. The traditions of the Greek Generations of the Gods and the Legend of the Five Suns are based upon astronomical cycles. These records are still preserved in the sky, while papyrus, tapestry, clay, and stone have vanished. Take a look at the mythological beings that are circling above us in the night sky. These are not phantasmagorical creatures but explicit beings from history and the great dramas of past ages.

The first astronomers were patriarchs, sages, and founders of their culture. Adam, the first man, was an astronomer. The patriarch Abraham of the city of Ur in Chaldea was a cosmologer. The primeval gods of the Egyptians—Hephaestus, Thoth, and Agathodaemon—were all astronomers who predicted the world flood and fire. Atlas, the patriarch of culture along the Atlantic coastlands of Fez-Morocco, was one of the most notable astronomers of all time. On the American continents flourished Quetzalcoatl, Kukulkan, Gukumatz, and Viracocha, founders of culture and astronomy and builders of pyramids and astronomical hierophany associated with the solstices, equinoxes, and the cycles of the planets. Even Thales (c.585 BC), first of the Greek philosophers, was an astronomer who predicted eclipses and marked the solstices and equinoxes (Diogenes Laertius, I.22).

All the profound tenets and fundamental notions are borrowed from cosmic physics. Astronomy is the elusive "Cup of the Holy Grail," under whose spherical vault the mysteries are revealed. The traditions of the Bible and Greek, Vedic, and Maya myth are all derived from astronomy and the cycles of heaven. The heavenly Grail Cup instructs us in the meaning of number, geometry, angles, measurement, and time. The most elusive and complex mysteries are all simple astronomy. The secret societies, the ancient temples of mystery and arcane knowledge, Brotherhood of the Knights of the Temple of Solomon, the Freemasons, and many of the world's great philosophies derive their knowledge and inspiration from astronomy and cosmology.

The Mexica-Maya-Andean culture perfected astrology in its quest to develop a better society created in conformity with the cosmic order of the heavens. Astrology was employed worldwide to confirm leaders and justify the rulership of certain families. Shamanism was used to establish a connection with the cosmic powers of the earth, the ancestors and past history of our planet. Astrology and shamanism are truly an important part of archaeoastronomy because they are based upon cosmic principles and therefore contain vital fragments of the first cosmology ever developed.

Astronomy permitted history, science, culture, and religion to flourish because it demonstrated a pattern, a design, and model in the heavens for humans to perceive and copy—a structure for the ultimate organization of all knowledge. The cosmological worldview of the ancient people supports the image of the universe as a place of comfort and fulfillment. What a cozy and wonderful world to live in where the night sky did not forebode gloom and darkness but rather shone forth the mighty presence of the Creator and his work. Carlos Milla agrees when he writes (p. 17), "Cosmic laws regulate the heavenly bodies and present a structure for our rituals, creating a science and a religion as one indivisible unity." Cosmology supports the traditions of all religions. Hebrew, Moslem, Christian, Buddhist, and others will appreciate discovering some of the cosmic roots of their special faith and beliefs that should strengthen and solidify their understanding.

The study of astronomy brought forth the cosmological worldview, which has permitted humans to make unimaginable advances around the globe. Every significant culture and civilization upon this planet was born out of the cradle of astronomy. And though this worldview was developed in the most ancient of times, it will never vanish, just as the stars will never cease to shine.

This book is a comprehensive overview of culture that was created by the observation of astronomy, the first of all the sciences. The focus of this perspective is as unusual as it is revealing. It is not just meant for students, professors, philosophers, and seniors. It is meant to open up a new world to people who have worked hard during their lives and did not have the opportunity to examine life through the medium of culture.

This work presents a wealth of powerful and important data from leading authorities around the world. Parenthetical information includes the dates of ancient and modern authors, relevant dates in history, the mathematics supporting the numbers and chronology, and clarifications by the author. In the interests of preserving clarity within an uninterrupted flow of information, this work will cite the page reference as close as possible to the author's name so that the reader does not need to stop and reread the paragraphs to check upon who said what.

—Thomas Karl Dietrich, January 2011, San Bruno, California

PART 1

A CONFLICT OF UNDERSTANDING BETWEEN THE ANCIENT AND MODERN WORLDS

This part concerns the dysfunctional transmission of the ancient worldview into modern times. Why do we not understand what these ancient people are telling us? What factors on their side, and on our side, lead to an uneasy and fractured communication of information?

CHAPTER 1

The Hereford Map

The Hereford map locates Jerusalem in the center of its hemisphere precisely between Europe, Asia, and Africa. One would immediately suppose that the reason for this special placement was to develop a Christian worldview. This is certainly true; but there are also some other reasons from history and astronomy that justify this placement.

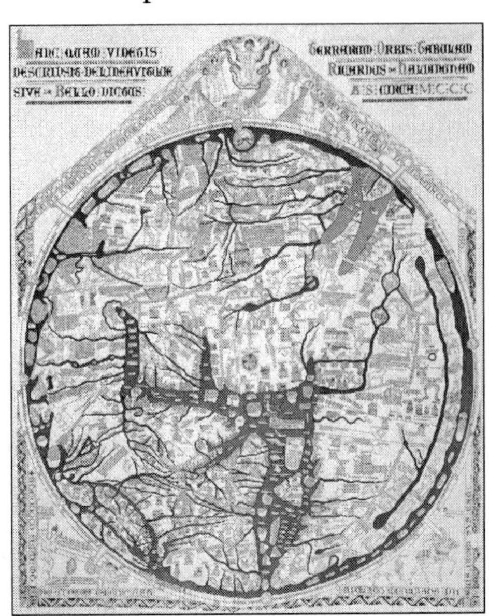

The Hereford map with Jerusalem in the exact center, the Island of the Garden of Eden at the top and the Straits of Gibraltar at the bottom, with Africa to the right, Europe to the left, and Asia at the top. Europeans were shocked at the discovery of the American continents which revealed another total hemisphere at the other side of the globe. Courtesy: Bing free images:nerissaafonso.com

Although the Hereford map appears to be the work of novices, its childish appearance belies many of its scientific and historical accuracies. For instance, it represents a nearly exact hemisphere of the globe with Jerusalem as the pole of a scientifically accurate *equidistant projection* of one-half of the world.

A.E. Nordenskiold in his *Facsimile Atlas, the Early History of Cartography* (1889) had already shown antique maps of Antarctica without ice, and the truly exceptional Dulcert Portolano which contained an accurate projection of the Mediterranean regions. Following Nordenskiold, Charles Hapgood produced the most influential book of the 20th century, *Maps of the Ancient Sea Kings*, concerning the preexistence of a highly advanced science and cartography that had flourished in extreme antiquity.

The Hereford map appears to be a remnant of ancient science based upon scientific projection techniques and longitude encompassing half a globe. The Middle-Ages in Europe and England produced a number of these gigantic wall maps, which were obviously a teaching tool covering a variety of disciplines from geography, religion, history, Biblical studies, Greek, as well as other ancient myths and legends. The magnificent scale of these charts made them easily recognized and absorbed by young scholars who were assembled in large halls and churches where the maps were prominently displayed. One might say that these monster maps presented a complete cosmological worldview encompassing God, nature, and man.

Triangulation of the Globe

Ancient cosmologers divided the globe into a hexagram containing points of divine incarnation and revelation. There had been an incarnation near Costa Rica in Central America, another upon the Canary Islands, and finally a divine birth that had recently taken place at Jerusalem. The last ancient prime meridian upon the Atlantic, near the Canary Islands, was even still protected as a sacred marker by the Phoenicians and continued in usage to the times of Myrinos of Tyre. Even the great scientist Ptolemy declined to alter this prime meridian even though Eratosthenes (276–195 BC) had suggested a new prime meridian at Alexandria. Eratosthenes was born in Cyrene in Libya, studied in Athens and Alexandria, and was appointed the third chief of the library of Alexandria.

Christian Propaganda

The appearance of Jerusalem, the place of the birth and crucifixion of Christ, at the very center of the map certainly suggests an effort to propagandize this new religion as the center of all human attention. Some might argue that this over centralization led to the zealotry and religious fanaticism of the Inquisition in both Europe and the American continents.

Unhappily, the hemispherical projection of the map, by definition, fails to include the American continents on the other side of the globe. And this has dire consequences for the native peoples in those areas who will be excluded from a joyful participation in the forthcoming history of the world. The Jerusalem-centric maps became a selective and prejudicial icon implanted in the worldview of the conquerors and world rulers of that time. The Jerusalem hemisphere was considered to be full of the light of inspiration and revelation. The American hemisphere on the opposite side of the globe was considered to be full of darkness, suggestive of the dead underworld and its history of dark, meaningless, and distant ages of the past.

The cosmological reason for placing Jerusalem as the pole of the hemisphere is that prophecy long ago affirmed that a new epoch and a divine event would happen here. The heavenly Jerusalem, the archetypal perfection, was thought to have come down from heaven to be briefly realized on Earth. Jerusalem had become the divine *mesomphalos*, a sacred center and the matrix of the world.

Hereford Map Records Historical and Mythical Places of Origin

Diodorus Skytobrachion, Diodorus Siculus, Hesiod, Apollodorus, and the Alexandrian poet Nonnos affirm that the Greek gods and myths originate in the vicinity of the Canary Islands and the African shores of the Atlantic Ocean at the place of the ancient Atlantic Prime Meridian. This is a fact that the Hereford map also affirms.

The Hereford map carefully places the Garden of Eden upon an island at the very top of the map in the Far East. Then the cartographers placed the Island Garden of the Hesperides (the Canary Islands) and localities from Greek myth at the very bottom of the map in the Far West, almost on an axis directly through Jerusalem and the Garden of Eden. This placement of the Mid-Eastern myth of Adam and the Greek myths on the periphery of the circle seems to suggest that Christ and Jerusalem are the fulfillment of all traditions of the past from the different corners of the globe.

The Hereford map represents the ancient Atlantic prime meridian (the Garden of the Hesperides) separated by 60° from Jerusalem, which in turn is separated by 60° from the Garden of Eden of Adam and Eve, a circular island in the Far East. Toward the mainland is a city said to have existed before the flood: the city of Enos, son of Cain, in the land of Nod. Farther southeast is the place where Adam and Eve went after their expulsion from Paradise.

The current Greenwich prime meridian is founded on the politics of civilization, power, and domination by the British Empire. The English tongue has become the language of global commerce, aviation, navigation, and diplomacy. The ancient prime meridians were founded upon divine revelation, science, and culture.

The Discovery of the American Continents

When the Americas were discovered, it posed an enormous philosophical, historical, and religious problem. This problem was that the Hereford map (and the many maps like it) had created an intellectual community of scholars brought up upon the teachings and propaganda of these half-a-globe representations of the world. It must have come as an awful shock to these scholars that there was another entire world full of people and their history residing on the other hemisphere of the globe!

Some concluded that God would never have abandoned these, his children, in a state of loneliness and exclusion from His care and mercy. Therefore in 1590 AD, an astute Roman Catholic friar, Jose de Acosta, formulated the idea that primitive Siberian hunters crossed an ice bridge upon the Bering Straits to an almost virgin territory bereft of humans and culture (Erickson, p. 56). The propaganda was initiated that the Americas were an undeveloped territory with a negligible population, no history, no megalithic architecture, and no astronomy, cosmology, or culture. This paradigm of the Americas has led to the justification of enslavement, genocide, and the destruction of scientific and cultural documents of native people throughout the entire North and South American continents. The real history of the American continents is, of course, one-half of all global history.

Details, Description, and History of the Map

In *The Hereford Map*, Scott D. Westrem has catalogued nearly 1,100 place names and inscriptions that appear on the calfskin chart (over 5 feet x 4 feet) produced around the year 1300 AD. Other maps of that period are: a 12th-century map by Isidore of Seville, now in Munich; the gigantic 11-foot-square Ebstorf Map (destroyed in a bombing raid over Hanover in WWII); the Lambeth Map; and the Sawley Map of Yorkshire.

Westerm tells us that the Hereford map and the OT maps (the letter "T" inscribed in a circle to present three sections of the globe) were divided into Asia, Europe, and Africa. The three parts of the globe were said to have been allotted to Shem, Ham, and Japheth, the sons of Noah. It may be wondered why Noah did not have six sons that they might also inherit Australia and North and South America? Westrem (p. xxii) gives us the most complete background information by reporting that Paulus Orosius, encouraged by St. Augustine, wrote a book entitled *Seven Books of History Against the Pagans* (completed 418 AD). Orosius traces "a divinely ordained movement of imperial power and inspired knowledge...gradually from east to west. Adam and Eve's banishment from the terrestrial paradise at the earth's Oriental extreme was the original movement in a series of events that brought human civilization—via India, Babylon, Persia, and Greece—to its ultimate geographical and moral end in Christian Rome. Orosius' false propaganda was powerful and persistent. In England, it was adopted by Gildas (c. 500 AD), Bede (731 AD), and Geoffrey of Monmouth (c. 1136 AD). Orosius' ideas allowed Europeans to claim that knowledge and progress came only from the East and had not as yet arrived in the Americas.

It is curious and coincidental that civilization and empire do indeed follow the astronomical cycle of the precession of the vernal equinoxes, which moves from east to west at a rate of 30° in 2160 years. But according to the ancient cosmologers, there is a greater cycle of the revolution of the Milky Way Galaxy that shepherds culture and revelation from the opposite direction, from west to the east—eventually inspiring every location of the entire globe. No people or tribes on Earth were left out of this divine distribution of science, culture, and religion.

Atlas of Morocco and the Forgotten Context of History in the West

The Hereford map faithfully affirms the testimony from the historians Herodotus and Diodorus Siculus, as well as the mythographers and the genealogists, Hesiod and Apollodorus—all of whom report that Mediterranean culture, their gods and ancestors, came from the Atlantic islands and the famous coasts of Fez and Morocco. The following locations are depicted upon the Hereford image:

The ancient river and city of Lixus, where Hercules defeated the earth-born giant Antaeus is depicted inside the Straits of Gibraltar on the Mediterranean. The commentator notes that the town of Lixus and Tangiers have been misplaced, and both cities should appear on the Atlantic seaboard (Westrem, p.369–389). However, the River Lixus' position and flow is seen under the name "Nuchul fluvius" next to Mt. Atlas, where the true Lixus should be. The map says that after Lixus comes Mount Hesperus, where "the monstrous Gorgons [a tribe of Amazons] live on islands in the Atlantic opposite the promontory." Further down the Atlantic coast are the monstrous races with many deformities, such as the Cyclopes, the one-footed, and a race of Hermaphrodite people. This is also said to be the land of the Antipodes, where people's feet are turned backward.

The second island beyond the Gorgons is Membriona, marked as zero degrees longitude by the ancient geographers (the ancient Atlantic prime meridian). Four islands southward of the Gorgons is the famed island of the Hesperides (the daughters of the goddess Night and later of Atlas, who guard the Golden Apples). Six islands away is the island of Adanum. Eight islands south of the island of the Gorgons comes the island of the Sirens. After these comes a mixture of the Canaries, also called the Isles of the Blessed or the Fortunate Isles. The 15th-century Irish *Book of Lismore*, compiled from much older material, tells about the voyages of St. Brendan, the navigator. One version explains that St. Brendan wished to reach an island "just under Mt. Atlas." This was a place where the holy man Mernoc went to recluse himself from the world—an island that was the "the first home of Adam and Eve," an earthly paradise. This is a confusion with the Island of Adam and Eve in the Far East. However, the confusion is noteworthy because Atlantic Africa was also a remarkable place of origin, namely of Mediterranean culture.

The Hereford map shows Mt. Atlas, and its legend reports, "extremely high: it is silent by day; while at night it flashes with fires and resounds everywhere with the noise of dancers as if in rituals with Pan; the music of flutes and the crashing of cymbals is heard all along the seacoast." The Atlantis people are also mentioned on the map as living nearby within the three sides of the triangle formed by the rivers Malva, Salum, and Dara. Such mountain music has always been heard on the Irish fairy mountain, Mt. Slievenamon. It may be noted that the earliest inhabitants of Ireland were from Morocco, and that Irish step-dancing is possibly derived from the goat-like dance of the primeval god Pan.

The Roundness of the Earth

Scholars of our generation were taught in school that people of the Middle Ages thought that the world was flat. This absurd falsehood was propagated by the American writer and humorist Washington Irving in his 1828 biography of Columbus and strangely accepted by American educators who allowed this untruth to be printed in their history books (Edward Grant in his *God and Reason in the Middle Ages* (2001) and John Grant in his *Discarded Science, Ideas That Seemed Good at the Time* (2006). It is true that the Phoenicians rigorously patrolled the Straits of Gibraltar, which was their lucrative gateway to their Atlantic trading empire for British tin and American tobacco and cocaine. Phoenicians furthermore advanced stories of giant sea monsters, the stagnant windless Saragossa Sea, and that ships that ventured too far out to sea fell off the edge of the ocean.

Paul Binding's wonderful book *Imagined Corners, Exploring the World's First Atlas* (p. 190) records, "Sphericity as the truth about the world never died. Rather, it went underground… Medieval cartographers simply did not see the Earth's roundness as a key feature; their religious interpretation of existence and notions of pictorial convenience led naturally enough to their maps showing disc-like Earths…"

Events That Changed the World and the Worldview

In the year of his death, Copernicus (1473–1543 AD) put forward the heliocentric theory. Almost 100 years later, the Holy Roman Inquisition (1610–1633 AD) accused Galileo Galilei of propounding Pythagorean (570–495 BC) doctrine that the Earth was round and that it moved. In one of his first manuscripts, Copernicus originally credited the Pythagorean disciple Philolaus (480–385 BC) as well as Aristarchus of Samos (310–230 BC) with the theories of the heliocentric solar system and the spinning Earth. Copernicus later struck their names from his *Revolution of the Celestial Spheres* and simply wrote, "The sun is the center of the universe…we revolve around the sun like any other planet."

Confirmation of heliocentricity and/or questions about a rotating and rounded Earth were put forward by Pythagoras, Philolaus, Heraclides (387–312 BC), Aristarchus (270 BC), Archimedes, Seleucus of Mesopotamia, Plutarch, Pliny, Nonnus, Martianus Capella (5th cent. AD Carthage), Aryabhata (476-550 AD), as well as the Persians Abu Mashar (9th cent.), 11th century Albiruni, and Nicholas of Cusa (1444 AD) supported by Puerbach and Regiomontanus (1426-1476 AD) (absoluteastronomy.com/topics, 2/28/10. Astro.cornell.edu, 5/16/10). Of course the phases of the moon demonstrate the roundness of that body, while lunar eclipses show the rounded shadow of the spherical earth. Also, the Greek geographer and explorer Pytheas (330 BC) of Marseilles traveled beyond the British Isles to the Land of the Midnight Sun, where he saw the sun orbiting above the horizon of the Earth, phenomena that would require a round and spinning Earth. The above references from classical and medieval times—coupled with the accusation of "Pythagorean doctrines" as heresy—prove that the Church was aware that ancient science believed in heliocentricity. The Church's real problem was not heliocentricity but that the Earth was to be removed from its sacred position as the center of the universe—the cardinal focus of life transmitted from God. Cosmologically, ancient science and the Roman Church believed that the Earth was cosmo centric (the center of the universe), regardless if the sun moved around the Earth or if the Earth moved around the sun.

It may have been that the Roman Church was reluctant to place its "ancient cosmological doctrines" on the table and in public view because it claimed to be the disciples of a new son of God who proposed very simple laws and basic moral rules of conduct—uncomplicated by a sophisticated science and worldview.

The embarrassment of the Church of Rome was shared by Galileo, who had transgressed the laws of intellectual property by failing to cite the names of Philolaus and Aristarchus in his manuscript. Because of the Church's and Galileo' secrets, neither party spoke the truth. Their combined silence has led to assumptions that do not accurately serve history. The assumptions are that this court case was the first attempt to separate science and religion. The second assumption is that Copernicus and Galileo were the geniuses who elevated mankind above the primitive idea that the universe moved around the Earth. In the most inappropriate circumstance of all, Galileo chose to humiliate the intelligence of Pope Urban II by putting the Pope's words into the mouth of his character Simplicio, "the simpleton," who defends Aristotelian geocentricism in the *Dialogue Concerning the Two Chief World Systems*. During a 1632 appearance before the Inquisition, Galileo was placed under house arrest.

The new telescope invented by Galileo was able to discern four moons of Jupiter, the mountains of the moon, and the phases of Venus. He allowed the philosophers and mathematicians of the Jesuit College at Rome to look through his telescope and confirm what he had observed. This confirmation was a vital part of the scientific method. It is interesting that the Roman Church did not abandon its argument against Galileo until 1992 AD, when

Pope John Paul II expressed regret over the Galileo affair and acknowledged the Church's errors. Of course, observation of the material fact of heliocentricity never did explain the unique and exclusive appearance of life on Earth.

CHAPTER 1.2

Croll-Milankovitch Climate Cycles

Cosmology attests that there is a fundamental connection between the universe (galaxy clusters, galaxies, and solar systems) and the life-giving Earth. This connection is correctly called "astrological" because stars, cosmic cycles, and planets directly cause natural events here on Earth. Modern science steadfastly denies astronomic and astrologic causes of events here on earth except in the case of climate cycles.

Scientific astrological cause is demonstrated by the findings of James Croll and Milutin Milankovitch, who showed a direct connection between astronomical phenomena and the climate cycles that we experience upon our planet. Beneficial climate cycles positively influence food production; which in turn stimulates population growth; which dictates economic trade, wars, and the movements of population. Therefore, climate has an all-encompassing influence upon history, the growth of civilizations, and the cycles of human advancement as well as degeneration and decline.

The information below is from George Kaplan of the US Naval Observatory, Astronomical Applications Department. Other information comes from National Climate Data Center (NCDC), UCD Paleoclimatology, National Environmental Satellite Data Information Service (NESDIS), and the NOAA.

Eccentricity of the Shape of the Earth's Orbit

The Earth's orbit around the sun changes over great periods of time from almost circular to elliptical. At the moment, the orbit is elliptical, and rotates around the sun in a matter of about 21,600 years. Numerous variations occur over a period of 413,000 years producing a general cycle of about 100,000 years.

The eccentricity of the Earth would not vary if it were the only planet orbiting the Sun. The Earth's eccentricity varies primarily due to interactions with the gravitational fields of Jupiter and Saturn.

Currently the difference between closest approach to the sun (perihelion) and furthest distance away (aphelion) is only about 5 million km, which allows for a 6.8% increase in solar radiation. In the future when the orbit is at its extreme elliptical extension and at perihelion, the amount of solar radiation would be about 23% greater than at our current aphelion position. Martineau writes (p. 12), "In recent years, far from diminishing Kepler's vision, Einstein's laws actually showed that the tiny space-time effects caused by Mercury's faster (and therefore heavier and time-slowed) motion when nearer to the sun affected the precessional rotation of the ellipses over thousands of years…"

In very simple terms:

The difference between the current 6.8% solar radiation and the future 23% solar radiation would result in a totally different climate here upon earth caused by the gravitational pull of Jupiter, Saturn, and Mercury. The entire solar system acts as a balancing equation.

Axial Tilt. 21.5–24.5° Range of Earth's obliquity.

Currently the Earth's axis is tilted at 23.44 degrees from its orbital plane around the sun. The range of tilt can vary from about 21.5 degrees to 24.5. During a period of about 41,000 years the angle moves from one position to the other and back again. The present tilt is about halfway between the extremes which may account for the high yields of food production which in turn is responsible for overpopulation and excessive pollution.

Obviously, a lesser or greater tilt in the Earth's axis would mean more extremes in solar radiation causing great changes in the seasons and agricultural production, as well as the ability for humans to work long hours during inclement seasons. Colder summers would allow more ice and snow accumulation near the Polar Regions.

Precession of the Vernal Equinoxes

Precession of the vernal equinoxes is the change in the direction of the Earth's axis of rotation relative to the Sun at the time of perihelion and aphelion. The complete cycle of rotation from one point and back again to that point is approximately 25,920 years.

The axis of rotation itself rotates like a top around a line perpendicular to the orbital planes creating a gyroscopic-like motion. This is due to the combined effects of the motions of the Earth, Moon, Sun, Jupiter, Saturn, and the other planets. The orbital ellipse of the Earth is also mutating the length of precession from 25,920 to 21,600 years. If summertime in one hemisphere corresponds with perihelion, there will naturally be an increase in solar radiation, but during the aphelion at winter that season will be much colder. Meanwhile the opposite hemisphere will benefit from a cooler summer and a warmer winter.

At the present time, perihelion occurs during the southern hemisphere's summer, and aphelion happens during the southern winter. Therefore the southern hemisphere's seasons tend to be somewhat more extreme than the northern hemisphere's seasons. The Earth also moves faster when one focus of its ellipse is the perihelion. All these minute variations combine over time to manifest significant astrologic influence on climate and life upon our planet.

Orbital Inclination

The inclination of Earth's orbit drifts up and down relative to its present orbit, with a cycle of about 70,000 years. Milankovitch did not investigate this three-dimensional movement.

More recent researchers noted this drift and that the orbit also moves relative to the orbits of the other planets. The invariable plane, the plane that represents the angular momentum of the solar system, is approximately the orbital plane of Jupiter. The inclination of the Earth's orbit has a 100,000-year cycle relative to the invariable plane. This 100,000-year cycle closely matches the 100,000-year pattern of ice ages.

It has been proposed that a disk of dust and other debris is in the invariable plane, and this affects the Earth's climate through several possible means. The Earth presently moves through this plane around January 9 and July 9.

Present Conditions

Our present perihelion occurs during the southern hemisphere's summer, and aphelion occurs during the southern winter. Thus the southern hemisphere's seasons should tend to be somewhat more extreme than the northern hemisphere's seasons. The relatively low eccentricity of the present orbit results in a 6.8% difference in the amount of solar radiation during summer in the two hemispheres.

The often-cited 1980 study by Imbrie and Imbrie determined that "Ignoring anthropogenic [human influence] and other possible sources of variation acting at frequencies higher than one cycle per 19,000 years, this model predicts that the long-term cooling trend which began some 6,000 years ago will continue for the next 23,000 years." More recent work by Berger and Loutre suggests quite the opposite by saying that the current warm climate may last another 50,000 years.

Conflicting studies and interpretations suggest that current science has not come to a specific conclusion regarding the interplay of the various astronomical cycles in which the Earth participates. It will require a very fine and articulated human mind to fully comprehend the total combination of all the variations of astronomical-astrological influence.

Rise in Ocean Levels

According to the IPCC 4th Report, the rise in ocean levels is 3mm per year since 1993 AD. The rise is attributed to polar and global glacier melting as well as "thermal expansion" of the hot water of the oceans created by warmer climate. In 1900 ocean levels were 100mm less than today. In 2100 the rise is estimated to be 500mm (19.685 inches) above today's levels. Future climate may become more violent and extreme, possibly creating 40 million climate refugees by the year 2080 (globalgreenhouse.com, 10/11/2009).

When water freezes, it expands in volume by about 10% but still weighs the same. Roughly 80% of our fresh water is locked up in glaciers, some of which are two miles thick. These glaciers cover 8% of the land and 2% of the oceans of our globe. If all this ice melted, ocean levels would rise about 200 feet (Tom Cwynar, Mdc.mo.gov, 10/11/2009). Again, we should not be frightened by such data until the one scientific mind can be found to digest and discover the cumulative effect of all the relevant information.

Modern Scientists Who Connected Climate with Astronomy

Modern physicists agree that climate change is caused by astronomical changes. Namely, the major players in determining weather cycles are axial inclinations; orbital eccentricities; declination of the orbits of the sun, moon, Earth, and the planets; and most important of all, the assessment of the cumulative effect of all these interrelationships.

Joseph Alphonse Adhemar (1797–1862) was a French mathematician. He was the first to suggest that ice ages were controlled by astronomical forces in his 1842 book, *Revolutions of the Sea.*

As we already know, the orbit of the Earth is an ellipse which is also revolving slowly around the sun. At this moment in time it so happens that the Earth is at perihelion (closest to the sun) during the northern hemisphere's winter solstice. During perihelion the Earth moves faster and therefore the cold winter period for the northern hemisphere is shorter.

Because of this, Adhemar reasoned that the southern hemisphere had more hours of darkness in winter and attributed the Antarctic ice sheet to this. Adhemar knew of the 25,920-year cycle of precession of the equinoxes and theorized that the ice ages occurred in this cycle.

One immediate objection to the theory was that the total insolation during a year does not vary at all during the precessional cycle, only its seasonal distribution. Another objection was that the timing was wrong. However, this could not be tested by the observations available at the time.

James Croll (1821–1890) was a 19th-century scientist who developed a theory of climate in Whitefield, near Wolfhill in Perthshire, Scotland. In 1859 he became a janitor in the museum at the Andersonian College and Museum in Glasgow in order to obtain access to the excellent library there.

From 1864, Croll corresponded with Sir Charles Lyell about links between ice ages and variations in the Earth's orbit. This led to a position in the Edinburgh office of the Geological Survey of Scotland. He published a number of books and papers that were at the forefront of contemporary science. Croll's many works included *Climate and Time, in Their Geological Relations* (1875) and *Climate and Cosmology* (1885). He corresponded with Charles Darwin on erosion by rivers. In 1876 he was elected Fellow of the Royal Society and awarded an honorary degree by the University of St. Andrews.

It may be generalized that Croll was too far ahead of his contemporaries in respect to his astronomical knowledge and theories. Most of the scientific community was unacquainted with the celestial and global cycles that were the foundation of Croll's work.

Using formulae for orbital variations developed by Leverrier (which had led to the discovery of Neptune), Croll developed a theory of the effects of variations of the earth's orbit on climate cycles. His idea was that decreases in winter sunlight would favor snow accumulation and he, for the first time, coupled this with the idea of a positive ice-albedo feedback to amplify the solar variations. He suggested that when orbital eccentricity is high, then winters will tend to be colder when Earth is farther from the sun in that season. Hence, during periods of high orbital eccentricity, ice ages occur on 22,000-year cycles in each hemisphere and alternate between southern and northern hemispheres, lasting approximately 10,000 years each. This idea is wrong but was not corrected at that time.

Croll's theory predicted multiple ice ages, asynchronous in northern and southern hemispheres, and that the last ice ages should have occurred about 80,000 years ago. Evidence was just then emerging of multiple ice ages, and geologists were interested in a theory to explain this. Geologists were not then able to date sediments accurately enough to determine if glaciation was synchronous between the hemispheres. More crucially, estimates of the recession rate of the Niagara Falls indicated that the last ice age ended 6,000 to 35,000 years ago—a large range but enough to rule out Croll's theory to those who accepted these measurements.

Croll's work was widely discussed, but by the end of the 19th century, his theory was generally disbelieved. However, the basic idea of orbital-forced insolation variations influencing terrestrial temperatures was further developed by Milankovitch and eventually triumphed in 1976, about 100 years after Croll's first book on this subject.

Louis Agassiz's concept of a "Great Ice Age" (c.1837) that led to the mass extinction of many creatures was disproved by the Scottish geologist Geikie, who found plant remnants between the layers of glacial deposits. Later research showed that there were multiple ice ages.

The Serbian civil engineer and mathematician, Milutin Milankovitch (1879–1958), in his *Mathematical Science of Climate and Astronomical Theory of the Variations of Climate*, discusses the collective effect of changes in the Earth's movements upon its climate. But because of the visionary pioneer work of Croll, the Milankovitch cycles should rightly be called the Croll-Milankovitch cycles. The following astronomical-climate causations are credited to Milankovitch: precession, rotation of the entire elliptical orbit over 21,600 years, and tilt of the Earth's axis between 21.5 degrees to 24.5 degrees and back again.

The combination of all of the above events produced the 100,000-year ice-age cycles of the quaternary glaciation over the last few million years. It was not until the advent of deep-ocean cores and the seminal paper by Hayes, Imbrie, and Shackleton—"Variations in the Earth's Orbit: Pacemaker of the Ice Ages" in *Science* (1976) that astronomical-climate theories became accepted.

Milankovitch studied changes in the eccentricity, obliquity, and precession of the Earth's movements. Such changes in movement and orientation change the amount and location of solar radiation (called solar forcing) reaching the Earth. There is much more land in the northern hemisphere than in the southern hemisphere. Sunlight warms land faster than the ocean. Every astronomical factor that increases the Earth's northern-hemisphere exposure to the sun naturally affects climate in that region.

There was a time when scientists argued against astrology, saying that the distance between Earth and the planets was so great that the effects of interplanetary gravity were almost nonexistent. Current astronomers admit that the gravitational forces of the planets, especially the giant planets Jupiter and Saturn, definitely readjust the orbit of the Earth. Even a child would understand that during the gas and mass stage of the formation of our solar system, there was a physical reason that everything ended up where it did. The laws of physics dictated the result, and therefore boundaries and relationships follow the dictates of this physics. Above all, "physics" cannot be conveniently dismissed in the middle of an argument—like a taxi—when one is done with its services as Schopenhauer once remarked. The universe functions as an interrelated and harmonious whole whose entire structure is woven through and through like that of a fabricated textile composition.

It is important to realize that a tiny change in astronomics—such as axial tilt, orbital eccentricity, and inclination—may have enormous consequences for life on Earth because of tremendous changes in climate. These changes are brought about by gravity and the interaction of bodies within our solar system. We can only imagine what larger cosmic forces lay in waiting or are currently influencing our galaxy. Today, contemporary science approves of astronomic or "astrological" cause. In the words of Richard Muller, UC Berkeley professor of physics at Lawrence National Laboratories, "Astronomy is responsible for almost all climate changes."

Because of the abhorrence of science to the very mention of the word "astrology," this section is important to reintroduce the importance of "astro" + "logical" affect and change. As was said above, all these minute variations in planetary mechanics combine over time to manifest significant astrologic influence on climate and life upon our planet.

CHAPTER 1.3.

Cultural Destruction by Emperors and Evangelists

The great warriors and their armies possibly eclipse nature in the utter extermination of culture, scientific temples, and information. Most appalling and humiliating of all is that they leave their seed among the conquered to further efface the unique racial strains of the citizens who survived the invaders' onslaught. A close review of the exploits of Alexander, Julius Caesar, William the Conqueror, Attila, Genghis Khan, Napoleon, Stalin, and Hitler will demonstrate an unbelievable destruction of prior human achievement. These generals, conquistadors, emperors, and dictators again prove that centralization of power in the hands of one person has a most deleterious effect upon culture. We now turn to one of the great rulers of the Orient, who best exemplifies the power of catastrophic human destruction.

In China: The Emperor Qin Shi Huang

In one of my lectures I said that Western culture from Rome, Greece, the Mid-East, and Egypt is one of the few genuine and intact traditions of myth and history that has come down to us. A young Asian girl then asked me, "What about my Oriental culture?" The answer is, "Your emperor burned your culture to the eternal detriment of all human history on this planet." It is sad to have to admit that the successors of Western civilization are guilty of destroying native records and culture around the entire globe. Again and again, the survival of intelligent humanity is challenged by natural disasters, but most devastating of all are the human predators of culture.

A terrible thing happened in the kingdom of Chin. An intruder, Lao Ai, who had masked himself under the pretense of being a eunuch, had fathered two children by the queen. Attempting a royal coup, Lao Ai sprang upon the 21-year-old legitimate prince and came close to killing him. It was a time in history when the Seven Kingdoms had fought for over 500 years for the ultimate control and domination of China (*The First Emperor,* the History Channel, 8/4/08).

The young king, Qin Shi Huang, narrowly escaped death and became gripped with an iron resolve to finish off all his enemies—those who surrounded him at court and those among the other kingdoms of China. He exercised these plans through the unrelenting administration of violence and force. In 235 BC he took the road to becoming the first emperor of all China. His family, the original Chin, had arrived in the region around 1027 BC as marauders on horseback. The Chin had followed a Spartan like obsession with military training and what one would term a military-industrial complex. They were the first to develop man-slaying meter-long swords of bronze welded with chrome, a technique not developed until 1937 AD in Germany. The Chin further introduced mass-produced, standardized, three-sided arrowheads that were so aerodynamic that they could meet their mark dead-on at 150 meters and fly up to 300 meters. To attain such performance, they developed the crossbow with standardized, interchangeable triggers. They originated the three-line alternating kneel-load-and-shoot stratagem, which proved to be a formidable defense in hard battle. Finally, the Chin fielded an army of half a million men, the largest the world had ever seen. Men were rewarded with promotions and land according to the severed heads of their enemies they exhibited back at their camp. In 1974, buried underneath the soil, 1000 life-size pottery soldiers, horses, and chariots were discovered. Further investigations have revealed that there are a total of about 30,000 unique and personalized images—all individually handcrafted—to protect the emperor, even in death. In 230 BC, the emperor had sworn to "unite all people under heaven!"

Qin Shi Huang was the ruler who built the Great Wall of China, where 1 million people were conscripted into labor with little food, water, or reward. 100,000 died in the course of this monumental construction, and many became a part of the edifice, walled up at their death. The Great Wall is about 4,500 miles in length. This cruel project, coming upon the heels of the Great Wars, soured the people against the emperor. His spies reported that his popularity was waning.

One of the Confucian scholars at his court had the effrontery to openly admonish the emperor of heaven, saying that the empire is doomed if the emperor does not listen to the past. Liu Siu, the emperor's prime minister replied, "In order to move successfully into the future—we must extricate the past!" This pronouncement was endorsed by an immediate edict by which 460 Confucian scholars were buried alive, while others were sent to work on the Great Wall. All bamboo books of history and other writings were consigned to the flames. Philosophy and history from outside of the state of Qin were also burned under the edict, "Burn the classics and bury the scholars." The only exceptions were those copies in the Imperial Library used for official purposes. After these atrocious acts by the young minister and his young emperor, a malaise seems to have enveloped the empire. A period of bad luck and bad omens settled upon the land. The emperor's propitiatory sacrificial tally; that he cast upon the sacred river this year had been returned to the palace by the "river ghost." The very heavens themselves were full of bad omens and the so-called "doom-star" comets.

Since his earliest nightmare of barely escaping regicide, it must be truthfully admitted that the emperor was always subject to psychotic paranoia following upon the heels of his megalomania. Now the emperor lived in perpetual dread with visions of assassins everywhere. He had many palaces built in order to confuse his enemies as to his true whereabouts. He moved restlessly from one palace to another pursued by his imaginings and never slept in the same palace bed twice. He traveled with two royal carriages to confuse his assailants. He was obsessed with immortality and had his musicians compose songs and poems about his immortal nature. In addition, he sent out explorers to search the world for any elixirs of youth.

We cannot refrain from commenting that this psychologically injured 21-year-old committed an ill choice when selecting Li Si as his closest advisor. The combination of two young people in power can only lead to disaster. The same may be said of a combination of two old people. Success lies in the combination of something borrowed, something blue, something old, and something new—that is, something from the present, the past, and the future. After the death of Qin Shi Huang, the nation that he had carefully sculpted into an empire broke out into a punishing civil war.

Divine right is the same principle throughout the entire world, for it comes from a cosmological "thinking model" common to all cultures. Within the Forbidden City in the heart of Beijing there is a circular ceremonial platform of three levels (*Globe Trekker* series: China 2008). These levels signified nature, man, and the Divine. The Chinese emperor would ascend these levels with much ceremony to be proclaimed the Divine and Rightful Heavenly King and the incarnate representative of God here upon the Earth. The heavenly emperor, Qin Shi Huang, was not serene enough to deal with his own personal demons. He was not strong enough to forget his personal misfortunes in order to lead an empire and serve his countrymen through good example and balanced judgment.

A number of China's olden traditions were resurrected through provincial schools and oral traditions. But in the main part, the Chinese people were deprived of their ancient and unique philosophy, cosmology, and culture. Qin Shi Huang will forever serve as the hallmark of the devastating capability of human-generated destruction and disaster.

Cultural Destruction by Evangelists –the Fraternity of Franciscan Friars

In July 1562 AD the Inquisition in Mani in Yucatan, under the guidance of the Franciscan friar Diego de Landa, burned 5,000 idols and 27 hieroglyphic scrolls. Though Bishop de Landa could not read these documents, he declared that they were "the works of the devil" and designed to delude the Maya and prevent them from accepting Christianity when it would be brought to them.

Two of de Landa's native informants, Gaspar Antonio Chi and Nachi Cocom, had told the Friar about the structure of their yearly calendar and also about the chronology of the Maya Long Count. In Mexico proper, Bishop Juan de Zumarraga was delighted to report having destroyed 20,000 idols.

Regrettably, it was just shortly after the destructions of the *auto-da-fé* in Mani that the superior Bishop Toral arrived in Yucatan. William Yates, in his translation of *Yucatan, Before and After the Conquest,* writes that Toral ordered the release of the prisoners that de Landa had incarcerated, and demanded de Landa's own return to Spain to stand trial before the Council of the Indies regarding his outrageous behavior. It is evident that de Landa's book, *Relacion de la Cosas de Yucatan,* was written in self-justification and explanation in his own defense before the council. This book would never have seen the light of day had de Landa remained safe and secure back in Yucatan continuing his self-appointed reign of terror upon the culture of the native inhabitants.

It is an absolute and incredible shame that this racial and cultural holocaust consumed the history of a gifted and scientifically advanced people! But it is well known that the evangelizers of the Americas were chosen from the roster of the hardened and experienced inquisitors of the Holy Roman Inquisition in Europe. Karl Taube, in *Aztec and Maya Myths* (p. 20), proclaims that,

> By the 1570s a growing anti-native attitude was shared by both the crown and the Franciscans. The great experiment had failed; there was no New World Utopia. The native populations were being decimated by disease, forced labor, and over-taxation. At least as disturbing were the growing indications that true conversion was not being achieved, and many were returning to their idolatrous ways, often with unholy blending of Catholic and native beliefs. In this light, religious works written in native languages were increasingly considered threats to conversion and even political stability.

Rafael Ancona, in his *History of Yucatan,* complains about the Ordinances of the Auditor, Tomas Lopez, regarding his direct authorization of the town removals of the 1550s, including the sanction of town burnings when necessary. This directive allowed the dominating Franciscan friars "more convenient doctrinal and ecclesiastical supervision." This effectively turned Yucatan into a "Franciscan monastery" founded upon Indian labor, which was supposed to be independent and above the regular Church authority. This infraction of power over native inhabitants was later duplicated in California, where it served to eradicate large numbers of original peoples through overcrowding in disease-ridden compounds in the ecclesiastical rancheros. Bishop Toral was not able to win the upper hand against the mighty organization of the Franciscan Order and retired back to Mexico. Indeed, he was so badly treated that, though he was a Franciscan himself, he left the hospitality of the monastery and took up lodgings in a private residence in the city. Toral described his Franciscan brothers as "men of little learning and less charity." Having passed the scrutiny of the Council of the Indies, Diego de Landa was promoted to provincial of the Franciscan Order as well as a bishop of the Church. In Yucatan he continued where he had left off, promoting his version of Franciscan ideology. Untamed and "absolved" of his crimes, he continued his eradication of the ancient ways through floggings and other illegal and criminal behavior. Especially merciless and humiliating was the destruction of ancient towns where the natives had lived and grown their own food for generations. Now they were removed to "doctrinal centers" around the missions that had been built upon the ancient holy sites of their temples. Here they had to accept what was given them and to become serfs to the governing religious order.

These religious orders had their own provincials and generals, but they were still subject to the bishops of the Church of Rome, who were regarded as descendants of the first apostles of Jesus. But in order to gain the upper hand over the recalcitrant natives, the religious orders asked for emergency powers to exercise plenary right in distant places. Diego de Landa had been sent to trial back in Spain because he illegally tried the Indians under the laws of the Inquisition. Indians were regarded under Church law as "infants in the faith" and therefore had to be treated like minors of tender age and cared for and protected as children. A formal commission of four bishops and three religious orders had met in Mexico on April 27, 1539, to order that whipping and flogging should not be used to enforce obedience to the church or in matters of faith. In spite of this order, many unspeakable violations were committed by many, especially by Tomas Lopez in the *Audiencia* of Guatemala.

William Gates further asserts that form letters—ostensibly signed by numbers of local Yucatan chieftains requesting the reinstatement of de Landa—that appeared in the great volume of *Cartas de Indias* were, in fact, all signed in what was obviously the same signature type. Later, Francisco de Montejo Xiu, governor of Mani, condemned these counterfeit letters as falsehoods and further related what had actually been done to his people.

There is a proclamation required of every Spanish captain and explorer upon landing in native territory. The gist of this document is that it is made in the name of the Kings of Castile and Leon—that God created us all but had given St. Peter charge over the entire human linage. Also that Rome was the best place fitted to rule the world. One of the previous Pontiffs had given dominion over these islands and mainland to the Catholic kings of Castile, who sent religious men to instruct the natives in the holy faith.

Unfortunately, the issue of native rights was not so simply resolved but was continually challenged for almost 100 years. In a papal bull entitled *The Sublime God* issued on May 29, 1537, Pope Paul III declared that the indigenous people of the Americas were rational beings with souls and that they had not been inspired by Satan. The Pope called for their immediate evangelization, while conferring rights to liberty and property. However 13 years later in 1550, Charles V, king of Spain and holy Roman emperor, summoned a council at Villadolid. For three long hours Jesuit theologian Juan Gines de Sepulveda argued that Indians were slaves according to Aristotelian logic. His rhetoric spoke in favor of the land-management system of the *encomienda*, whereby the Indians were Christianized but enslaved and bound to the land, working for the profit of the owners.

In response, Dominican friar Bartolome de Las Casas testified for five days that the Indians should be treated like Europeans in their shared humanity given by the grace of God. Las Casas won over the king's ear in favor of his arguments, and while the encomienda was officially abolished for a time, it was reinstituted when Peruvian settlers claimed that they could not continue sending riches to Spain unless the Indians were under their total control. So unfortunately—while many listened to the humanitarian pleas—economics driven by greed and supported by fallacious arguments eventually won the day over the crushed hearts and souls of the native people (drarchaeology.com/culthist/origins.htm, 7/2009).

The destruction of Mesoamerican scientific observation and records is beyond comprehension. The above horrific accounts can only sadden both God and man. Every country is permitted to ensure its survival by protecting its borders with armies and weaponry. But what really surpasses belief is the idea that European culture was high and above native culture because of its self-appointed mandate to convert the world to a new religion. Every religion claims to be a special covenant and private relationship between one people and God. But the Creator's spirit and light shines upon all people, including "the just and the unjust." Our Earth is a special material realm inspired by spirit and energy in a drama of change and time. We live upon a stage of conflict between civilization and culture—where civilization represents the drive of political power and culture represents the cosmic law of balance and harmony. The cosmic worldview proclaims that there is no nation that is exalted above the other. Elitism, exceptionalism, and national and racial superiority are delusions that imagine that God sanctions the reconstruction or destruction of the culture of other people. Civilization proclaims that life is stagnant and nonexistent without change. Both statements are true and describe the nature of our planet and ourselves—half ethereal and half material.

<u>*Destruction of Documents By the Aztec*</u>

One of the basic laws of this world is that the expansion of civilizations lies at the root of the destruction and falsification of documents. John Bierhorst, author of *History and Mythology of the Aztecs: The Codex Chimalpopoca* tells us that, in approximately the year 1430 AD, the Aztecs had ensconced themselves in the ancient city of Tenochtitlan and began their conquest of the surrounding regions of Mexico. The ruling elite decided to burn the old pictographic histories, which they pronounced as containing "falsehoods." Bierhorst continues, "Presumably the books that replaced them exaggerated the deeds of the upstart Aztecs and codified the legend that the Aztecs themselves had founded Tenochtitlan [Mexico City]."

Again Bierhorst writes, "A hundred years later the [new Aztec] books were burned again, this time by Spanish missionaries who, in the wake of the Conquest of 1521, rushed to eliminate whatever might remind the native people of their pre-Christian past and might thus inhibit the work of conversion. Once again new histories rose out of the ashes." One of the native authors of the *Annals of Cuauhtitlan* repeatedly disparages the old gods as "devils" and "sorcerers" who tricked the people into performing human sacrifices. The old cliché seems to hold true that history is indeed written by the victors.

Carlos Milla Villena tells us that many of the olden traditions of astronomical holy days in Peru were eradicated and mistranslated by the agents of the Inquisition, such as the astrologer Friar Juan Polo de Ondegardo. The Andean religion had a cosmological foundation, and therefore all their astronomical science was thought to stand in the way of their conversion to Christianity. The most ancient sacred icon of Andean star-religion was the constellation of the Southern Cross, the *Cruz del Sur.* Villena reports that the Southern Cross is reported to have only been discovered in recent times by Vasco de Gama (p. 27).

But as in all instances around the world, documents miraculously make their reappearance—as the Bible says, "Nothing is hidden that will not be revealed." Fray Diego Duran emphatically stated that none of the olden books escaped the autos-da-fé. The renowned chronicler Bernardino de Sahagun claimed, however, that many of the old books were safely spirited away to hiding places and could be consulted for reference, as he himself did on many occasions.

CHAPTER 1.4.

The Lisbon Earthquake

All cultures of the world report episodes of the Creation and Destruction. There is the Legend of the Five Suns of the Mexica-Maya-Andean culture, which says that creation and destruction goes in cycles. Because there is so much similar information coming from all times, it seems reasonable to say that humankind and its civilizations are periodically destroyed—plummeting humankind back into the Stone Age and the lives of primitive hunters and gatherers. After a time, these survivors rise up again. Human existence on this planet is subject to many natural disasters and greater cycles of creation and destruction. Humans are so versatile and successful that they would soon overrun the planet if they were not held in their place by the challenging forces of nature.

The *Timaeus* (22) of Plato recalls the travels of Solon in Egypt. One of the Egyptian priests who was of a very great age observed to Solon:

> O Solon, Solon, you Hellens are never anything but children, and there is not an old man among you—in mind you are all young, there is no old opinion handed down among you by ancient tradition, nor any science which is hoary with age... There have been, and will be again, many destructions of mankind arising out of many causes; the greatest have been brought about by the agencies of fire and water... Once upon a time Phaeton burnt up all that was upon the earth... Now, this is in the form of a myth but really signifies a declination of the bodies moving in the heavens around the earth.

The Egyptian priest finishes by saying that unfortunately, just as people are beginning to advance, natural disasters destroy their civilization and send them back into a primitive state of life. One may notice that the Egyptian priest connects myth with very ancient but factual natural events here on Earth.

Along with countless natural disasters, human advancement is always threatened by human intervention through religious agendas and fanaticism, greed, corruption, and wars. But the most detrimental of all is the policy of the centralization of artifacts and information—where one disaster could irreparably wipe out the legacy of an entire culture. Whether it is libraries, museums, the printing press, the Internet, or the internationalization of one prominent language above many local languages—all efforts of centralization invariably threaten the preservation of ancient data and local microcultures.

A close study of the ancient national assemblies in Ireland reveals a system of perfect oral recitation of the many provincial historical poets. After each presentation, there was a period of challenge, rebuttal, and the final and agreed correction of historical data. Once this *Feis* was dismissed, everyone took their local and national history home with them. The numerous provincial *seanachie* poets were the most effective and secure means to safeguard traditions over long periods of time.

Details of the Lisbon Quake

The great earthquake, tsunami, and subsequent fire that hit the city of Lisbon on November 1, 1755, generated an extraordinary chain of human events. The astrological configuration prompting these events is unique. The positions of the planets in relation to the geography precipitated a powerful reaction of nature as well as an astounding human response.

In his book *The Lisbon Earthquake*, T.D. Kendrick writes that this event brought the characteristic age of popular optimism of the first half of the 18th century to an end. The publication of Voltaire's *Candide* finalized the pessimism of Europe reflecting upon this earthquake, which was the worst catastrophe to strike Europe since the eruption of Mt. Vesuvius and the destruction of the city of Pompeii (79 AD). The quake lasted about 10 minutes, beginning at 9:30 AM on Saturday, and consisted of three distinct shocks separated by intervals of about a minute. An entire fleet of vessels was swept out of the harbor. Some estimates put the loss of human life at 60,000 persons. A pilot on the Tagus River had observed that on the night previous to the great earthquake, October 31, that the turn of the tides was two hours late. He also noticed the same tide delay on December 10, after which two more shocks took place on December 11.

On the modern seismic scale—judging from paintings, drawings, and reports—the quake was between a 9 and 10 magnitude on the scale. Like the 1906 episode in San Francisco, a fire subsequently erupted, fanned by a northeast wind, and lasted nearly a week. This conflagration greatly increased the destruction begun by the earthquake and ripped through central Lisbon, annihilating 20 parish churches, including the home of the Inquisition. The fire consumed the material wealth of the people; destroyed many priceless works of art; and ruined the great libraries with their collections of ancient maps and charts, numerous specialized archives, plus a valuable library of Marian literature. This was a loss to all of humanity, indeed. All these priceless treasures were taken away from the world—forever—as a warning that cultural treasures should not be housed in cities by the ocean. In the case of Lisbon, nothing in those libraries had been copied that we know of, and indeed, a most remarkable treasure was lost relating to the history and science of these unique Atlantic regions where the gods of the Greeks, Egyptians, and Mediterranean peoples were said to have been born.

The actual area affected by the earthquake was very large, encompassing the southwest corner of Portugal and a great portion of North Africa. It was felt in northern Spain and in France as far as Bordeaux, as well as in Switzerland, Brittany, and northern Italy. Waters in rivers and lakes were suddenly disturbed as far afield as Loch Ness in Scotland and in Scandinavia. Apparently, the massive quake hit the entire Atlantic seaboard and in Morocco destroyed the towns of Meknes and Volubilis, which had been continuously occupied for over 3,000 years. These Moroccan cities were in the heartland of the most ancient Atlantic peoples, as well as the ancient Phoenicians who supplanted them. Huelva, Mequinez, Tetuan, and other olden towns were destroyed in the regions of Spain.

It would seem that the epicenter was located out in the Atlantic, because 20-foot seismic waves from the southwest crashed into the port at 11:00 AM, an hour and 20 minutes after the earthquake. Similar waves reached the West Indies at 6:00 PM that day. It should also be noted that there were 30 aftershocks within a week and up to 500 aftershocks until August of the following year, 1756.

Interestingly, the All Souls' Day quake produced many stories of miraculous happenings during and after the quake, including instances of wonderful healing. Many of the renowned miraculous images of Lisbon churches were preserved. The quake was actually foretold by a nun, Sister Maria Joanna Lourical.

Voltaire wrote a poem about the Lisbon disaster, followed by his famous novel *Candide*, in which he disparages the "Best of all possible worlds" optimism of thinkers like Leibniz. The effect of the quake was quite momentous in that it served to quell the self-assurance of the world at that time and to make people more introspective, realizing the momentous power of natural forces. By virtue of this great realization, the cities and nations throughout Europe generously sent money and goods to the afflicted people of Lisbon.

In Conclusion

It is the nature of the world and the astronomical cycles that humans and their civilizations advance and then are periodically destroyed. After these cleansing events humans are then thrown back into a primitive state to start all over again. In olden California, many of the ancient tribes were hunter-gathers, yet their cosmology was extraordinarily well advanced (K&M, p. 419). Prior to these discoveries, it was theorized that hunter-gatherers were a primitive step in the evolution of humans long before they could attain any scientific or astronomical knowledge. This idea is just not true. The Juaneno tribe of San Juan Capistrano said that God made the world spherical in shape and that it rested in his hands. The California Chumash did not have astronomers, because all members of society understood aspects of astronomy. They raised a "sun stick" for the winter solstice, recognize the equinoxes, and painted rock art on these occasions as a celebration of these events. Their religious leader became "sun priest" on the astronomic occasions, and 12 of his assistants were called rays of the sun. They also used light plays and shadow-casters. The Chumash say that Shaq the "Turtle" was once chief of the Land of the Dead and that the souls travel westward along the Milky Way. The California Pomo showed bundles of record sticks that demonstrated they had kept records of astronomical events in bundles of 512 years.

Ancient human remains and their artifacts have been found under many layers of geological deposits in deep mining operations. Every culture tells us a story of how their society was destroyed by water, fire, wind, or earthquakes. The Anasazi seem to have been ruined by extended drought. The Hindu speak of insufferable overpopulation, while the Maya and the Cambodian people of Angkor Wat appear to have succumbed to their own overdevelopment and the unsustainable expansion of their cities. People who love the rugged scenery of the shore lands of the oceans are engulfed by tsunami. Those who live on the beautiful Caribbean are annihilated by the monster hurricanes that stalk those regions. The survivors of Atlantis speak of the calamities of tremendous earthquakes. North Africans tell of the erratic course of the chariot of Phaeton and the fires from heaven that parched their lands into a barren desert land. The Babylonians and Jews have preserved the report of the devastating world flood, and the ancient inhabitants of Mexico have carved pictures of their volcanoes erupting as survivors view the devastation as they paddle by in their canoes. Natural disasters continually check the civilizations of the world, but each of these catastrophes is followed by a tale of the survival of a few intelligent people who rekindled the flame of hope and started all over again. God has planted enduring hope and a capacity to forget into the nature of humans so that they may successfully survive every calamity. Mankind has been psychologically conditioned to survive natural disasters.

Humans are drawn to the beauty of rugged landscapes sculpted by the forces of earthquakes, volcanoes, landslides, tsunami, hurricanes, floods, and the erosion of wind and water—which all contribute to vistas of exceptional beauty—forgetting the power of these very forces that will annihilate their homes and cities in the future. These sculptures of brute nature should warn rather than attract us to settle in their midst. But, of course, the most favored human habitations are upon rivers near picturesque ocean coastlands that illuminate the imagination and stimulate the mind. The rivers and oceans are the water supply and the avenues of transportation and commerce. Such places likewise attract a cornucopia of wildlife, fish, waterfowl, and other animals for our sustenance. These favored places also supply the alluvial deltas for our agriculture. In a word, we seem to be drawn to a picturesque arena where natural forces lurk and conspire to bring about our downfall and destruction. It seems as if the natural beauty entraps us to come closer in order to be more perfectly ensnared by earthquakes, storms, erosions, and tsunami. But it is in these coastal bays and river-delta environments that cosmological thinking originated by tracking the recurring revolutions of the bodies of the heavens.

Beauty truly ensnares us. Look at Holland, Venice, and New Orleans—all cities built upon small islands within old swamps. These islands were casually fortified against storm surges by embankments that served to isolate those islands from the prevailing wetlands. This artificial barrier caused the subsoils underneath these islands to shrink, dry out, and subside. Formerly these islands were supported by a wet spongelike foundation. Now that sponge was forced to lose its moisture and shrank in size; and consequently the lands above sank and sank until they were below the surrounding water levels of the tideland swamp. Since its first inhabitation, New Orleans has sunk 28 feet below the level of the surrounding swamp. Again, we never seem to learn. The very shopfronts of the mercantile establishments in Pompeii in Italy are built from the quarried blocks of lava from the previous eruption of the volcano Vesuvius.

CHAPTER 1.5

Precocious Pyramids

Politicians and government-funded science are constantly trying to promote the impossible notion of continual human progress in a universe driven by cycles of birth, maturity, degeneration, and decay. Humans are born, live, mature, grow old, degenerate, and die—after which they are born again—if we adhere to the logic of cosmic physics. Societies and nations are subject to the same cycles accentuated by corruption, wars, famines, diseases, and natural disasters. There are cycles in science and technology where previous ages have turned out superior products and achievements. Archaeologists continually uncover superior arts and artifacts below the layers of geology. Schliemann at Troy and Mycenae attested to superior finds in the most ancient levels of his archaeological excavations. Schwaller de Lubicz also was confounded by the cycles of degeneration and renaissance of Egyptian art and artisanship throughout his research in Egypt. The more ancient megalithic structures have been found to be superior to the more contemporary buildings. These cycles of inspiration and inventiveness, followed by degeneration and decay, are purposely passed over and obscured by science influenced by corporate and political agendas. On the evidence of his lifelong study of the wonders and precision of ancient astronomy, Charles William Johnson stated that, "Human civilization must be far older and its secrets more profound than what is generally inferred from the available historical and archaeological evidence."

Science Frontiers (#184, July 2009) discloses new insights about the amazing 2,000-year-old analog computer found in the Aegean Sea capable of performing astronomical computations impossible to duplicate until the 18th century of the modern era. The turning gears of the Antikythera device mimicked the motions of the heavens. A tiny inscription on the device says that it can predict the starting dates of the Olympic Games. Today's games are held every four years, while the ancient Olympics only started on the full moon closest to the summer solstice. The Antikythera mechanism uses an ingenious gearing system to calculate the phases of the moon over a 19-year Metonic cycle as well as solar and planetary motions.

The Maya say that, at one time, the gods drew lines and pictures upon the Earth to mimic the stars and the constellations of the heavens that were being formed at the same time. There are more of these cosmic representations being discovered around the world in addition to the famous Nazca lines. *Science Frontiers* (#182, March 2009) reveals that there is a possibility that the Nazca lines may have been a historical superalmanac of changing constellation pictures:

> It now seems that the miles of geoglyphs we see are just the last page of a larger "book." Earlier "pages" of Nazca lines can be detected by crisscrossing the wide sandy tracts, where the visible lines are drawn, with a sensitive magnetometer... The geoglyphs visible today are the most recent stage of a prolonged construction process during which the whole complex of drawings was constantly added to, remodeled, obliterated, or changed by use. Some of the magnetic anomalies thought to represent lines are weaker than others and may represent either lines less-walked-upon, or a still deeper page of Nazca Lines.

William R. Corliss, the publisher of *Science Frontiers*, asks, "How many pages of drawings are there?"

In his book *The Egypt Code* (2008), Robert Bauval laments that for over two centuries the astronomical alignments of the pyramids were disregarded or held to be meaningless. Yet he says that the base of each pyramid was positioned to the astronomical directions using star alignments (p. xvi). The air shafts of the largest pyramids were aligned to important star systems such as Orion, Sirius, and the circumpolar stars. Pyramids were given star names like "Horus is the Star at the Head of the Sky." The ceilings of the pyramid chambers were covered with canopies of five-pointed stars. The interior walls of the pyramids were covered with references to their star religion, and the starry world of the *Duat.*

Megalithic structures invariably present astronomic sight lines as well as light and shadow plays based upon equinoxes, solstices, and other astronomical phenomena. Megalithic architecture represents high technology in precision crafting, transportation, and setting of enormous and heavy stones. The most important fact about supermegalithic structures is that they do not represent an advance or progress in building; but rather, the oldest of all the megalithic works are the best and largest while the newer works are smaller and less advanced. In this context, the newer megalithic structures represent degeneration from an older advanced state of engineering. Many of these buildings are the oldest structures on the planet and are said to have been erected before the great world flood. This is not only an Egyptian phenomenon because it is repeated in Tiwanaku and Puma Punku in Bolivia where the more ancient megalithic work is more advanced than the later workmanship. Therefore, megalithic architecture demonstrates the cyclical nature of human activity, which repeatedly goes through stages from advancement to decline and rejuvenation.

William R. Corliss (*Ancient Structures*, p.70, 85) compares the weight of individual stones at some of these supermegalithic locations:

- Baalbek Monolith 1,100 tons
- Calle de los Muertos, Mexico 635 tons
- Baalbek Trilithon 620 tons
- Khafre Pyramid base, Giza 500 tons
- Valley Temple, Egypt 200–500 tons
- Jerusalem underground 350 tons
- Great Pyramid 200 tons
- Tiwanaku 130 tons

- Tonga 100–150 tons
- Puma Punku, Bolivia 100 tons
- Osireion, Egypt 100 tons
- Browne's Hill dolmen, Ireland 100 tons
- Temple Rock Jerusalem 60–90 tons
- Hagar Qin, Malta 20–57 tons
- Stonehenge 50 tons
- Nan Madol, Ponape 40–50 tons

While modern cranes are able to lift some of these stones, the crane operators admit that they would not be able to set stones of this weight and size in place to form the structures that ancient people have created.

The Pyramids at Giza

Some have recorded that the Giza pyramids express the size and orbits of the sun, moon, Earth, and planets. Others have imagined that they describe the universe. In *The Giza Power Plant* (pp. 125–150), Christopher Dunn makes a credible case that the Great Pyramid acted as a seismic resonator of the Earth's regular vibrations, as a reliable and inexpensive source of energy. The emperor Napoleon even slept in the coffer of the King's Chamber, where he had a profound spiritual experience that he would never speak about again afterward.

Everywhere in the world, ancient astronomical sites were built above powerful underground water spirals and springs that reacted to the sun, moon, and planets when they entered into a geometric relationship with one another and in reference to that particular geographic location. In her book *Maya Art and Architecture* (p. 46), Mary Ellen Miller says that throughout Mesoamerica a pyramid represented *altepetl,* a "water mountain" placed above a symbolic cave and its attendant springs beneath the pyramid. Miller also relates (p. 65) that Schele and Mathews have proposed that the pyramid at Chichen Itza may be thought of as Snake Mountain, just like the Coatpec pyramid in Mexico

City. Snakes and their serpent knowledge are related to structures built over sacred water spirals. Of course, the Castillo pyramid at Chichen Itza is the famous one and shows the shadow of a snake writhing down the balustrade of the pyramid staircase during the equinox.

In 2008 our Egyptian guide at Luxor told us that the stones at the temples of Luxor and Karnack were erected by magic. How strange and reminiscent of the monoliths of Stonehenge, which were moved from Ireland by the magic of Merlin. The structures at Chichen Itza, Tikal, and also Tiwanaku in Bolivia were also built by magicians all in one night. The terms "magician" and "all in one night" are mythological code for "structures so ancient that no one remembers the time or the actual names of the builders." It could be said that when we encounter a technology that we do not understand, we call it magic. Today, King Arthur would certainly consider cell phones, GPS, and the Internet as astounding forms of magic.

The Giza pyramids are also magic. The building technology and geometry of these pyramids are so advanced that we are forced to formulate a new theory of anthropology—namely that intelligent human life has always existed on the planet and that we have been preceded by a number of advanced scientific cultures. The well at Syene in Egypt was certainly used to recheck global measurement long before it was employed again by Eratosthenes to determine the size of the globe.

Martin Grey (sacredsites.com) has compiled some excellent information about the highly advanced pyramids at Giza:

The highly polished limestone refacing stones laid upon the slopes of the Great Pyramid were 115,000 in number and weighed about 10 tons each. Remnants show that they were dressed on all of their six sides to tolerances of .01 of an inch. They were set with mortar so closely that a razor blade cannot be inserted between them. The Egyptologist Flinders Petrie wrote, "Merely to place such stones in exact contact would be careful work, but to do so with cement in the joint seems almost impossible; it is to be compared to the finest opticians work on a scale of acres." Herodotus, in the fifth century, reported on the casing stones covered with inscriptions of strange characters. The Arab historian Abd el Latif recorded that these inscriptions were so numerous that they could have filled "more than ten-thousand written pages." William of Baldensal in the 14th century said that the stones were covered with strange symbols arranged in careful rows. In 1356 AD a great earthquake leveled Cairo. The resident Arabs robbed the pyramid of its beautiful casing stones to reconstruct forts and mosques and the new city. The large stones were cut and redressed, which obliterated the wisdom that they were intended to pass down to humanity.

Martin Grey continues to say that there is further evidence that the pyramids were not the creation of the dynastic Egyptians. There are watermarks on the stones halfway up the pyramids. Silt sediments rising to 40 feet around the base of the pyramid contain many seashells and fossils that have been radiocarbon dated to be nearly 12,000 years old. These sediments could have been deposited in such great quantities only by major sea flooding, an event the dynastic Egyptians could never have recorded because they were not living in the area until 8,000 years after the flood. Watermarks were noticed halfway up the casing stones before they were removed (a height of 400 feet above the present level). Thick encrustations of sea salt were also found in the interior of the pyramid, corresponding to the height of the watermarks on the outside. There are still salt encrustations found on the walls of the Queen's Chamber.

In the words of the Egyptians themselves, it is recorded by Manetho (Appendix I) in his *Aegyptica* that the god Thoth, the first Hermes, wrote the history of Egypt in the sacred language of the hieroglyphs before the time of the great flood. Long after the great flood, Agathodaemon, son of the second Hermes (*Hermes Trismegistus*), copied down ancient wisdom and science from the hieroglyphs made by the ancient god Thoth who reigned before the great flood.

The Alignment of the Great Pyramid to the cardinal points has a variation of less than .06% in any direction. It also functioned as an enormous sundial, casting its shadow to the north on a field of stone paving and its reflected sunlight to the south, accurately marking the equinoxes and solstices. The original perimeter of the pyramid exactly equals one-half minute of latitude at the equator (which makes each side equal 1/8 minute of equatorial latitude). These measurements show that the builders knew the dimensions of the globe as precisely as if these had been determined by modern satellite surveys.

Precision in Mathematics, Geometry, Astronomy, and Workmanship

Many savants have demonstrated that the Great Pyramid at Giza was built upon arcane geometrical principles that interact within its structure. Intelligent researchers throughout the ages have discovered that the Egyptians easily handle the concepts of pi, $\pi = 3.14$, and the Golden Mean, phi, $\phi = .618$, as well as the methods of squaring the circle and creating the pentagram. But it should be almost inconceivable to us that this one pyramid could demonstrate all of these concepts as interrelated aspects of one spatial form. Interested geometers should seek a copy of *Pyramid Geometry* by the noted scholar Leon N. Cooper who demonstrates the efficiency of the numbers 11 and 22. Yet, Martineau in *Quadrivium* (p. 32) shows that the moon is related to the earth by a factor of 3:11; while the height of a pyramid and the diameter of a circle are related to the side of a pyramid and half the circumference of a circle in the factor of 7:11.

Many investigators of the pyramids, temples, and artifacts of Egypt have been astounded by the accuracy and high technology that is displayed in their construction. Egyptians even created a monument that contained a seismic deterrent by inserting a course of very large stones at one of the higher courses of stone in order to defeat the transmission of destructive seismic waves.

Concerning the difficult methods of dealing with giant blocks of extremely hard stone, we will rely on the information gathered by Christopher Dunn in *The Giza Power Plant, Technologies in Ancient Egypt* (1998). Mr. Dunn is a fabricating engineer who describes the unbelievable precision of accuracy that he noticed in his visits to Egypt. Signs of this incredible perfection were already noted by Napoleon's army of scientists and savants in the early 1800s and also in the early 20th century by the famous archaeologist Sir William Flinders Petrie.

Christopher Dunn revisits some of these early investigations and, through his own experience, finds that there is demonstrable evidence that the early inhabitants of the Nile and Giza Plateau used sophisticated high-speed saws, drills, and core drills. This is because hand-driven tools could not possibly create the markings in the extremely hard diorite and granite stones that he personally examined and evaluated by virtue of his own professional use of modern high-speed tools. Dunn's book and website are highly recommended. His observations are as follows:

- All the machining marks were those only to be found in manufacturing machinery of today. There were saw jumps and redirections that could only occur when a blade is cutting faster than the tradesmen could immediately notice and control. These saw marks—which were misplaced, restarted, and backed out again—were noticed already by Petrie.
- There were cuts that did not go through the stone but dead-ended in a corner or in very deep cuts. These types of cuts could not be made by long hand-drawn saws, even if they were assisted by grinding silicates or even saws impregnated with diamonds.
- All of the large drilled holes showed the continuing rifling marks throughout the long bore holes, which are consistent with high-speed drills. This is because a low-speed process would polish and obliterate the markings as it proceeded down the hole. Also, the examples of core holes are deeper than any known archaic equipment has been able to reach.
- At the rock tunnels of the Serapeum at Saqqara there are many carved granite stone boxes similar to the one found in the main pyramid at Giza. These 80-ton boxes with their 27-ton lids are amazing in their incredible precision of total orthogonal perfection. The insides, outsides, tops, and bottoms are all absolutely square and parallel to each other and themselves to 5/100,000 of an inch.

This is a degree of manufacturing that modern technology could only duplicate on very limited and small-scale custom work.

- Dunn saw evidence of what could only be evaluated as contoured saw cuts from saws that were able to slice concave and convex spherical radii. Corners in granite boxes were mitered to 5/32-inch radius gage.
- The Great Pyramid sits upon a solid limestone rock outcropping that was leveled by the Egyptians prior to construction of the pyramid. A survey using modern instruments determined that this area had been leveled to within 7/8 of an inch over the total area of 13 acres.
- In 1881, Petrie measured the descending passage, which is partially carved from the living rock and partially constructed of quarried stone. He was amazed to discover that his survey showed a miniscule quarter-inch difference in tolerance over the entire length of 350 feet of quarried and positioned stone.
- In the Cairo museum there are stone jars and bowls so finely machined and perfectly balanced that they inspire awe and wonder. One bowl in particular, a schist bowl with three lobes folded toward the center hub, is an incredible piece of work. Many of the 30,000 vessels found in the Step Pyramid of Zoser (2650 BC) were tall vases with long, thin, elegant necks and widely flared interiors. These curious vases were created from solid rock of extreme hardness—diorite, basalt, quartz crystal, and metamorphic schist. Even today, we have not yet invented the instruments that could carve out bulbous interior shapes through long narrow necks of hard rock. It will be remembered that the incredible savant, polymath, doctor, and architect, Imhotep, lived at the time of Zoser and introduced many new forms of architecture.
- Christopher Dunn cites Piazzi Smyth, the great supporter of John Taylor's original work, as saying, "There appears to be further an even commensurability of a most marvelous order,

between the weight of the whole Great Pyramid and the weight of our planet earth [in terms of scale equated to weight]."

Ancient Tools

I was repeating the remark that, "The base of the Great Pyramid is founded upon a rocky outcropping of limestone that was leveled off to 7/8 of an inch over 13 acres" to an acquaintance of mine who replied, "Yes, isn't that amazing—considering that they only had primitive tools?" This statement typifies exactly what is wrong with our treatment of ancient history:

- Nobody could seriously imagine that people equipped with simple tools could possibly level off 13 acres of limestone as well as build to the amazing specifications and tolerances that are displayed in Egypt.
- But archaeologists *have not* as yet discovered the methods or the tools by which such, work has been completed. From our other readings we have learned that tools and technique were classed among the royal possessions of the king, who was sometimes called the "chief carpenter," a term analogous with our builder-architect. The Roman Pope is called the *Pontifix Maximus*, the "chief bridge builder." Building practices were trade, national, and royal secrets and, as such, the direct source of the ruler's power and the security of the state. Therefore, tools and instruments were regarded the same way as the maps and trade routes of the Phoenicians. They were kept private as trade secrets and under lock and key, and they were most often willfully destroyed rather than allowed to fall into enemy hands. Peter Tompkins writes (*Great Pyramid*, p. 264), "Funk-Heller says the basic meter from which the cubit was derived had to be kept a deep secret, presumably so that all the calculations, including the means for obtaining the exact length of the year, would remain the sole property of the officiating priests." Also, it has been remarked that the paucity of artisan tools in Egypt was the result of the practice of collecting them after a day's work, since they belonged to the king, who safeguarded these instruments of

superior technology. It is also possible that the original builders of the great works of antiquity purposefully destroyed their tools, their architectural plans, and all records in order that they could not be duplicated by others and that they might be remembered in history as a people who had achieved the impossible. Subsequent carvings showing stones moved on rollers lubricated with oil and pulled by large gangs of workers could well have been created to further deceive later generations and to perpetuate the idea of a mysterious and supertalented people. In his new work, *Lost Technologies of Ancient Egypt*, Dunn cites (p. xii) Arlan Andrews, who says that, "When civilization fails for any reason, metals of all kinds become precious commodities. They become knives, spearpoints, scrapers, fish hooks, even plows. Ancient Egypt underwent numerous upheavals caused by droughts, earthquakes, civil wars, religious strife, and foreign invasions. During the times of collapse, the advanced metal tools that the ancient Egyptians used were probably disassembled, cut apart, or melted down. What wasn't immediately used would corrode and disappear after thousands of years."

- In 1853 ground crystal lens resembling telescope lenses were found at Nineveh among deposits dated 600 BC. Astronomical clay tablets from Nineveh record objects in the sky that are only visible with the use of optical assistance. Clay tablets from 747 BC at the British Museum describe four moons of Jupiter and seven moons of Saturn. The Babylonian year is recorded as 365 days, 6 hours, and 11 minutes, which is within 2 minutes of modern reckoning (ancient-wisdom.co.uk/crystal.htm 6/25/10).
- Archaeologists rationalize that until they can find sophisticated ancient tools, they have the right to say that the Egyptians did it all "with primitive tools." They justify this falsehood by pleading the scientific method of determining fact from observation. What cannot be found cannot be placed into the scientific equation.

- Every expert in every trade from stone carvers, masons, and engineers who lift and place heavy objects by cranes all testify that technology found in Egypt is above today's capabilities and could not be replicated by even today's most advanced and modern methods.
- The physical evidence—as evaluated by experts in the field—prompts the archaeologists to proclaim that many aspects of Egyptian work are beyond our present comprehension and abilities. The incredible close tolerances, precision shaping, finishing, polishing, the huge multisided limestone casing stones, and especially drilling of granite have never been explained. The mohs ratings for the hardness of the limestone and granite exceed the mohs hardness of the tools found in Egypt. Some of the superhard stones, like obsidian, could not even have been dinged or dented by any tools found by the archaeologists.
- Finally, none of the construction of any of the major ancient works in Egypt could have been completed in today's intensely hot climate. These projects belong to eras of long ago, when a much milder and cooler climate prevailed in these regions.

The Pyramid Is a Model of the Earth

After reading the Greek sources—such as Herodotus, Diodorus Siculus, and Strabo—the French surveyor of Napoleon's Egyptian campaign, Edme-Francois Jomard, was the first to conceive of the idea that the pyramid was a structure whose dimensions mimicked the dimensions of the Earth. Jomard was convinced that the Egyptians had developed an advanced science of geography and geodesy and that perhaps the pyramid reflected a portion of the length of a geographic degree. Further up the Nile at Thebes, General Desaix discovered a circular stone zodiac that portrayed the recognizable zodiac constellations in an ancient position somewhat different from their modern declinations. This allowed Jomard to rightly presume that the science of Egypt must be very ancient indeed. However, the temple that housed this antique star map was covered with relatively recent Ptolemaic inscriptions dating from the period shortly after Alexander. It later turned out that Jomard was correct to believe in the advanced ancient knowledge of the Egyptians. The temple that displayed the zodiac had been remodeled on many occasions far into the distant past. It should always be appreciated that Napoleon's army of soldiers and savants helped to illuminate our regard for the ancient scientific past as well as sparking an Egyptian renaissance in Europe.

Another of the unsung heroes of research was a poet and essayist, John Taylor, the son of a London bookseller born in the early 1800s. Peter Tompkins, in his excellent *Secrets of the Great Pyramid* (Ch.6), tells us that this investigator never set eyes upon the noble structure. Taylor used the ideas and measurements of Jomard and the French savants and those of Howard-Vyse and drew "from them a set of conclusions," writes Tompkins, "the most far reaching thus far about the origin and purpose of the Pyramid."

Taylor (d. 1864) was a gifted mathematician and amateur astronomer who analyzed the scale models of the pyramids that he fabricated. He was puzzled by the particular angle of 51 degrees, 51 minutes for the pyramid faces instead of the regular equilateral triangle of 60 degrees. Taylor read classical Greek accounts concerning what the Egyptian priests had told about the surface of each face of the pyramid. Taylor concluded that they had been designed to be equal in area to the square of the pyramid's height. He then discovered that if he divided the perimeter of the pyramid by twice its height, it gave him a quotient of 3.114, remarkably close to the value of pi. "In other words," writes Tompkins, "the height of the Pyramid appeared to be in relation to the perimeter of its base—as the radius of a circle is to its circumference. This seemed to Taylor far too extraordinary to be attributed to chance...if so this was a demonstration of the advanced knowledge of the builders." Taylor's thesis proclaimed that, "The pyramid had been built as a record of the true measurements of the Earth."

Not only was the pyramid in exact proportion to the oblate-spheroid shape of the Earth but units of time and cycles could be deduced from the measurements of its size. Ancient astronomical systems, as well as those that we use today, use the sexagesimal numbers 6, 60, and 360. This sexagesimal system is so ancient that it cannot be said to originate with any one nation. It is truly a part of universal scientific culture. Jomard, John Taylor, Piazzi Smith, and, later, William Fix have shown that the perimeter of the Great Pyramid's sockets equals a half minute of equatorial latitude, or 1/43,200 of the Earth's circumference. This is very important because—irrespective of feet, meters, cubits, or miles—the Earth is proportionally 43,200 times the size of the Great Pyramid. The perimeter (all four sides) of the base of the pyramid represents the true and exact equator of the Earth in the proportion of 1:43,200. This proportion was said to equal ½ a degree (4 x 1/8 degree per side = ½ degree per perimeter) of the equator, which results in the following equation:

> If ½ degree (of a 360 degree circle) =43,200 units; then a full degree would be a circle of 720 units (360 x 2 = 720). Then, 43,200 divided by 720 = 60 which is one of the key units in the sexagesimal system, especially related to the interior angles of 60° of equilateral triangles and the hexagram used in global measurement.

In addition to these unique mathematical relationships, there are many other exact relationships. It seems almost incredible that the height is also in this proportion: The height of the Pyramid including the platform equals 1/43,200 of the earth's polar radius (which is different to the equator). 2,160 years is the sexagesimal value for the precession of the vernal equinox through one sign of the zodiac, or 30 degrees. Then, 2 x 2,160 years = 4,320 years = 2 zodiac signs or 60 degrees, which again is one of the key basis of the sexagesimal system.

These multiplicities of proportional relationships of the size of the pyramid relative to the Earth, as well as the chronological astronomical cycles' relationship to the geometry and scale of the Great Pyramid, seem incredible and beyond human abilities. The Great Pyramid is the jewel of an all-comprehensive expression of technology, structure, mathematics, geometry, geophysics, and chronology. Even though its shell cladding was removed—including its instructions, directions for use, and explanations—the Great Pyramid is so perfect that it explained itself to the many intelligent amateurs who deciphered its meanings. The Great Pyramid embodies the "mystery of the Sphinx"—namely the explanation of the cosmic unity of the proportion of man, pyramid, Earth, solar system, galaxy, and universe. It should be admitted that the Great Pyramid at Giza is the ultimate temple, a stone mandala, and a model of the cosmos.

Could it be possible that the other two pyramids on the Giza Plateau also represent the cosmic means and extremes in the size, shape, and precessional cycle of the Earth during the course of all time? Is the Giza Plateau a historical picture of the changes of the Earth over epochal ages? These changes would be in the size, orbit, velocity, and speed of revolution of our planet during the long history of the Earth within our galaxy, within our universe.

The Giza Pyramids must also be regarded as cosmic temples to the Creator God, the sublime architect of the universe. In Peru, precision and exactness were required in all holy structures that celebrated the Divine. Both sacred and scientific went hand in hand in the worldview of the ancient cosmologers. In their perspective, the pyramid would have represented a mandala and an earthly temple of the universe. The Mixtec reported that the pyramids near Mexico City were "the road to the gods"—a perfect temple of communication with God.

More Examples of Precision

William R. Corliss, in his book *Ancient Structures* (pp. 169–205), touches upon many of the anomalies and engineering enigmas discovered at the Great Pyramid. He reiterates that the size and transportation of the many large blocks is not at issue because all of this could have been accomplished by simple mechanics and a large, well-organized workforce. He focuses upon extreme precision and technological anomalies that are not concurrent with the era in which the Great Pyramid is thought to have been constructed:

- The triangular sides of the pyramid are concave in an opposite curve that exactly emulates the precise curvature of our Earth. Preserving this accuracy while ascending the sides of the pyramid without "twisting" the courses seems a construction capability that is beyond belief.

- Graham Hancock and Robert Bauval brought forward the ideas that the Giza pyramids were an earthly image of the three stars in the belt of the constellation of Orion, whom the Egyptians worshipped as their national god, Osiris. Moreover, the pyramid's relationship to the River Nile is the same as the Orion stars' relationship to the Milky Way, the great galactic river in the sky. Because of changes in our perspective due to precession, the stars of Orion's belt rose exactly with the Milky Way in emulation of the position of the Nile and the Giza Pyramids exactly in 10,500 BC, when the precessional cycle was in the constellation of Leo. Ptolemy reports that the solid signs like Taurus, Aquarius, and Leo are most suitable for building monuments that will stand for great periods of time. The extensive studies of Schwaller de Lubicz confirm that Egyptian culture went through several cycles of architectural, scientific, and artistic surges and depressions of greatness and degeneration from the absolute sublime to the incompetent.
- The 35th course of blocks, at the height of the King's Chamber, which is 100 feet high, weigh about five times as much as the average block within the rest of the structure. The neighboring Pyramid of Khafre has all the largest blocks at the base level. Curiously, these blocks are so large—500 tons—that some suspect that these belong to some older culture that erected these monolithic stones for another purpose than a pyramid foundation. The quarrying, transportation by boat, and precision setting of even the average 70-ton granite blocks seems beyond the capabilities of Fourth Dynasty stone masons. This monster-size 35th course is the seismic course implanted to defeat the earthquake shockwaves.
- The logistics and social organization required to procure, process, and place one multi-ton stone block every 2 minutes and 17 seconds, 12 hours a day for 20 years (=2.3 million stone blocks) is unrealistic. There are over 30 recognized theories concerning this incredible construction. If the historians are wrong, and we assume

a period of 100 years to construct, then one block would have to be set every 11 minutes. Modern field tests show that humans can wrestle multi-ton stones on sleds and drag them a few feet. The idea of raising multi-ton stones several hundred feet high and setting them perfectly at a rate of 2 to 11 minutes per stone is not possible.

- There is an unexplained absence of spoiled or rejected blocks that should be in evidence in the quarries.
- The gleaming, polished limestone casing stones at the base were 12 feet long, 5 feet high, and 8 feet wide and weighed between 16–20 tons each. They had a very complex shape in order to rest on the core stones and also to present a perfectly polished slanted face to the outside. They were cemented together by an extremely thin film layer (no thicker than a man's nail) of cement of an unknown formula. Petrie found that the mean variation from a straight line and a true square was but 1/100 of an inch on a length of 75 inches. This staggering accuracy is equivalent to the most modern optician's straight edges. Optical precision in limestone using copper chisels is unlikely. It has also been asked why the Egyptians demanded such tight tolerances over such large areas. The Egyptians demanded .010-inch precision when modern stonework only requires .25-inch precision. These kinds of tolerances are beyond belief.
- Thirty-ton granite blocks make up the walls and ceiling of the Queen's Chamber. Their joints are so fine that a knife blade will not fit between them. This would have been difficult with limestone—with huge, superhard granite blocks; it is little short of a miracle.
- The King's Chamber is composed of 100 70-ton granite blocks and nine ceiling blocks weighing 50 tons each. The engineering logistics involved in creating such a chamber at a height of 150 feet above the ground are stupefying.
- The king's sarcophagus is a manufacturing anomaly. It is carved from a single block of chocolate-colored granite from an as-yet-

> undiscovered quarry. The Egyptians' drills apparently cut through this hard quartz-crystal-impregnated granite with speed and ease, judging from the marks on the sides of the stone. Today's granite drills advance at 0.0002 inch per turn. The Egyptian drills advanced an absolutely incredible 500 times faster at 0.1 inch per revolution. Some granite artifacts from this period seem to have been turned upon a lathe, which sounds preposterous to modern tradesmen. Again, there are an incredible number of these identical 80-ton boxes and their 27-ton lids in the stone tunnels of Saqqara.

Precision Astronomical Sighting Tool

The position of the pyramids at 30 degrees north of the equator should alert us to the fact that they were constructed to map both the heavens and the earth as well as to possibly establish a microcosmic concord between the positions of the stars of the galaxy and the universe and the layout of the geography of the Earth.

In *Secrets of the Great Pyramids* (Ch. 12), Peter Tompkins discloses that Arab historians repeatedly affirm that the Great Pyramid had originally been designed "as an astronomical observatory and that it contained reproductions of the celestial spheres…yet none could put forward a sensible solution as to how its steep polished sides could be climbed as an observatory."

Before the turn of the last century, the British astronomer Richard A. Proctor published *The Great Pyramid, Observatory, Tomb, and Temple.* He found a reference by the neo-Platonist Proclus that the pyramid had been used as an observatory before its completion. Proctor theorized that, "The Pyramid might have made an excellent observatory at the time it had reached the summit of the Grand Gallery, which would have given on to a large square platform where the priests could observe and record the movements of the heavenly bodies."

Most intriguing of all the anomalies is, of course, the Grand Gallery, which Tompkins describes in *Mysteries of the Great Pyramid.* The gallery likely served as a precision astronomical sighting tool. The many unusual intricate nuances of design could not have been made for some casual purpose. It looks like some part of a machine whose purpose is beyond our ken. It has been discovered that the granite plugs that seal off the Grand Gallery and the King's Chamber were made to look as if they had been slid into place, but they are actually cemented to the floor of the passage. It is assumed that this passage was the Egyptian equivalent to the housing of a telescope, which could have accommodated mirrored- or optical-lens telescopes. Its scientific purpose seems beyond question, but whatever careful calibrations were discovered by this instrument is not apparent. One could make up an interpretation that the king was the chief astronomer, who, like Atlas before him, discovered the round circuit of the stars. His burial chamber was placed above this instrument. His magnificent sighting tool and his home in the afterlife were therefore enshrined in the heart of the pyramid.

The Astronomical Mirror

Like their Egyptian counterparts, the Mesoamerican pyramids are extremely sophisticated. Just like the many rings around Stonehenge, the Teotihuacán pyramids near Mexico City are said to reveal the exact proportion of the size of the orbits of the planets around the central feature of the giant Pyramid of the Sun. In modern astronomy, overhead transits of stars are captured in a pool of reflective mercury. The Maya also used pools of water and seaside caves with holes in their ceilings to observe important transits of stars and planets. At Teotihuacán there is a raised fountain-pool in front of the Pyramid of the Moon in which the stars and planets were tracked by the light of their reflection.

Some pyramids produce light-and-shadow shows during the equinoxes. These pyramids are also sensitive to such acoustical effects as the sound of clapping hands, which reverberates like they cry of a Macaw. Most astounding is the stair railing ending in a serpent's head that produces a slithering action along the stepped pyramid at Chichen Itza. This process is called a *hierophany*—a holy show. Anthony Aveni (*Skywatchers*, p. 299) quotes several observers and authorities regarding the undulating shadows of the sacred serpents descending the staircases of the Castillo pyramid at Chichen

Itza during both the vernal and autumnal equinoxes. I have witnessed this impressive show, and the perfection of the shadowy movement is so realistic that one must believe that no ordinary science and technology created it.

The Great Pyramid also put on a light-and-shadow show. There is a crease in the middle of all the four faces of the Great Pyramid at Giza. During the spring and autumn equinoxes, half of the southern face is in shadow, while the other half catches the rays of the sun. This phenomenon lasts for about four minutes and compares to the light-and-shadow show of the snake descending the staircase of Kukulcan's pyramid in Yucatan. Another shadow-and-light show also occurs at the equinoxes on the Pyramid of the Sun in Teotihuacán by Mexico City.

Tim Stouse (timstouse.com/great pyramid, 1/31/11) tells us that the Great Pyramid is located at the center of the greatest extent of landmass on the Earth. The pyramid was originally covered with 144,000 hard polished white limestone casing stones weighing about 15 tons each. This polished white stone easily reflected light from both Sun and stars, and could most likely be seen from the Moon. As the concave sides of the Great Pyramid produce a light-and-shadow show during the equinoxes, there is a further possibility of an extremely advanced type of holy show. Perhaps, therefore, we might imagine that the Giza Pyramids of Egypt may once have produced a hierophany by means of the reflection of astronomical objects upon its highly polished surfaces of its granite casings. It may well be that the entire complex of pyramids and satellite structures all functioned together as actors in some gigantic cosmic drama of astronomy by bringing the heavens down to be reflected upon the slopes of the pyramids as well as transferred upon the surrounding pavements. This mirror show would have been impressive during moonlight, as well as mirroring the blazing sunlight in a surreal image upon the surrounding plateau areas. But without this highly polished mirror casing the pyramids are like a blind person, because they cannot see the heavens.

This mirroring would also have shown eclipses of the sun and moon, transits of the inferior planets, and possibly the entire solar system through angles formed with the other pyramid members. Again, the polish and shade of granite may even have shown the blazing sun alongside the major and brighter stars of the day sky. Visitors to Egypt would have been shown that the people along the Nile had extraordinary knowledge of the universe—to such an extent that they were able to bring the cosmos virtually down to Earth. Such knowledge, magic, and control over cosmic phenomena would have made these scientists the envy of the world.

There Are Many Other Pyramids around the World

Most of us are astonished to find out that there are 50,000 known ancient pyramid-like structures all around the globe. The pyramids outside Mexico City are nearly equal in volume and size to those in Egypt. While the Great Pyramid of Cholula in Puebla, Mexico, dates from 200 BC and is an astounding one-third larger in volume (1476 x 1476 feet square base) than the Great Pyramid in Egypt (756 x 756 feet square base).

There are giant pyramids in the China Pyramid Complex near Taiyuan Space Center in Shanxi Province. In total, 70 pyramids are located in this area, but they have only recently been investigated. Curiously, the main complex has a configuration of three pyramids like those upon the Giza Plateau. Again, the Chinese government is reluctant to disclose much information about their pyramids. We do know that they are aligned to the cardinal directions and toward Gemini and are placed upon the ground like the constellation of Gemini. Some of them are flat-topped like some of the Mexican pyramids.

Pyramids have been reported in Japan, Java, Indonesia, Bolivia, Burma, Tibet, as well as 26 in Peru. Even in Bosnia there are several pyramid-shaped mountains related by specific orientations—in one of which, caverns, stairways, and architectural forms are just now beginning to be examined (bosnianpyramid.com, 1/24/11).

The 59-foot-tall Akapana pyramid in Tiwanaku, Bolivia has been plundered of its stones for railroad and church building. At this location and nearby Puma Punku are many examples of stone duct-works, core-holes, and stones that look like they were carved by machines. At Huaca Grande, there are 26 pyramids over a 540-acre site, including the eroded pyramid at Tucume. At Huallamarca and Pachacamac, Peru, there are impressive step pyramids with ramps.

Conclusion

The Great Pyramid at Giza, the perfect granite caskets in the underground caves at Saqqara, and the multi-faced stones at Puma Punku are clearly at a level high above our abilities to replicate. They belong to a technologically advanced culture that we cannot explain. Along with these amazing creations are abundant remains, artifacts, and sophisticated ancient sites that proclaim a worldview and a philosophy driven to the zenith of their expectation and imagination. In other words, these ancient people had gone as far as they could go pursuing their unique goals before time and the destructive cycles of nature terminated their game. These people are not a chapter in human evolution, progress, or development. They are their own unique and epochal episode in universal history. And there will come a day when our modern, advanced, and unique brave new world will travel that identical road, swallowed up by the natural cycles of creation and destruction that have been spoken about by all peoples of every culture since the beginning of time.

Part 2

The Ancient Cosmic Worldview

CHAPTER 2.1

"Cosmothink"—*Thinking in Cycles*

The cosmic worldview of ancient people took into account the context of the entire universe in order to explain life here on our planet. They attempted to create a comfortable and rational view out of the chaos of nature and the astronomical cycles of the heavens. They also realized that the great astronomical cycles imposed a tremendous regulator grip of fate and preordained order upon the system and that in order to escape this determinism, you must know how fate operates and where "freedom of the will" begins and where it ends. In order to perceive human freedom, one must know the limitations of fate. One must be both a philosopher as well as an astrologer-cosmologer.

In *Skywatchers* (p. 222), noted archaeoastronomer Anthony F. Aveni writes how the ancients marked the movements of the sun, moon, planets, and astrocycles within the layout of complex sites such as the pyramids outside of Mexico City. But he is forced to admit, "In our modern scientific attempts to understand the natural world, we also seek to attain a predictive advantage over nature, one which affords a measure of control over the environment. To accomplish this task we employ complex instruments to extend our senses and devise a rigorously defined formal system of logic... But are the thought processes of modern people...very far removed in basic structure from their ancestors' form of thought?" Mainly, however, ancient people painted an image of the friendly skies of order and rhythm formed by a Creator God as opposed to the chaos of chemical reactions and explosions proposed by modern science.

In the conclusion to *Early Man and the Cosmos* (1984), Evan Hadingham considers the problem of the difference in worldview between ancient and modern man. He asks the general question as to how and why ancient astronomy was carried out. Was superstition rather than science their motivation? Hadingham also questions interpretations regarding ancient sky-watchers as members of religious orders and astronomer-priests forming specialized colleges for training "wise men" to serve and give power to an elite and royal society.

Hadingham summarizes (p. 245) by saying that:

> The order perceived in the heavens provided a model that gave form and meaning to the actions of people on earth. Whether their needs and decisions revolved around the right time to plant corn, or the proper place to raise a cairn or pyramid to honor a dead lord, the cosmic order provided them with guidance and justification. This conscious use of the sky to create and reinforce social values was quite different from the attitude of an astronomer today. Of course we know that the path of modern scientific inquiry is influenced by economic and political forces; indeed if we look beneath the proverbial objectivity of the scientist we might find his calculations serving such ends as guiding missiles and spy satellites. However, it is the essential and explicit concern of ancient astronomers with human affairs, as well as with beliefs about the natural order, that distinguishes their thinking from ours today.

Hadingham continues by remarking that scientists often lose their objectivity when they try "to people the prehistoric past with ourselves in fancy dress as R.J.C. Atkinson once said." The religious or astrological preoccupations of early astronomers are sometimes dismissed as unimportant or as obstacles that prevented the observers from making true scientific progress. The distinction between religion and the "practical" or the "scientific" is meaningless in the case of the Maya. Hadingham (p. 246) says, "A mystical unifying conception was the motivation of their mathematics and astronomy. It was expressed in a holy framework of number cycles, to which nearly all their observations of the sky were related...buildings were not observing devices, but instead symbolized the divine celestial and earthly relationships perceived by the Maya." Finally, he proposes (p. 249) "We begin to value the complexity and logic of other schemes of thought besides our own. We realize that our framework of ideas developed from only one system of thought out of many that have passed into obscurity. The perspective of other peoples, sometimes glimpsed across a gap of countless generations, reminds us of the shortcomings of our own outlook..."

The Egyptian priest criticized Solon and the Greeks for thinking like children, saying that none of their sciences were "hoary with age"; that is, they lacked long-term records and experience. What exactly do long-term records and experience show us? They tell us something very important in life; namely that everything proceeds in cycles. Things and events are born, and then they mature, degenerate, deteriorate, and die. Astronomical phenomena show that things are reborn afresh, resurrected, and continue by proceeding in similar cycles over and over again. "Thinking in cycles" presents a totally different way of looking at the world—a cosmological worldview where even cycles are working within other cycles.

Every human understands this worldview because of their experience of the day-and-night cycle of every day, the phases of the moon, the cycling seasons of the year. Even above our casual experience there are magnificent celestial cycles formatting new global climates and environments upon which the future characters of history will perform.

Hadingham has begun to suggest that contemporary science is the handmaiden of the military, corporations, government bureaucracy, and politics. It is in the interest of these combined forces to promote a worldview of evolution and progress forward from a lowly and more primitive plane.

Straight-line thinking is goal-orientated, easy to indoctrinate, and readily acceptable because it is partially true. All the ideas from straight-line thinking are like graphs that represent parts and segments of a true cycle of events. The temporary economic prosperity of the last housing-appreciation bubble was partially true as values kept rising, but since every marketplace operates in cycles, it became inevitable that the bubble would burst. This was because everything was stretched out of form, from credit availability to mortgage qualification to sustainable high-reward employment.

Straight-line thinking purposely subverts, ignores, and destroys "information which does not support the progress of man."

Indeed, if there were straight-line human progress, we would have achieved it long ago. Human evolution comes about after global and regional catastrophes when mankind is thrown back into a primitive state of the hunter-gatherer when cities, infrastructure, and agriculture are annihilated by great natural disasters and global wars.

Political evolution is again a cycle of complete change from one system to another: from kingship to democracy to socialism to communism to dictatorship.

The big bang theory is also a part of the cycle. Vedic astronomers have continually held that the universe expands into many themes and vistas and then recedes back into itself and into a sleeping and dormant state before rising again. Their traditions spoke of the 100 years of the life of the god Brahma, which equated into 311,040,000,000,000 human years. At the dissolution of the Vedic universe, Brahma would recede into the sleeping god Shiva. After all this, the cosmos would once again be reformed and exploded into life again.

Science itself admits that Pangaea is indeed a cycle and that we are now halfway through the second formation and dispersal cycle.

The Egyptian priest represents the antiquity of culture. Solon represents the infancy of emerging city-states. Wherever we look on the globe, there is a battle between the new and the old a battle between civilization and culture, a conflict between the exuberance of youth and the over-assurance of age. "Thinking in cycles" leads to the realization that the world is very old and that intelligent humans have been around for a very long time experiencing large-scale annihilations by many natural disasters, different cosmic dramas, and histories dictated by the cycle of the spiraling Milky Way Galaxy.

The Cosmic Ocean of the Universe, the Celestial River of the Milky Way, and the Local Rivers on Earth

All energy and spirit comes from the celestial ocean (which we call the universe) to the individual galaxies. The individual galaxies transfer this universe energy throughout their own constituent parts. Therefore, ancient people regarded the Milky Way as the conveyor of all energy, life, sustenance, and inspiration. They even symbolized their own rivers as images of the Milky Way and also called this celestial river of stars by the name of their own stream, whether it was the Yellow River, the River Maya, or the Nile. The universal ocean is depicted by zigzag water symbols on the sides of the Circular Zodiac of Dendera that frame the circle of the constellations. Wavy zigzag bands symbolizing the celestial ocean are also found on the sides of the pyramid of Quetzalcoatl at Teotihuacán in Mexico.

There is a reference to the Maize God, who is conveyed on his journey by the "cosmic canoe." Indeed, the Egyptian gods travel by boat through the cosmic ocean. Maritime cultures are the most knowledgeable about astronomy, which is their map of the skies to direct their progress over seas and to guide them to safe anchorages through the ebb and flow of the tides. Rivers that flow through rich agricultural deltas toward ocean bays provide the best settlements for commerce and industry near the abundant supplies of fish, game, and waterfowl.

Ancient people believed that the energy of the universe is transferred to the sun at the center of our solar system. Our Earth is juxtaposed within our solar system so that it may gently and safely receive portions of this cosmic energy. This juxtaposition accounts for the changes and irregularities in nature and human beings. Perfection in form cannot be directly delivered to our planet. But those who have studied celestial mechanics can see beyond change, irregularity, and chaos to perceive the ultimate perfection and formal design of the cosmos.

The Ancient Common Worldview and Global Language of Cosmic Thought

Ancient cosmic thought divides the universe into a trinity made up of the Creator God, humans, and the garden planet Earth. Humans were thought to stand between the divine and matter and therefore share in the nature of both being creatures half-material and half-divine. Andean and Maya cultures characterize this trifold division of the cosmos as the realms of the condor (heaven), puma (life between heaven and earth), and the serpent (earth). Every imaginable culture has adopted the motto "On Earth as it is in heaven," attempting to recreate an earthly mandala of the perfections of cosmic physics, synchronicity, balance, and harmony that appear in the heavens:

- "Astronomy is the mother of cultures," says the Peruvian professor Carlos Milla Villena in *Cultura Andina* (p. 37).
- In the Forbidden City in the heart of Beijing there is a circular ceremonial platform of three levels. These levels signify nature, man, and the divine. The Chinese emperor would surmount these with much ceremony to be proclaimed the divine and rightful heavenly king and the incarnate representative of God here on the Earth. This sort of formal ceremony did not vary throughout the ancient world. The emperor was under strict command to obey the cosmic order. In Chinese astrology, the moon is considered to be the prime minister of the sky who rules sternly. Also, the grand astrologer of China had 28 officials, corresponding to the 28 mansions of the moon upon the celestial sphere.
- The *Nihongi, Chronicles of Japan from the Earliest Times* tell us that the ancient Japanese held a cosmological worldview. Their traditions speak of the Milky Way, the heavenly image of their "Tranquil River," and of the 500-branched true *Sakaki* World Tree. They also speak of their gods being born from the great anthropological body of the High God—one god from the forearm, the left foot, the right leg, and so on.

- Imhotep was the renowned architect, medical doctor, and advisor to the king of Egypt. He also carried the title "chief of the observers," the regular title of the astronomer priests of Heliopolis. According to Egyptian manuscripts, Imhotep prophesized the legend of the seven fat cows and the seven lean cows coming from the Nile to prepare Pharaoh to store up provisions during the prosperous years in order to survive through the drought. According to I.E.S. Edwards (Bauval p. 30), the chief of the astronomers was represented wearing a mantle adorned with stars. It may be assumed that Imhotep made his prediction through astronomical means to predict weather cycles and flood levels of the Nile.
- In Greek-Egyptian lore, Hercules, the student of the astronomer Atlas, was called "star-clad." The Blessed Virgin Mary, astrologers, and cosmologers are portrayed in "star mantles," representing their love of the heavens and connection with the universe. In *Maya Cosmos* (p. 394), Linda Schele reports that the Maya kings dressed themselves as the embodiment of the Milky Way Galaxy. This took the form of impersonating the Waka Chan tree, the holy ceiba tree, whose gentle five-petaled, white flowers replicated the stars of the galaxy. The blossoms come into flower on the Mayan "day of creation" and only open during the night and close against the heat of the day. The fruit comes on the spring equinox, showing that the ceiba is attuned to the cosmos.
- In his *Update on the Aryan Invasion Debate* (1999), Koenraad Elst speaks about an element of Hebrew culture from Babylon and Egypt that is fascinated with mysteries of Kabalistic lore and numerical representation of astronomical data in ancient traditions, "Thus the Bible, written by a satellite culture of the astronomically astute Babylonians, used the device of enciphering astronomical data in all kinds of contingent numerical aspects of the narrative, e.g. the ages of the antediluvian patriarchs in Genesis turn out to be equal to the sums of the planets' synodic cycles (period from one conjunction with

the sun until the next): Lamech dies at age 777, which is the sum of 399 (number of days in Jupiter's synodic cycle) + 378 (Saturn's); Mahalalel at 895 = 116 + 779 (Mercury + Mars); Yared at 962 = 584 + 378 (Venus + Saturn). Similarly, the symbolism of 12 and 13, referring to the lunar months in a year, is omnipresent in the Bible: 12 sons of Jacob plus one daughter; 12 tribes of Israel with a territory plus the one priestly tribe of Levi; 12 regular apostles of Jesus plus the one substitute for the traitor Judas, Matthias; the "13-petal rose" as Talmudic symbol of the Torah. The ancient symbol of the Jews was always the seven-branched candlestick representing the seven planets."

- Kelley and Milone cite (p. 433) the work done by Reichel-Dolmatoff (1965) on the Kogi, or ancient Tairona people, of the isolated Columbian Sierra Nevada region on the Caribbean near Santa Maria. He describes the rigors of the training of a young astronomer-priest, called a *Mama*. These tribes still have and use many of the antique articles of their ancestors, such as the concave obsidian mirrors for observing the sun, the so-called "smoking mirrors" of the Mesoamericans. Preservation of their heritage has been possible because of the extreme steepness of their terrain from sea level to the highest regions of the alpine snow peaks. The unique and fiercely independent Kogi nation managed to survive and keep their ancient culture totally intact even into our modern times. They are a people imbued in a cosmological worldview. While they were in training, their novice priests awoke at nightfall and spent the entire night studying. They returned to bed before sunrise because they were not allowed to see the sun for nine years. The studies included local traditions, myths, history, and astronomy. After the period of nine years, the novices were sent home for a while to consider if they wished to continue with another nine years of rigorous training, diet, and abstinence from women and indeed all other society. The key information that one can immediately see is that the Kogi do not regard astronomy as a separate department in their world of science and activities. For them, as with all cosmologically minded people, astronomy is the framework of their religion, science, history, myths, and traditions. Cosmology is the life's breath of their culture. Curiously, when intrepid missionaries scaled their mountain passes to bring them the word of Jesus Christ, the Kogi responded that this was already known to them as a part of their traditions and that Catholicism is simply a corrupted version of their own religion.

- Cinematography has made a comedic performance out of ancient Native American costume and ritual dance. The snake dances of the North American and Mesoamerican native people are enacted in tune to the cosmic cycles like the dragon dances of the Asian people celebrating the cycles of their lunar zodiac. The dancing and flowing Asian dragons symbolize the River of Milk, the Milky Way Galaxy. These performances are in imitation of cosmic cycles and astronomical events. Hunbatz Men in *Secrets of Mayan Science/Religion* (p. 118) says that the illumination and auric energy of a Maya priest is represented by the feathers surrounding the subject's head. Planetary astrology was certainly part of Maya science and shamanism. These general kinds of headdresses were common to both continents of the Americas, and it seems that they represented a "divine halo" symbolized by the circle of feathers.
- Throughout the world, people have made ritual sand paintings and mandala as models of their perceptions of the universe. Stone alignments track the courses of the sun, moon, and stars. The Temples of Angkor Wat, Jerusalem, and the Great Pyramid were designed as astronomical replicas of the cosmos. Even in one of the oldest cradles of civilization high in the Andes of Bolivia, "The Tiwanakans left us a cosmic vision of the world: Earth was created for mankind, and mankind for the veneration of the gods, a concept in which humans, like the planets and stars, were part of a cosmic equilibrium (J. Escalante in *Tiwanaku—Cultural Patrimony of Humanity* La Paz, Bolivia, 2001)." Kelley and Milone

record that the most complex mandala that they have ever seen is that of Garbhadata, a Chinese Buddhist mandala brought to Japan in 806 AD, in which over 300 deities are represented along with 28 lunar mansions and 12 signs of the zodiac around a square center holding eight gods around a central supreme god. Chinese cosmology comprehends the entire universe, including God, nature, humans, colors, substances, elements, geometry, and numbers.

- Some of the greatest treasures of human art are related to astronomy: the Aztec calendar stones, the Coyolxauhqui stone, Circular Zodiac of Dendera, and the marble statue of Atlas holding the celestial sphere.
- Everywhere upon the face of the globe we find ancient stone alignments and temples orientated to the north polar axis of the Earth, the equinoxes and solstices, and the rising and setting of significant stars and asterisms.
- Mazes and labyrinths depict the back-and-forth weaving of the different clockwise and counterclockwise movements of the cosmic cycles creating the mystic tapestry and drama of life. In many medieval churches, pious believers meditate and say their prayers while following the winding route of the mazes. Most of the great mystery schools and cults employed these mysterious puzzles in their initiatory rites and celebrations, accompanied by holy chants and the tunes of instruments mimicking the heavenly music of the spheres. The blindfold represents the darkness of the universe whose secrets are to be revealed. The secret is that these initiations are of cosmic origin.

Similar Astronomy

It seems beyond coincidence that cultures around the world have focused upon the same aspects and problems of astronomy. It is remarkable that crystals and granite-bearing crystals are found at sacred and burial sites in Egypt, England, Scotland, Ireland, China, India, Peru, and California. Crystals seem to work in some mysterious electrical fashion in connection with underground water emanations (ancient-wisdom.co.uk/, 1/24/11).

- Another common astronomical feature found in China is the use of equal double hours: 12 to the day and 12 to the night. It is also amazing that most of the world was familiar with the fact that the center navel of our Milky Way Galaxy is universally regarded to be near the bright star, "A" Sagittarius, shown as the arrow point in the constellation of the archer.
- Almost every culture around the globe has a very special regard for the star Sirius, the asterism of the Pleiades, and the constellation of Orion, which are all found in the same region of the sky.
- Advanced astronomy around the world calculated the moon's Metonic cycle of north and south standstills over a period of 18–19 years. This cycle dominates the layout of Chaco Canyon, home of the Anasazi in Arizona; sites in Scotland; and Chankillo and Qenko in Peru. In China the Metonic cycle was called *chang* and became the basis of their world cycle of 23,639,040 years.
- In many parts of the world, the divine right of kings and the legitimacy of ruling families has been based upon specific astronomical cycles, especially eclipses of the sun and moon when they fall upon the exact geography of a kingdom. In some instances, eclipses required a ruling family to abdicate and give place to a new family. Chinese and Mesoamericans held strong beliefs that changes in the ruling families—as well as government and society—occurred during solar and lunar eclipses.
- Chroniclers of the past throughout the world linked ancient history with the zodiac and all the constellations of the heavens. This system rehearsed and celebrated all ancient and mythic events every year as the sun passed through the signs of the zodiac creating an anniversary of every event of the past even from different cosmic cycles. Myth was thus safeguarded and encoded in a cocoon of astronomy permanently written in the sky. Many of these events were from the far distant past and rightly belonged to the slow and ponderous cycle of the Milky Way.

Cosmic Games

Livio Catullo Stecchini (*Secrets of the Great Pyramid* p. 295) says that the origin of foot and chariot races, such as the Olympics, were ritual imitations of the courses of the planets of the gods in the heavens. The ballgames in the great ball court of the Maya city of Chichen Itza were likewise in imitation of celestial events. Ancient people regarded the zodiac as a heavenly racecourse in which the sun, moon, and planets revolved—a highway about 14 degrees wide to allow the 7-degree north and south declinations of the planet Mercury. The Giant's Ring near Belfast may well have been a ritual site for horseraces in imitation of the sun and planets of our solar system. Sacred buildings and labyrinths, board games, card games, and dice games were all constructed upon cosmological models. Kelley and Milone in their encyclopedia of astronomy (p. 499) say that the image of the sun as a charioteer spread throughout the Mediterranean world, where ever-more-elaborate racecourses were designed as cosmic images. During the Byzantium period, astrological themes seemed to dominate the design of hippodromes.

In China, astrological divination tools later became board games. One metal plate indicated the four cardinal directions of the Earth. Centered upon this was a round spinning disc divided into the 28 days of the moon's influences. Some plates depicted an outer circle of 36 animals, like the *decans* of Egyptian astronomy.

The normal deck of cards is divided into four major suits of hearts, clubs, diamonds, and spades representing the four cardinal directions and the four seasons of the year. There are 52 cards in total representing the 52 weeks of the year. There are 13 cards in each of the four suits. The number 13 is the holiest of astronomic numbers.

Ancient Icons of the Cosmos—The Winged Serpent

The snake has always been an image of wisdom. Because they live in the earth, they are especially associated with the natural sciences. By the simple expedient of attaching wings to serpents, it raises their level of knowledge to that of the heavens.

The dancing Chinese dragons in the New Year parades represent the celestial Yellow River, a depiction of the stream of the Milky Way Galaxy. In Egypt, every important temple entrance is surmounted by the winged solar disc flanked by serpents. The Egyptians were, of course, masters of symbols and the above mentioned symbol simply expressed would read as, "Welcome to the temple of cosmological knowledge."

Egyptian temple with solar disc supported by winged-serpents. Author photo

In the American continents, the "plumed, winged, or feathered serpent" was the instructor of the cosmic sciences. Quetzalcoatl is simply translated as "winged-snake." Other versions of his name are Gucumatz and Kukulcan. His famous pyramid at Chichen Itza exquisitely demonstrates astronomical knowledge by signaling the date of the equinoxes through shadowplay showing the cosmic serpent slithering down the side of the serpent-headed balustrades of the great staircases of the pyramid.

The heavenly snake slithering down the pyramid of Chichen Itza. Author photo

In Teotihuacán near Mexico City are the great pyramids of the moon, sun, and Quetzalcoatl, as the divine spirit. His temple has alternating symbols of the plumed serpent, the rain god Tlaloc, and the mythical *cipactli*—"the crocodile that symbolizes the fusion of earth and water" (*Teotihuacán*, p. 14). There are wavy bands around the feathered serpent to symbolize the cosmic ocean, which is the universe.

The Cosmic Milk

All ancient people believed that energy, spirit, sustenance, inspiration, and divine food and drink came from the galaxy. In *The Milky Way and the Cosmic Soma*, David Frawley insists that the Milky Way provides the cosmic soma, the nectar of immortality and the drink of the gods. This heavenly manna-like drink is said to be related to the side of the Milky Way where it crosses the zodiac signs of Taurus and Gemini.

The renowned goddess Hathor of Egypt offers her milk-full breasts to replenish the Milky Way galaxy. She is the spiritual hostess who communicates with humans and the divine. In Greece, the goddess Hera—consort of Zeus—offered her exposed breasts to perform the identical function. While in Mexico, it is Coyolxauhqui who is the milk goddess. The god Shiva, in special hermaphrodite form, fills the same necessity of keeping divine drink of inspiration flowing.

Is it so very reassuring and comforting that on the other side of the globe in the high mountains of Mexico Coyolxauhqui shows her pendent breasts to replenish the Milky Way. The Coyolxauhqui-Hathor-Hera-Shiva link concerning a cosmic mother is an unbelievable expression of global correspondence, similitude, and concord. How could this idea be common to all cultures of the globe? It is utterly amazing that such powerful concepts entered the culture of so many diverse peoples around the planet. These icons necessitate an advanced astronomy and science to have figured out the complexity of the Earth's dependent relationship with our galaxy and our universe.

Cosmic Cycles

Ancient scientists recognized these cosmic cycles:

- Daily rotation of the Earth
- Cycles and phases of the moon
- Annual revolution of the Earth around the sun
- Precession of the vernal equinoxes
- Cycle of the Milky Way, which is the rotation of our galaxy
- Revolution of the Milky Way galaxy throughout the universe (one should remember that the Milky Way rotates or spins on its axis while it also revolves in an orbit around the universe)

To keep track of all these contrary revolutions, the ancient astronomers used the 12 signs of the zodiac as a clock with many hands marking the many cycles. Thus was born the most elegant scientific instrument, which provided a single calibrated context for objects moving and changing positions relative to one another upon the panorama of the skies.

The Planets

The Planets were originally called "angels," which in Greek means "messengers, prophets, and heralds." The planets have also been called "the wandering stars" and "the capricious goats" because of their occasional backward or retrograde motion. They were also called the *Egregori*, the "watchers of mankind," and "the teachers of astronomy," according to Manetho (third century BC, *Aegyptiaca*, p. 11). This reference of the planets as teachers is the origin of the notions of alien contact from a celestial source. According to Palaephatus (second century BC), the first and most ancient gods of the Egyptians were the sun, moon, and the five planets (p. 23). The planets were often referred to as the spinners and weavers of fate in Greek, Atlantic, and also (K&M, p. 451) Kogi traditions. The cosmic music of the planets, the music of the spheres, was called the fairy music and the song of the Sirens of the sea, luring sailors to their death.

The Importance of Eclipses

In ancient times, only a "prophet" in the particular service of a king was permitted to make statements about "possible cause" being generated by the sun, moon, planets, and stars. This was considered acceptable because a king or a queen was deemed to be a chosen and accepted agent of the sun and the moon, almost as an incarnation of these heavenly bodies. The actions of ordinary human creatures were too complicated to predict because of the complexity of multitudes of genetic interaction, the geography of birth and environment, upbringing, and education. Royalty, however, were the agents of the kingdom, whose fate became intertwined with the fate of the nation. They governed by divine right as viceroys of the sun and moon.

The rulership of all ancient cultures was based upon the claim that members of one olden family were the descendants of the sun and the moon. Just as the sun and the moon were the rulers of the sky, the sons and daughters of the sun and the moon were the rulers of the Earth. Even as late as the 18th century, King Louis the XIV resurrected this ancient paradigm by proclaiming himself as the Sun King. If you are powerful enough, you can easily proclaim yourself to be almost anything. But what happens when there is an eclipse of the sun or the moon? If your scientists and astrologers have predicted the eclipse, you can easily put any spin on the astronomical events that you like, for example saying that it is a sign to attack your weak neighbors. However, if the eclipse catches you unawares, it is a sign that your people may depose you from the kingship. And this scenario has happened throughout history. Divine right of kings is founded upon astronomy, through which it fails or thrives.

From these traditions came one of the most fundamental rules of astrology—namely the prediction, observation, and analysis of solar and lunar eclipses and the first new moon of the New Year. Indeed, it is required of every competent astrologer to look at and discover the meaning of each and every new moon, quarters, and full moon. Ptolemy says that the sun and moon are marshals of every prediction, for they are the prime cause. The planets are, for the most part, powerless unless they are associated with the sun and the moon by conjunction, opposition, or a strong geometrical relationship.

Of course, it is *not* the intention of this book to promote *astrology* but to investigate ancient classical astrology because it contains the seeds of cosmology. And it is *not* the purpose of this work to legitimize all myth but only ancient cosmological myth because of the astronomical data within.

The Earth

Ancient astrology recognizes the Earth as a unique and holy place in the universe. Earth must be some kind of focus of the cosmos because it is a garden that permits life to be formed. The Earth is connected to the universe in a special way. One of the consequences of this viewpoint is a moral mandate to appreciate and honor life. The other is that the cosmos must be viewed from an Earth-centric platform in order to be understood. This does not mean that ancient people did not know that the sun was the focus of the solar system. In fact, the argument with Galileo was never about heliocentricity; the argument was about cosmology, namely removing the Earth from the central focus of the universe. The Milky Way transforms energy from the universe to the sun at the center of its system. If the Earth were at the center of this system, it would burn and be destroyed. But the Earth has been offset in a special way to receive energy from the universe and sun in mild and favorable proportion. The cosmologers looked at the harmonious position of the Earth within the solar system wherein it is perfectly surrounded by opposite natures:

Sun—	Mercury—	Venus—	Earth—	Mars—	Jupiter—	Saturn
hot	dry	moist	—	hot	moist	cold

Modern science recognizes the importance of the planet Jupiter, whose massive size deflects meteors and space debris from hitting the Earth. The position of Jupiter is balanced between the planets of the solar system:

Mercury–Venus–Earth–Mars–***Jupiter***–Saturn–Uranus–Neptune–Pluto

Ancient scientists viewed the heavens from the platform of the Earth. Their astronomy centered upon the major "standstills of the heavenly bodies," such as the solstices of the sun, the major and minor standstills of the moon, and the standstills of the planets in the sky. If the Earth were the center of the solar system, there would be no "standstills" (other than our moon) because everything would continually circle our planet. It is Earth's very position within the solar system that creates the circumstance of the standstills of the planets. And theses "standstills" assist in creating the diversity of life and the ever-changing face of our planet caused by climate and the geological disasters.

From a heliocentric view, the orbit of Venus makes a circle around the sun. From a geocentric view, the orbit of Venus makes a five-pointed pentagram star in the sky during its standstills in the heavens. The lines within this pentagram are all in golden-mean (PHI ϕ, .618) relationship to one another. The human body, human architecture, growth, and creation in nature are all modeled upon the golden mean proportion. This certainly must indicate that the off-set position of the Earth in the solar system is the reason for its success as a garden of life. Indeed, the Earth is in the position of a cosmic blender, creating a cosmic frappe by combining the forces of the universe in one focus of the cosmos. Again, it is unquestionable that Venus' positions in the sky seem to communicate PHI .618 to humans and the Earth. Martineau writes (*Pattern in the Solar System*, p. 23) that the relationship of Venus and Earth is 5-to-8 extended out to 55-to-89 (55 + 89 = 144) produces the golden-mean proportion (89 ÷ 144 = .618). Martineau also demonstrates that Earth and Mercury kiss 22 times in seven years, a synchronism that produces a close approximation of pi π, 3.14 (22 ÷ 7 = 3.142857).

Religion, Law, and the Moral Order Taught by Cosmic Physics

One of the laws governing our solar system states that the total eccentricity of the planets of the solar system must stay constant, provided that all planets revolve around the sun in the same direction. If the orbit of one planet increases its eccentricity, then the others must decrease in eccentricity sufficiently to strike a balance. The abovementioned astronomical law of physics presents an inescapable mandate of the natural law and the moral order of the universe. If one could coin an opinion relating cosmic physics and natural law to human laws, commandments, and morals –it might read as follows:

> It seems reasonable to believe that every change in the cosmos—from the universe, down to the galaxies, solar system, as well as life on Earth—causes an adjustment within the entire system. Cosmic physics implies order and adjustment toward a state of balance. This law of physics is our constant and visible reminder that the universe teaches us that harmony must prevail in the heavens and upon the Earth.

Human commandments and morals such as thou shall not worship false gods, covet, bear false witness, steal, or murder decry any interference with life because of the concept of equal partnership and worthiness in the universe. Indian philosophers went so far as to respect the "being" of a common fly whose existence was believed to be of equal importance with all other forms. The moral reason "not to do wrong" is that by doing wrong you will not only harm others but also yourself and the physics of the order of the universe, in addition to offending God, the creator of all.

Le Chatelier's Principle (1850–1936) says, "Every change of one of the factors of an equilibrium brings about a rearrangement of the system in such a direction as to minimize the original change." P.S. Laplace (1749–1827) and J.L. Lagrange (1736–1813) generalized that the total eccentricity of the planetary orbits of the solar system had to stay constant, provided all the planets revolve about the sun in the same direction. If the orbit of one planet increases its eccentricity, that of the others must decrease in eccentricity sufficiently to strike a balance. The same sort of constancy holds for the inclination of a planet's orbit to the plane of the ecliptic. In 1787 Laplace was able to show the moon was accelerating slightly more than could be earlier explained. This he attributed to the fact that the eccentricity of the Earth's orbit was very slowly decreasing as a result of the gravitational influence of other planets.

Astronomical laws indicate the existence of a woven cosmic tapestry of balance and interrelationship. It is easy to see how this science could be applied to human law, morality, and ultimately human religion. Precepts such as "worship only the 'highest,' the Creator God," "Love thy neighbor as thyself," and "Thou shalt not steal nor kill" are rules that directly evolve from the cosmic physics of equality and harmony. The very idea of truth, justice, and harmony originates in the perfect motion of the heavens, galaxies, stars, and planets. Our icon of blind justice holding a balance scale comes from the Egyptian image of the scales weighing a feather of truth against the heart of an individual. Throughout the world, the feather is a symbol for the sky. In the Coptic schools of present-day Egypt, the feather is the symbol of *Maat*—the truth and balance of the cosmos.

The whole requires all of its parts to function and thrive. Everything has its virtue and its place. Every person has their dignity, talent, and uniqueness. The laws of heaven are simple and easy. No one is special, exempt, or exceptional. Killing, harming, lying, cheating, and stealing disturb the balance of the cosmos. "The ends do not justify the means" because there are no "permanent ends' in the cosmos of cycles. Special distinctions and agendas are contrary to the harmony of the universe and render it dysfunctional.

Destruction of the Ancient Chumash Culture in California

Crystals in the Sky by John Peabody Harrington and Ernest Underhay reveals the sophisticated cosmological worldview of the California Chumash and other California tribes hitherto regarded among the most backward of hunter-gathers. The Chumash created the finest rock art of astronomical symbols in North America. Hadingham describes (pp. 110–23) their beliefs:

> The winter solstice was the most critical moment of the year. It marked the annual finish of a nightly ball game played by two teams of sky people, one led by the Sun and the other by Sky Coyote, the North Star, with the Moon acting as scorekeeper. The game was an opportunity for the most powerful celestial beings to assert their influence and so upset the balance of nature. Everyone participated in the mid-winter ceremonies when the high chief put on the robes of the "image of the Sun" and his twelve assistants imitated the rays of the sun. A "sun stick" with a skewed angle was placed in the ground which represented the axis of the Earth. There were dances which dramatized the soul's journey along the Milky Way to reach the land of the dead. The Chumash astronomer controlled the calendar and named the children by determining their astrological character and destiny. The astronomer also guided the young men through their "vision quest" toward manhood. He was also a doctor to the community as well as a shaman who controlled weather and executed magic paintings. Their cosmology also contains the quartz crystal house of the Sun, and the Moon who controlled health and the menstrual cycle.

California boasted a population of 300,000 native people and 75 different languages with 300 dialects. This population was guided by ritual organizations of the far-ranging Antap cult. Only the wealthy elite qualified as members of this organization, which even had its own esoteric language. The cult staged the astronomical dances and ceremonies, as well as the storing of provisions and distribution of food in bad times.

Many of the solar observatories and astronomical rock-art sanctuaries have been plowed under by California developers, and even today these extraordinary sites are not protected. It is only a matter of time before this aspect of ancient California is totally forgotten. Therefore, the little that we know now will become even less.

Anthropologists' scheme of human development and evolution suggests that agriculture is key to consistent supplies of food that in turn allow humans to develop science. The hunter-gatherer tribes of California totally negate this theory and show that astronomy is a cultural mother science to all of humanity.

CHAPTER 2.2.

Cosmic Order and the Milky Way

The Cosmic Kingship of Divine Right

Eleanor Mannikka in *Angkor Wat, Time, Space, and Kingship* writes (p. 51) that according to Brahmanical cosmology, a good king can eradicate the *kali yuga*, the age of dishonor, strife, and war. The good king can then institute the golden age of justice and harmony, the *krta yuga.* Furthermore, Mannikka (p.58) explains that "Time, divinity, and the king are inextricably co-joined... Neither time nor place, divinity nor humanity, celestial nor terrestrial realms are independent of each other...a celestial and terrestrial pivot of time and place, generated by heavenly gods or earthly kings in a parallel conjunction, has an enormous philosophical scope."

Egyptian cosmology exactly bespeaks these principles where the cosmic order is guided by Maat, the seated goddess wearing the ostrich feather called "the feather of truth," which is used in the judgment scene when a person's heavy heart is weighed against the weightless feather of heavenly truth. According to Shaw and Nicholson (Bauval, p. 15) Maat represented the divine order of the universe from the moment of creation. It was the power of Maat to regulate the seasons, the movement of the stars, and the relation between men and God. The concept was central to their ideas about the universe and morals. Kingship required imposing order and preventing chaos. The function of the king as the representative of the gods was to preserve the original harmony of the universe.

Egyptian iconography clearly presents this cosmic trusteeship. The king assumes the stewardship but with the responsibility to perform the role of Maat, that is, to rule with discernment and justice. Divine right is a two-way covenant. For, according to the Heliopolitan creation myth, there was a time when the sky goddess Nut and the earth god Geb were locked in tight embrace as one perfect harmony. But now the king needed to restore harmony and balance and the cosmic law, Maat.

Anthony Aveni says (p. 245) that, "Maya architecture…clearly delivers the message to the people that the power of the ruling elite is mandated from heavenly ancestors. The city is a microcosm of the divine, designed to facilitate a dialogue between the people and their gods, with the rulers taking center stage as mediator." Aveni again speaks (p. 288) of the context of the sacred site as a holy cosmic city ruled by the Maya king as the viceroy of the Creator God. He says, "We have only begun to understand the cosmic blueprint which govern the structure of Uxmal and surrounding sites… The example of the Palace of the Governor shows how Mesoamerican art and architecture created models of social reality and served the purpose of creating societal bonds." Aveni mentions the work of Linda Schele and Mary Miller, who have given examples of the way that,

> ceremonial structures function to identify the ruler with forces that order the cosmos… The Maya farmer standing below this building for some ritual occasion, saw his ruler standing at the pivot of this symbolic program that represented the movement of heavenly bodies as they rose and set. Behind his ruler he saw the sun and its twin, Venus, actually rise in the east and sink in the west duplicating the symbols on the monument that defined social and cosmic order. By taking his place at the apex of the symbolic program, the king declared himself to be the causal force that perpetuated this order.

The temple-palace in front of which the Maya king stood portrayed the sun and Venus rising in the east on one side of the temple and the sun and Venus setting in the west on the other side of the temple. In all these matters, science, astrology, and rulership were combined. A perfect harmony between the heavens, man, and the Earth was achieved, verified, and approved. Architecture, social usage, and astronomy supported the right of cosmic kingship.

Aveni (p. 255) cites Sanders and Webster, who say, "Copan's great plaza...a space large enough to accommodate the entire population of the polity for the celebration of ceremonies that enjoin religious ideas with political propaganda." Aveni continues to remark that king Yax Pac instituted the *ahua* principle that the king was conceived supernaturally and derived his power directly from the sky deities thought to be his ancestors.

Yax Pac's temple complex was a virtual three-dimensional map of the Maya cosmos that must have awed Maya peasants. The south side carries symbols of the underworld, the north those of the afterworld (afterlife), while the middle of the site represented the world of today, where the king's throne was placed (p. 256).

Aveni (p. 259) finishes by saying that the astronomical observatory became "a tool for acquiring information from the Maya's planetary guideposts, the gods who revealed themselves to be the true source of power and authority, the legitimizing agents in a belief system embedded in both the public and the private sectors of Maya society."

Politics and Astrology

The politics behind the divine right of kings certainly supported the development of astronomy. The science of astronomy would not exist without astrology. Every ancient society demanded productivity from every activity. Who would pay the astronomers? Astronomy had to have a realistic and practical side. Therefore, the astronomer had to predict accurate outcomes for natural and political events. The astronomer had to forecast the agricultural cycle, including variations of scarce or plentiful harvests. In the political realm, the astronomer and his staff had to present annual paintings showing prognosticated events that affected both king and state. Astrology was the hardworking sister of astronomy that paid the bills to justify the study of the stars and especially the history that happened under certain planetary configurations and the natural and climate events that occurred under specific astronomical cycles.

In order to make all this work, especially prognostication, the astrologers kept records of great natural and political events and connected these with cycles and aspects of the planets and heavens. Record-keeping became the sustaining essence of astrology. The more accurate, older, and far-reaching the historical records, the more valuable they were to serve the body of data that the astrologer was able to consult. It is the hard work of the astrologer–record-keeper that has preserved most ancient mythological cycles of the great gods and world epochs of creation and destruction. The astrologer's livelihood depended upon his historical skills in preserving that which was cosmically accurate and true. And it was this evidence that gave life to future interpretations of the cosmic cycles.

Susan Milbrath writes in her introduction that many of the best-documented astronomical images of the Maya seem primarily concerned with divination. Maya astronomy is really astrology (Thompson, 1972) but not in the sense of personal horoscopes. The astrological texts in the codices often deal with cycles of illness, the fate of crops, and weather, somewhat like our own *Old Farmer's Almanac.*

All ancient civilizations believed that stars were gods and that their rulers derived power and legitimacy from their connection with the cosmos—both in life and in the afterlife of the ruler (Milbrath, p. 11). As in the Old World, astrologer-priests correlated events in the lives of rulers with celestial events (Milbrath, p. 3). Indeed the term "star wars" comes from the Maya predilection of starting wars according to celestial configurations. Their rulers could also be called "star kings" because events of their lives were dictated by astrology. Milbrath says (p.271–3) that "events in Chan Bahlum's life seem to be linked with Jupiter's retrograde motion." She continues to say that the Temple of the Foliated Cross at Palenque is orientated to the setting point of Deneb, the brightest star of the Northern Cross, while the Southern Cross was linked to the "heir-designation" date and the actual accession to the throne by Chan Bahlum in 684 AD.

Milbrath also says that stellar imagery is also prominent in an important image of apotheosis in the Temple of Inscriptions at Palenque that houses the tomb of Chan Bahlum's father, Pacal II. Here the texts do not say that he died but that he "entered the road" at the place where the ecliptic crosses the Milky Way at Scorpio, the portal to the Underworld region of the Milky Way. Study of the Sarcophagus lid suggests that the deceased Pacal entered the Milky Way near Scorpio and ascended to heaven on the Southern Cross to reach his planet Jupiter.

The Milky Way Galaxy

Though the Maya accounts often feature the sun and Venus and planetary astrology, their basic idea is that our solar system, the Earth, and its inhabitants derive all their energy from the Milky Way, our home galaxy. The Milky Way, of course, gets its energy form the universe and the Creator God of the cosmos. Therefore it should be understood that the zodiac (so highly regarded by European, African, and Asian cultures) has little significance for the cultures of the American continents. The zodiac does not transmit spirit and energy. The zodiac is only a convenient expression of the movement of the sun which does transmit spirit and energy. The zodiac is also used as an abstract of the rotation of the Milky Way to permit yearly religious anniversaries to be celebrated, including creation and destruction cycles, as well as the cycles of the generations of the gods beginning with Adam.

Andean cosmologers actually created huge earthworks of cavities in the ground that accurately depicted the directional projection of the Milky Way at the winter solstice (Milla Villena, pp. 42–8). This means that these astronomers were checking the movement of our solar system relative to the galaxy.

All religions speak of holy sustenance of manna, soma, itz, milk and honey, spirit, and cosmic sap. The satisfying waters and the bread of life refer to emanations from the Milky Way that feeds our every intellectual wish and material want and desire.

Susan Milbrath on the Milky Way

Milbrath (p. 10) writes that a zodiac-like sequence from Yucatan reveals specific animal constellations. The constellations on the sky bands depicted by the Maya are linked specifically with imagery of the ecliptic crossing the Milky Way. In the Classical Period, the Milky Way is depicted by the cosmic monster, with his two heads symbolizing the crossing points of the ecliptic (the zodiac) and the Milky Way. Some rulers like King Pacal were transposed into the planet Jupiter, while others were transformed into Venus after death. Usually, most people traveled the "soul's road," upon the Milky Way, in order to reach their celestial abode.

Milbrath (p. 279, 283) carefully distinguishes between two sections of the Milky Way: the underworld, or the black road (where the ecliptic crosses between Scorpio/Sagittarius), and the upperworld, or the white road (where the ecliptic crosses between the borders of Taurus/Gemini). The Milky Way is also represented as a male and female pair known as Citlaltonac (where the stars shine) and Citlalcue (star skirt (reminiscent of the star mantles of the Egyptian astronomers, the Greek astro-goddesses, and the Virgin Mary). Again, the Milky Way is a celestial river, a stream of blood (as sacrifice or sustenance) or celestial dew, or a serpent or dragon. The ritual of baptism in an earthly river seems to symbolize the soul's resurrection and rebirth during its journey through the celestial river of the Milky Way.

Milbrath writes (p. 251) that,

> Constellations located at the intersection points of the Milky Way and the ecliptic seem to be especially important in Precolumbian Maya cosmology. The Pleiades are represented by the rattlesnake's rattle in Yucatan, an image that is also found in central Mexico. Orion's Belt represents a turtle constellation, but other stars in Orion may be linked with the Hearthstones of Creation. Scorpio is a scorpion in the northern Maya area, but to the south it may be a skeletal serpent known as the White-Bone-Snake. There is a fish-snake constellation in the region of Sagittarius, a star group associated with the Quadripartite God forming the rear head of the Cosmic Monster. The Cosmic

> Monster itself seems to embody the Milky Way, and the two areas where it intersects the ecliptic represent opposite seasons. Itzamna... may symbolize the entire sky, his four bodies formed by the two sides of the Milky Way and the two sides of the ecliptic. A similar configuration is suggested by the four roads of the Popol Vuh.

The Milky Way is, of course, the heavenly river of spilled milk, sometimes referred to as a net of fish transformed into this celestial stream. Milbrath tells us (p. 253) that in the Classical Period, disembodied eyes and crossed bones represented the night sky and the starry underworld (portrayed on the Vase of the Seven Gods). The Milky Way is equally generative and destructive, creator and destroyer of the great cosmic ages and epochs. In this sense, the Milky Way is the ravaging and destructive cosmic monster (Milbrath p. 275). The cosmic monster has reptile skin; a sky-band body; and deer ears, eyes, antlers, and feet. The Milky Way bestows the nimbus, or halo, upon those born under its divine auspices, like St. Francis and Padre Pio in modern times.

Crossing Points of the Ecliptic and the Circle of the Milky Way at Gemini/Taurus and Scorpio/Sagittarius—Portals of the Milky Way

Our solar system is a part of the Milky Way, which we see as a milky circular band crossing the ecliptic on the borders between Taurus and Gemini and on the other side of the ecliptic on the borders of Scorpio and Sagittarius. Stars and star groups in the vicinity of Taurus/Gemini and Scorpio/Sagittarius are extremely significant for the ancient people who regarded them as portals of energy and spirit, doorways to heaven and to the underworld and hell.

The entrance to the underworld is Scorpio/Sagittarius (Milbrath p. 265), somewhat like the Christian idea that the soul must first descend into hell (*xibalba be*) for some days before it may ascend into heaven. Sagittarius is portrayed in Mayan art as a fish-snake, the skeletal snake, the White Bone Snake, and the snaggletoothed dragon. The constellation of the Southern Cross represents the holy ceiba tree, the place where the souls of the dead climb up into heaven and the land of milk and honey, to become transformed into stars once again (Milbrath p. 270).

In the region of Taurus/Gemini are located Sirius, Orion = "Heart of Sky," Orion's belt = Turtle and/or three hearthstones of creation or "the fire drill," Pleiades = rattlesnake, and Castor and Pollux—the brightest twin stars in the sky—which may be associated with the twin dwarfs and also with the copulating peccaries. This region is also identified with the plumed serpent and hurricane, the stars Rigel and Betelgeuse, and the patron bird, the owl (associated with Mercury). The stars in Orion are linked with the maize god and the world tree as a cornstalk and as the Foliated Cross (Northern Cross). Milbrath, citing Lamb, writes (p. 251) that Yucatan Maya refer to a star as the spots on a jaguar and a deer. Stars are called "the flower of the night and the flowering sky; as well as eyes of the night." Individual stars may be represented as birds, such as how Rigel and Sirius are represented as woodpeckers (p. 253).

In Maya art, diametrically opposite (180°) constellations such as Turtle (Orion's belt) and Scorpio may appear *next to each other* on a sky band to indicate the astronomical opposition of these opposite places. Milbrath (pp. 253–264) shows images of the cosmic turtle's shell, upon which appear the three bright stars of Orion's belt. Milbrath says that the Yucatan Maya called the Pleiades *tzab,* "'the rattlesnake's rattle." The tzab were special insignia of the priests who carried a short stick with rattlesnakes' tails attached to it. The association of the Pleiades carries over to the Chicchan serpent, a feathered rain serpent connected with agricultural fertility since Olmec times. The rain-productive planet Venus appears in the vicinity of the Pleiades between mid-March and mid-June. The Chicchan serpent in the Madrid Codex takes the form of a hook. The Pleiades and constellation Perseus appear as a natural pair resembling a bent serpent (like the symbol of the rain god Chac) in the Madrid Codex. Chac rides the Chicchan serpent when he is pouring rain from his jar. The rainy season is associated with the sun's entrance into the regions of the Pleiades and Gemini. At Chichen Itza, the feathered-serpent columns with rattle tails and the sun, Venus, and the Pleiades are all associated together at the Temple of the Warriors.

In Egyptian cosmology of the Milky Way, the *Book of What Is in the Underworld* is set out in 12 chapters or hours, which mark the hours of night, the places where the souls, the gods, and the spirits stand—the gate of the western horizon. This is the knowledge of the power of those in the netherworld.

Corliss reports *(Stars, Galaxies, Cosmos,* p. 8) that the Dutch astronomer Kapteyn announced that the peculiar motions of stars around us are not at random; they fall into two streams that move in opposite directions in the plane of the Milky Way. The convergent point of one stream is located between Orion and Gemini, while the opposite convergent is located near the northern border of Sagittarius, not far from the currently accepted center of our galaxy, which is the black hole. Graham Hancock has also written an entire book about the connection of the Pyramids of Giza and other global sites with the stars of Orion's belt.

In *Maya Cosmos* (p. 394), Linda Schele reports that the Maya kings dressed themselves as the embodiment of the Milky Way Galaxy. This took the form of impersonating the Waka Chan tree and the holy ceiba tree, whose gentle five-petaled white flowers replicated the stars of the galaxy.

Hunbatz Men, the noted Mayan daykeeper and teacher, informs us about the cosmic philosophy of the Maya in *Secrets of Mayan Science/Religion.* In fact, Hunbatz Men begins the very first chapter saying that the Maya believe that everything, from food to knowledge, comes from the Milky Way galaxy. They refer to the galaxy by the name "Ge" which has two symbols in art, namely a bent form like our letter *G*, sometimes shown like the sacred spiral of the conch shell and also in the shape of an ellipse when it represents notions connected with zero. The *G* represents a frontal view of the galaxy, while the "()" represents a side view. The sacred *G* and the Milky Way stood at the forefront of almost every culture of these continents, stemming from the most ancient tribes and cultures, such as the Mexicas; Teotihuacans; Zapotecs; Xochipilli culture of Xochimilco; Totonac; Chavin people of Huantar, Peru; along with the Inca and Aymara. In his *Genesis de La Cultura Andina*, Carlos Milla Villena confirms throughout his book that Andean culture is founded upon the reverence of the Milky Way galaxy. The letter *G* also appears in Masonic symbols and is said to represent the geometry of the universe. The bent-form *G* also appears as the bent nose of the Mayan rain god as well as on the Temple of Hochoob of the cosmic monster in the design work of the eyes and around the entrance.

Hunbatz Men explains that the Maya used the power of the Milky Way and the positions of the planets to perform sacred procreation in tune with the cosmic law so as to create wise and talented children. Hunbatz writes that for the Maya and the Chimu of Peru, sexual activity and propagation were governed by planetary knowledge and natural laws. Rituals were performed and the priests taught the responsibilities inherent in engendering children. The priests used sacred calendrical calculations to avoid unplanned children. He says that European culture ignores the connection of sexual relations in tune with the cosmos (p. 138).

North American tribal culture was also based upon an astronomical foundation. The Tsimshian council of astronomers read the heavens for portents regarding food production and supply. Their head astronomer was called "moon reader." The Inuit called the Milky Way "the track across the sky." The Micmac of Nova Scotia called the Milky Way "the singing stars, and the firebirds." The California hunter-gather Chumash say that Shaq the Turtle was once chief of the Land of the Dead and that the souls travel westward along the Milky Way.

The Cosmic Monster

While the Aztec, Maya, and Andean cosmologers had great regard for the Milky Way, they also understood that the great epochal ages of the galaxy end with catastrophic flood, fire, wind, and ice. The cycle of the Milky Way is the cause of great periods of creation, life, maturity, degeneration, destruction, and death. But after destruction and death comes a new epoch of creation and regeneration. For the seed is buried in the ground and must die before it can burgeon forth again in the springtime. Dualism reminds us that in order to have creation, we must also experience destruction. This is the law of the creative and destructive natural cycles that move through the stages of moist-hot-dry-cold. Moist is birth, hot is maturity, dry is degeneration, and cold is death.

Tlaloc, the rain and lightning god, as the Cosmic Monster at Chichen Itza. Author photo

Therefore the cosmologers reminded themselves and all people that one must stand in awe of the galaxy that has the power to conceive and destroy. When one goes to such sites as Chichen Itza to see the Temple of the Nunnery, one is struck by the badly conceived and executed image of Tlaloc (supposedly the rain god) over the doorway. These giant face images always seem to be done as a cartoon diagram or a badly sketched icon. But if one realizes that these are meant to be representations of the cosmic monster, then one appreciates their placement, size, and delineation.

There is no more gripping image of the Cosmic Monster who is the black-hole matrix, the mouth of the galaxy, at the Temple of Hochoob, a model of which appears at the National Museum of Anthropology in Mexico City.

Model of the Temple of Hochob showing the black hole matrix of our Milky Way Galaxy as the mouth of the cosmic monster. Author photo.

Everything in the Mexica-Maya-Andean worldview is centered on dualism. Two Creator Gods speak (and even argue), and this dichotomy creates the world. Dualism represents the poles of the creative cycles and destructive cycles. Just as the Milky Way Galaxy is sometimes conceived as the cosmic monster, the Earth—our mother—is sometimes imagined as the Earth monster in the form of a caiman. Taube reminds (p. 73) that the New Year's ceremony is celebrated in terms of the destruction and recreation of the world. The Aztec gods carry a skull, a sign of the underworld, on their belt not to lose sight of the inevitable—namely personal death and the demise of history and culture.

Both the Yucatec Maya and the Aztec have a story about the dismemberment of the Earth monster. The 13 Katuns invariably begin on the day name Cipactli, which means "caiman." The Mani and Tizimin versions of the flood also mention the killing of a great Earth caiman known as Itzam Cab Ain, Giant Fish Earth Caiman, which is identified with the Earth as well as the flood (Taube, p. 69).

Although they are often adversaries, Tezcatlipoca and Quetzalcoatl now recreate the heavens and earth as allies. With the aid of other deities at the four corners of the world (and four divisions between those corners), eight gods now rise up the sky. In another Aztec creation myth, Tezcatlipoca and Quetzalcoatl fashion the heavens by dismembering the great Earth monster Tlaltecuhtli, who is dual-sexed and sometimes merges with the caiman Earth monster. In another version, Tlaltecuhtli is so voracious that she is equipped with gnashing mouths at her elbows, knees, and other joints (Taube, pp. 36–7). Xiuhtecuhtli is identified with the Milky Way, which is represented as a Tamoanchan tree with two crocodile heads that form the upper and lower jaws of the Cauac monster, Tonacatecuhtli.

Milbrath says (pp. 282–5), "We can conclude that the Cosmic Monster is one of the main images of the Milky Way in both Classic and Post Classic times. During the Classic period, its two heads represent a form of opposition [dichotomy] that seems to reflect seasonal duality." Milbrath also points out that the quadripartite Creator God Itzamna personifies the four celestial roads of white (around Taurus/Gemini), black (around Scorpio/Sagittarius), red (the sun's path during the dry season), and green/yellow (signifying the rainy season and the maturity of the yellow maize crop). Itzamna has four aspects: red to the east, white to the north, black to the west, and yellow to the south. *Itzamna* is translated as "the magician who has knowledge of the creative power, magician who gives birth to life on earth, and wizard of the water." *Itz* refers to liquid drops of dew, tears, milk, and semen. The Milky Way is often called the "dew road," which dispenses the manna, the spirit of life and sustenance to the world.

CHAPTER 2.3.

The Secret Writings of Sir Isaac Newton

Sir Isaac Newton (1643–1727) is of tremendous importance in the history of the culture of astronomy. Newton represents a bridge between the ancient and modern worldview. He is a physicist and the inventor of the modern telescope. And he is also a cosmologer of the ancient order because he accepts the truth of ancient myths as he attempts to place Hebrew, Greek, and Egyptian traditions into a uniform context of cosmic order and chronology.

Newton was an extremely eccentric personality who was involved in clandestine societies and was even one of the early advocates for the establishment of a Jewish state. In fulfillment of his duties as a minister and teacher, he was oftentimes observed lecturing to an empty hall, bereft of all occupants save himself. Edmond Halley, the observer of the famous comet, once asked him about a problem in astronomy, and Newton enthusiastically explained the matter, a subject that he had resolved 20 years earlier but forgot to bring to the attention of science because he was insecure about some of the details. One cannot help feeling a kindred empathy for Newton and all philosophers who are caught up in their deep cogitations in their own private worlds unknown to most of humanity.

Newton was indeed complex, an intellectually haggard creature for whom anyone would have felt sympathy had they understood the breadth of his contemplations and the deep chasms that stood between the areas of his investigations. One of the best lines ever penned about the deep character of

Newton was by the poet Wordsworth, who captured the psychology of the great man as, "Forever voyaging through strange seas of thought—alone."

Newton's invention of the reflecting telescope in 1668 captured the attention of the scientific community and set him onto the road to fame. He was elected Fellow of the Royal Society in 1672. In 1689 and also 1701 he was elected Member of Parliament for Cambridge University. In 1696 he was appointed Warden of the Royal Mint. By 1703 Newton was chosen as president of the Royal Society.

Newton's reclusive and crotchety nature has been cleaned up and "made nice" for the sake of his great reputation in the world of science. Imagine the dismay when Newton's secret papers suddenly turned up at Cambridge. The college immediately disavowed these works of fantasy and put them on the auction block, that some value might be gained from this embarrassment.

We all know about Sir Isaac Newton's contribution to cosmic physics. His conception of gravity is still "up to the minute" science because it has been observed in operation by the Hubble telescope during the collisions of far-distant galaxies in the universe.

What many people are not aware of is that Newton had a secret passion for universal history which he combined out of Bible traditions, Greek mythology, and ancient cosmological lore. In fact, he spent more of his time on Earth trying to riddle the facts and written traditions of religion, myth, and Bible folklore than he spent on what we would today call "real and observable science."

This is the reason for our fascination with Newton. In all his so-called secret activities, Newton behaved exactly like an ancient cosmologer whose activities involved the cultural cohesion of astronomy, history, myth, science, and religion.

Newton's fascination with science, history, and religion brands him as a true cosmologer. He was the first of the moderns to return to the connection between celestial forces and the physical laws that govern life on Earth. The moon, the apple, and the Earth illustrate the ancient cosmological adage, "On earth as it is in heaven." Whether the story is apocryphal or not, Newton deduced that the force that caused the apple to fall to the ground from the tree in his garden during a full moon was the same universal force that also held the moon in an orbit around the Earth! Gravity holds heavenly bodies together. Heavenly bodies influence weather on Earth, which controls food production, which affects population growth, which prompts economic markets and the inclination toward wars, etc, etc, etc. In a simple word, the argument of cosmic physics brings all subjects onto the table of discussion. The cosmologer is forced to consider history and religion as a possible byproduct of the agency of physics acting over an immense period of time. While physics cannot overwhelm human agency and human freewill, physics affects nature and thereby does contribute a considerable amount of weight to every calculation and argument.

Really, though, Newton was doing what he thought that he should be doing, as every cosmologer had done before him. The task of the cosmologer was to keep track of the astronomical events and doings in the heavens, keep track of the time and the cosmic cycles, and to be cognizant of the creation and destruction cycles of the universe. The cosmologer puts his immense studies to use in order to prophecy the future. Newton consulted the Bible and felt that he understood that the end of the world would occur some 2,060 years after the appearance of Christ.

Ancient cosmologers stood at the pinnacle of human knowledge. They were the doctors of philosophy who knew the movements of the heavens, the natural history of the Earth, and the universal history of humankind. It was they who prepared the forecast for the following year for the king and the nation because they were the embodiment of all knowledge. They were the highest advisers to the State. They were those who wore the cloak emblazoned with stars—the cherished star mantel.

Newton realized exactly who these ancient cosmologers were. He attempted to match their skills by gathering together human traditions from the Bible and classical myth into one universal history of the world. This achievement, combined with his contributions to science, would assure his reputation for all time. He would become the master cosmologer of the

Modern Age, whose acumen had joined the past with the present in order to discern the future. Newton would complete a balanced worldview of global history, science, and religion.

Such achievements would truly be glorious, however, Newton would fail in his ambitions. He was born just a bit too early and missed the forthcoming revolution in geology; the Egyptian renaissance brought home to Europe by Napoleon; and the stunning revelations of Vedic, Hindu, Egyptian, and Maya astronomy. In his *Solving Stonehenge* (p. 62), Anthony Johnson says that many intellectuals like Sir Isaac Newton and William Stukeley were convinced that the ancient world once possessed a body of knowledge that had been lost and corrupted down the ages, "Yet scholars of the time had no other 'chronology,' relative or otherwise, than those provided by the Bible and the Classical texts." This aptly describes Newton's position. The only ancient and esoteric knowledge that he possessed was associated with the "Templars" of the Temple of Solomon traditions brought to Europe by the Crusaders during the Dark Ages. The only chronology that Newton possessed was the chronology from Hebrews of the Old Testament.

Almost half of Newton's lifetime was spent on his esoteric studies of myth, and Bible chronology. These revelations have only recently been brought to light through the PBS documentary *Newton's Dark Secret*. Newton was an astoundingly avid reader, who apparently understood that the ancients had achieved "the great understanding of the world and the universe." Newton recognized the validity of ancient Greek myth as prehistorical accounts of the deep past. And he conspicuously attempted to join these ancient Greek myths with Biblical myth and Biblical chronology. But this effort proved to be too enormous for Newton.

Newton was, after all, an astronomer who would have recognized that all the constellation pictures were based upon mythical gods and heroes from the far-distant past. Did it not occur to him that the heavens might represent a chronological calendar of events and that the zodiac might be some sort of sky clock? The zodiac and constellations belonged to an ancient cosmological culture, and the Old or New Testament was not a facile doorway to understanding astronomical culture. Newton failed to see what was directly under his nose, especially as a noted astronomer. He understood that there was some secret process of encryption at work when he imagined that myths—like the tale of Mars, Venus, and the net of Hephaestus were clandestine alchemical formulas. Why could he not see that the zodiac and constellations were encryptions of cosmic history and a wonderful astrochronology stored upon the sky?

The Secret Societies

Some accounts portray Newton as a dedicated activist determined to free all of science from the oversight of the Roman Catholic Church. After the infamous trials of Galileo at the hands of the Inquisition, Newton was obviously cautious and discreet. Newton was too clever to be convicted of any antigovernment or anti-Papal activity. Yet the wealth of information suggests that where there is much smoke, there must be some fire. Newton has been accused of being a virulent anti-Catholic, an Illuminati, and a member of those organizations which actively move against the Roman Church. Laurence Gardner, author of *Bloodline of the Holy Grail,* writes concerning the ancient heritage of the Scots Templars and Cistercian Monks:

> In Stuart England, the early Freemasons of Charles I and Charles II were men of philosophy, astronomy, physics, architecture, chemistry, and generally advanced learning. Many were members of the country's most important scientific academy, The Royal Society, which had been styled the Invisible College, after it was forced underground during the Cromwell Protectorate...Early members were Robert Boyle, Sir Isaac Newton, Robert Hooke, Christopher Wren, Edmond Halley (Halley's Comet), and Samuel Pepys.
>
> Not only was Newton the President of the Royal Society, but he was also Grand Helmsman of the Priory Notre Dame de Sion. The original Order of Sion which had certain Grail connections, had been inaugurated by the Knights Templars to accommodate Jews and Muslims within their Christian organization. Until 1188 both

> organizations were united under the same Grand Master. They were noted exponents of religious toleration, which enabled them to be influential diplomats in both the Jewish and Islamic communities... denounced as 'heresy' by the Catholic Bishops, which was instrumental in the Knight's excommunication by the Church of Rome in 1306... Sir Christopher Wren (1632–1723)...was Grand Master of the esoteric Order of Rosicrucian's...So too had been Robert Boyle...Sir Francis Bacon...Benjamin Franklin...Thomas Jefferson...were Grand Masters of this Order as well.

> Gardner continues to say that there were certainly genuine landscapes of tolerance in such places as Toledo in Spain, where Christian, Jew, and Moslem lived in blessed harmony. There is an enormous amount of controversy about the Priory of Sion, which has actually included cases in the French courts. What is noteworthy is that the Priory rejects the dogma of the Holy Trinity of God, and the Divine Nature of Jesus Christ. Though Newton was a devout and pious man, he also rejected these two principles. Gardner affirms that Newton claimed the pre-eminence of the Judaic heritage as an archive of divine knowledge and numerology. Newton was wholly conversant with Universal Law, sacred geometry...an authority on early religion.

Gardner continues, saying,

> The Stuart Kings were at the very forefront of Scottish Rite Freemasonry, which was founded on the most ancient of all arcane knowledge and Universal Law. Newton admitted that the true inspiration of the *Law of Gravity* was Pythagoras' 'Music of the Spheres', a concept dating back from the 6th century BC. The Stuart's Breton heritage was closely allied to the noble families of Bologna and Jerusalem...the *Invisible College* of the Royal Society emerged—a college that within a brief period of Stuart patronage revealed some of the greatest scientific discoveries of all time.

Later Gardner writes that the Grail Code obliges those in hereditary or elected authority to concern themselves not only with the power but with the obligations of "service" and "duty."

Newton was closely associated with the renowned Robert Boyle, son of the notable Earl of Cork, "the richest man in the world" and confederate of Cromwell. Boyle and Newton were the most prominent of the founding fathers of the Royal Society. It was Boyle who coined the nickname "the Invisible College" because of his deep-seated fear of the Jesuits, who had prosecuted Galileo. It was also reported that two of Newton's most promising disciples followed the Arian heresy, which believed in the human nature of Christ and denied his divinity. "There was an Arian movement especially within the Church of England. Its leading exponents, William Whiston and Samuel Clarke, were among the prominent scientists of the day and disciples of Isaac Newton in both their scientific and theological views" (holy-catholic.org/arian, 6/10/06). Newton admittedly had difficulty with many of the key dogma of Catholicism. He struggled with many of the orthodox traditions of his religion—admitting Jesus as the son of God but not equal, and certainly not of a trinitarian nature or aspect. Most scientists of that epoch supported the Unitarian Church, which Benjamin Franklin specifically brought back to America from his travels in England.

Newton's Personality

Newton had a reputation for crotchetiness and feuded with his peers, such as Flamsteed, the Astronomer Royal, and even John Locke, the associate of his closest friend Boyle. Newton was ever reluctant to publish his research because of much jealously and unpleasantness with his contemporary Robert Hooke. This fellow member of the Invisible College had been hired by Boyle as an assistant because he recognized his scientific abilities. Hooke is credited with the "watch anchor escapement" mechanism, which revolutionized chronometers. Hooke had always challenged Newton to explain not only what gravity does but continually posed the question, "But what is it?" It is unfortunate to recall that Newton has been accused of failing to preserve the only known portrait of Robert Hooke. Partly because of this animosity with Hooke and that he was not happy with his initial calculations regarding the laws of gravity, Newton suspended publication for 20-some years. Newton was a perfectionist who never published anything that he was not steadfastly sure of.

In 1684 the astronomer Halley asked Newton a question about planetary motion. Newton explained that the key to the theory of gravity was the idea that one body could attract another across empty space. To Newton's great contemporaries, Descartes and Leibniz, this notion was medieval and magical. They subscribed exclusively to "mechanical" explanations, in which bodies influenced one another only by a direct series of pushes and pulls.

Grand as it was, Newton's *Principia* left a few loose ends in the celestial scheme. These were knitted up by Pierre-Simon Laplace (1749–1827) in his *Celestial Mechanics* to show that the mutual gravitational tugging among the planets would not cause the solar system to collapse as Newton had feared. When Laplace gave a couple of these volumes to his friend Napoleon shortly before the latter's coup d'etat, the future emperor promised to read them "in the first six months I have free." Napoleon did glance through the volumes, for he later asked Laplace just where God fit into the perfected Newtonian system. Laplace gave his famous answer, "I had no need of that hypothesis."

Though Newton had a perceptive wit and a tenacious bent of character, this was unfortunately coupled with a very limited and parochial viewpoint. The trouble was that he was a recluse by nature who never traveled outside his little realm. His lectures were so intolerably boring that he was mostly left alone speaking to the walls. He is said to have only laughed once in his lifetime, when someone asked him what use was Euclid. His laughter was occasioned by the fact that Euclidian geometry proved to be a gateway to the modern sciences. As an incorrigible recluse, Newton chose to live his life among his 1600 books and his interminable calculations. Our theme celebrates Newton as a cosmologer of wide interests from physics and history to theology. This theme is supported by the fact that Newton's library contained more books on humanities than books on math and science.

Newton spent the larger part of his academic lifetime working on his secret project—a reconciliation of Greek myth with the chronological timeline of the Bible. Newton's private preoccupation with these myth and Bible mysteries occupied a full two decades of his life. This was during the period between his discovery of the law of gravity and the publication of his masterwork, the *Principia Mathematica.* He isolated himself from society because he was too busy unraveling his own clandestine and beloved world of the laws of nature, physics, history, myth, and religion. He had become an addict of his own passion to rediscover cosmological philosophy, which contained the mystery of mysteries: the true relationship of God, nature, and man. The fulfillment of this dream would have exalted him to the ranks of the greatest thinkers of all time, but more importantly, it would have resolved one of Newton's most searching dilemmas—the reconciliation of science and religion.

Because of his vast reading, Newton became aware that the ancient natural scientists like the Druids were actually priests who studied astronomy. Newton obviously craved a scientifically inclined deity, as is revealed in *Aubrey's Brief Lives*, where it is written, "For him, a God who could create a mechanical universe—who could create matter in motion, obeying certain laws out of which the universe as we know it could come into being in an orderly fashion—was far more to be admired and worshipped than a God who created a universe without scientific law."

Newton's Legacy

Sir Isaac Newton's legacy continues to excite. Recently, science has confirmed the existence of "dark matter" through the collision of two large clusters of galaxies (NASA, 8/21/06). Dark matter responds to the same forces of gravity that Newton theorized concerning the apple, the Earth, and the moon. This means that our little microcosm of the Earth works under the same rules as the mighty galaxies of the universe. Scientists are now able to say (sciencedaily.com, 8/22/06), "This result also gives scientists more confidence that the Newtonian gravity, familiar on Earth and in the solar system, also works on the huge scales of galaxy clusters."

Through his discoveries of the principles of light, Sir Isaac Newton invented the modern mirrored telescope in order to eliminate distortion. His model was 40X, through which he could discern the movements of the moons of Saturn. This prototype is still the basic form and principle of all modern telescopes, up to the most sophisticated space probes used on satellites.

Newton is recognized for his contributions to the laws of motion:

1.) If a body is at rest, or if it is in motion, it moves with a uniform velocity, until it is acted upon by a resultant force.

2.) The rate of change of momentum of a body is proportional to the resulting force and occurs in the direction of the force. Force = mass x acceleration.

3.) If body *A* exerts a force on body *B*, then body *B* exerts an equal but opposite force on body *A*, the law of action and reaction.

Calculations for the volume and area of a pyramid were found in Egypt in 1800 BC. Newton refined and contributed to the mathematics of calculus to such an extent that it became the language of modern science.

Contemporary Knowledge

The astronomer Kepler (1571–1630) connected the creation story of Adam with astronomy a full century before the secret works of Newton. Kepler calculated that one of the great trigons of the conjunctions of Saturn and Jupiter had occurred in a special relationship to the zodiac on 4000 BC, near the date of Adam, according to Hebrew scripture. Newton agreed with this figure and further conjectured that the world would come to a catastrophic end in 2060 AD, following the 12,000-year cosmic period suggested in the Bible. Though, some have said that Newton prophesized the end of the Holy Roman Empire on this date. On the basis of Hebrew chronology, many evangelist sects expected the conclusion of the world in 1997 AD.

Advancement in the study of geological strata was only taught in the Museum of Natural History in France in 1741, when modern mining prompted an interest in geology and the long-term changes in the Earth's crust. Darwinism brought forward ideas about lengthy changes and the evolution of nature. While it was not until 1749 that Georges-Louis Leclerc, the Comte de Baffon, challenged the Hebrew 6,000-year creation barrier by proclaiming that the Earth was 75,000 years old. This revelation by the Comte was pronounced a mere 22 years after Newton's death.

Maynard Keynes and the Disclosure of the Secret Documents

When Newton's *Secret Writings* were discovered at Cambridge, the administrators would not accept them into their collection because they felt that these nonscientific writings would diminish the premier scientific reputation of Sir Isaac Newton. (*Newton's Castle*, tqnyc.org, 2008).

Therefore, in 1936 this curious cache of Newton's writings—journals and personal notebooks deemed to be "of no scientific value" was announced to be coming on sale at Sotheby's in London. The winning bidder was the economist John Maynard Keynes (1883–1946). After perusing his purchase, Keynes delivered a mildly shocking lecture to the Royal Society Club in 1942 on the event of the tercentenary of Newton's birth. Keynes began his lecture with the pronouncement, "Newton was not the first of the age of reason. He was the last of the magicians" (cftech.com/brain, 2007). Obviously Keynes did not understand what Newton had so earnestly wished to accomplish—to understand cosmology in all its glory.

John Maynard Keynes made a name for himself as the British Finance Department representative at the Versailles Peace Treaty in 1919. Keynes wrote several books, including *The Economic Consequences of the Peace* in 1919, followed by *A Revision of the Treaty* in 1922, in which he advised that the reparations that Germany was forced to repay were too large and would lead to the ruin of the German economy and consequently to further conflict in Europe. John Maynard Keynes was correct in his political predictions based upon his economic perspicuity.

Keynes' *The General Theory of Employment, Interest, and Money* (1936) established the modern concept of macroeconomics and the worldview of the economy as the driving force behind government. Keynes is credited with the political and fiscal policy that governments should act to control and stabilize economic and market recessions, depressions, and booms. Today, in the shadow of the economic collapse of 2004–2010, people are beginning to blame Keynes' ideology. This is unreasonable, because no one could have imagined the level of corporate and political corruption that would develop within the United States.

Keynes purchased Newton's secret and unpublished notebooks and brought these treasures to be housed in the National Library in Jerusalem. One might surmise that Keynes hoped that some brilliant scholar could penetrate Newton's concepts about the interrelation of history, religion, and physics. As Keynes had liberated the economy from the great private bankers and encouraged governments to attempt to control their own national economies, he naturally admired Newton and Boyle, who had created modern science by liberating it from the constraints of traditional religious establishments.

The Chronology of Ancient Kingdoms

One of Newton's secret works was his universal history of the world, *The Chronology of Ancient Kingdoms.* More than 700 years before Newton's time, Albiruni (973–1048 AD) had written *The Chronology of Ancient Nations.* Born in Uzbekistan, Albiruni was a great scholar of many things but most especially history and astronomy, which were Newton's prominent interests. As a leading astronomer of his time, Albiruni openly discussed the rotation of the Earth upon its own axis. As a historian, Albiruni dispassionately catalogued the chronologies of other nations without emendation or criticism.

Newton followed the Hereford map by accepting the accounts of the Greek "Generations of the Gods" and the legends of Atlas in Morocco, Saturn, the Atlantians, Neptune, Titians, and the Giants. Yet, in his introduction he writes that, "The Greek Antiquities are full of Poetical Fables." Newton is also not favorably disposed to the reports of Herodotus regarding 17,000 years from Hercules to Amosis and 15,000 years from Pan to Amosis and that the Chaldeans have observed the stars for 473,000 years. In his introduction, Newton makes the following statements, which define his worldview of history and religion: "The religion of both Jews and Christians ought to be the standing religion of all nations...the priests of Egypt have so magnified [exaggerated] their antiquities."

Examples of excerpts from Newton's work are as follows:

> According to the Cretans, Neptune, the lord of Africa, [whom the Greeks call Poseidon] is the son of Saturn [Cronus]. Poseidon invented tall ships with sails, and is regarded by all mariners as lord of the sea. For his eldest son Atlas, who succeeded him, was not only Lord of the Island *Atlantis,* but also Reigned over a great part of *Afric,* giving his name to the people called *Atlantii,* and to the mountain *Atlas,* and the *Atlantic Ocean*."
>
> *1015 BC.* The Temple of *Solomon* is founded. *Minos* Reigns in Crete expelling his father Asterius, who flees into Italy, and becomes the *Saturn* of the Latines. *Ammon* takes Gezer from the Canaanites, and gives it to his *daughter, Solomon's wife*; and sets up pillars at the mouth of the Red Sea.
>
> *1000 BC* Sesac, son of Ammon, invades Africa, Spain, and India... his nephew...Prometheus...Ethiopians...Pan...Libyan women... Minerva...Libyan Amazons...
>
> *964 BC* His brother Egyptus...Thoth

Conclusion

Whether or not Newton was a member of secret societies, an early Judeo-Christian, or a fervent anti-Roman Catholic is not material to our theme. The Invisible College and all reactionary movements overstep their own good intentions. What should be brought forward here is the cosmological scope of Newton's life, research, and passions. As a true cosmologer, Newton delved into myth and ancient history, as did Kepler (1571–1630), Beyer (1564–1617), and most other astronomers before him.

Yemima Ben-Menahem, one of the curators of the Newton exhibit at the JNUL commented, "Newton believed there was wisdom in the world that got lost. He thought it was coded, and that by studying things like the dimensions of the Temple of Solomon, he could decode it (jnul.huji.ac.il/dl/mss/newton, 1/24/11)." Newton did indeed discuss the exact dimensions of the temple, which he believed mirrored the arrangement of the cosmos.

Newton is important in the history of cosmology because he is a scientist who still recognized the importance of a unified worldview, which includes God, science, and man. Newton is ever reluctant to completely separate science and religion. Newton must be considered a modern scientist because his cutting-edge mirrored telescope is still the standard of today and his expression of gravity has been proved to apply to galactic physics and the most current scientific investigations such as dark matter.

Newton is a true modern scientist who saw that history, myth, science, and religion are all part of the cosmic context. It is absolutely astounding that such a closeted parochial man traveled to such heights in his intellectual musings. Whether his journeys into these realms were pleasant sojourns or torturous and nightmarish jaunts of agony, we will never know. He appeared to be a lonely and isolated personality. Yet, in reality, his mind walked in the company of the stars and among the past histories of humanity.

CHAPTER 2.4.

The Alexandrian Poet Nonnos of Panopolis

Nonnos of Panopolis is the lynchpin that locks in the connection between astronomy, natural disasters, history, and myth. He was most fortunate to have lived in the post-Alexandrian era, when an enormous amount of traditional material had been assembled from the four corners of the world. This traditional material was freely and openly available and no longer scrupulously guarded by a religious or political elite.

Aristotle took great pains to teach the principles of natural science and philosophy to Alexander of Macedon. Unfortunately, these studies did not captivate the interest of the great empire builder. Alexander was charmed by the mythology of the god Dionysos who had traveled and conquered the world. Dionysos was attractive to Alexander because of his military exploits but also because Dionysos was a benefactor who introduced grapes for wine and the cultivation of grain for bread and beer to a great part of humanity. Alexander was driven by the challenge of duplicating the achievements of Dionysos as a brilliant field marshal and, more importantly, as a benefactor of humanity—a task that the creation of the Library of Alexandria certainly accomplished in many respects.

We may find it difficult to share Alexander's interest in Dionysos. The legends of the superpower Atlantis, home of advanced science and technology, sound more interesting to us. But at the time of Alexander, the Near East was alive with the expectation of the coming of the messiah, whom some people called the reappearance of the new Dionysos. Indeed, history recorded several appearances of Dionysos and his avatars over great reaches of time. This meant that Dionysos was a true cosmic god whose character was a direct creation of one of the great epochal periods of the cycle of the Milky Way.

The Egyptian poet Nonnos of Panopolis produced a giant compendium of the accumulated facts about the various incarnations of the god Dionysos in 48 books. The *Dionysiaca* of Nonnos weaves a cosmological tapestry of the wars of the gods, natural disasters, cosmic changes, cycles, and even long-term movements of the positions and configurations of the constellations of the heavens. Nonnos intimates that the heavens put on a heavenly drama acted out by the pictures depicted by the constellations. Namely, the stars and asterisms documented the events that transpired in heaven and which were consequently enacted upon the Earth. This was like a stage show or a modern drive-in movie. Over time, these constellations actually metamorphosed from their original figures into the characters of the more recent history of the world.

Nonnos tells of outrageous and catastrophic natural upheavals and disasters. His history is nothing less than a cosmological and natural history of the world. He expounds on all matters of human and natural history but also describes the great expectation that the world has in the coming of a new Dionysos, who will restore justice and peace to the world.

Ancient astronomy, astrology, and cosmology is all about the Earth as the focus and center of everything. The power and influence of the universe, the galaxy, sun-moon-planets are all directed upon the Earth. Even astronomy is only concerned with the positions of the planets and all celestial objects in respect to the Earth.

Of course, the ancient people knew that the Earth traveled around the sun—but who cares? The mechanics of the solar system allows the cosmos to transmit gentle increments of energy to our planet. Heliocentrism is the key to understanding the mechanics of the solar system, but it is only one aspect of cosmic mechanics; and certainly is not the key to understanding the universe.

Long before Galileo and Copernicus, astronomers of the ancient world knew the mechanics of the solar system. In 498 AD Arybhata presented a book of astronomical and mathematical theories in which the Earth was spinning on its axis and the periods of the elliptical orbits of the planets were given in relation to the Sun. Even in the Dark Ages, Albiruni had expressed the sun-centered theory in 1026 AD. While Nonnos writes in the late fourth century AD: "Helios, central navel of the seven traveling planets."

He repeatedly refers to the sun as the *mesomphalus*, the midnavel and focal turning post of the circling planets (41.347).

Students of classical literature are amazed at the corpus of Greek and Roman manuscripts dedicated to ancient myth and astrology. The reason for so much information is because myth and astrology are departments of cosmology, the prevalent worldview of the ancient world.

Myth and astrology go hand in hand because, when they are brought together into a cosmological context, they confer meaning upon one another. Then, all of a sudden, these absurd accounts convey accurate history, chronology, and geographic location representing valuable records of scientific observation covering immense periods of the past. Astrology needs to be placed back into the strict cosmological context from which it has been allowed to escape. Mythology must be regarded as very ancient information that was transmitted across several cultures that translated the names into the idioms of their own languages. This type of history is older than years could express. It was therefore defined in terms of placement among the twelve zodiac signs acting as a general clockface of universal time showing the positions of all the cosmic cycles. We will see that this cosmic timepiece is convenient, effective, and absolutely accurate.

Nonnos of Panopolis connects astrology and myth through astronomy. He gives us a full-blown model of how this ancient system works. Others who have recognized the astronomical system of history are the French savant Charles Francois Dupuis (1742–1809); Franz Boll (1867–1924); R.A. Schwaller de Lubciz (1887–1961); Giorgio de Santillana and Hertha von Dechend, authors of "Hamlet's Mill" (1969); and Michael O'Kelly (1982). It was O'Kelly who suggested that, in the case of Newgrange, mythology was the vehicle for the transmission of astronomical knowledge. Many others have attempted to connect myth with cosmology in order to give a historical and scientific validity to these ancient tales. Of course, it is all too obvious that all of the heavenly constellation pictures represent mythological persons and mythological forms—a proof in itself that myth and history are forever forged together with astronomy. Hopefully, it will be possible to disclose the true ancient systems of cosmic chronology in which ancient history—formatted as myth—is placed within the context of astronomical cycles.

Nonnos' main contribution to knowledge is his explicit display of cosmic forces of the universe helping to direct history, nature, science, and religion. The main feature of Nonnos is that he truly describes a universal worldview of natural and human history. This gathering together and comprehension of everything is truly an extraordinary achievement and a true representation of the philosophy of cosmology held by the priest-scientists of not only of Egypt but throughout the ancient world. Nonnos' work may be the only extant example of true "cosmological thinking" of the cosmological worldview and philosophy.

Nonnos writes (*Dionysiaca*, 35.309) that Zeus proclaims, "And I offer you a worthy reward; for I will place in Olympus a circle, image of that flow named after Hera's milk, to honor the all famous sap of your savior breast."

This circle of Hera's milk is the cloudy image of millions of stars that make up our spiraling circular galaxy, the Milky Way. The Egyptians attributed the milky appearance of the galaxy to the stream of milk from the breasts of their own sky goddess, Hathor. The idea of a flow of divine nourishment from the human breast is a beautiful picture and a wonderful human analogy, for the appearance of our galaxy in the night sky truly resembles a stream of flowing milk. This image exactly represents the cosmological idea that our galaxy communicates power, life, and sustenance from the divine source in the universe. Our galaxy, the Milky Way, is a transfer station for the divine power of the universe to convey life to our solar system, sun, moon, and planets, which in turn transmit this energy and life to our own fruitful planet. The lactation of heaven is the fount and source of our being and intelligent inspiration. These notions are beautifully presented in the image of the children of the Earth suckling their mother's milk from heaven.

Ancient people regarded the Milky Way as the only avenue of communication with the universe and their creator. In our modern era we are wrong to think that ancient people only held rudimentary concepts based upon sun-moon-planetary astronomy. There is enough hard written evidence and folkloric tradition to proclaim that ancient culture was based upon remnants of a superastronomy that existed in the deep reaches of the past.

There is very little known about the poet Nonnos, who lived sometime before 500 AD. The birthplace of our poet was the ancient *Apu* or *Khimmin* in ancient Egypt, which the Greeks called Khemmis and Panopolis, the city of the god Pan, or Min, as the local inhabitants called him. Min was portrayed ithyphallic, and so the Greeks associated him with fertility and the god Pan, the half-goat god of nature and sexual generation. Panopolis served as the capital of the Panopolitan Nome and was one of the most important towns of upper Egypt. Another prominent citizen from Panopolis in the late fourth century was Horapollon, the poet-scholar who taught in Alexandria. According to Strabo, the town was a center of trades and industry inhabited by weavers and stonecutters. The tapestry work found there is the archetype of the famous Gobelin work—the art form that was later reestablished in France. Numerous Christian manuscripts have been discovered there, including an apocalypse according to Peter. It may be assumed that there must have been a significant library, a temple archive, or a Coptic enclave to account for such materials. It may be presumed that many of the Egyptian priests converted to Christianity, as was the case in Ireland. Such conversion would have provided a very learned population that could preserve and cross-pollinate cultural traditions. This would have been an excellent environment to stimulate the young poet Nonnos.

During the time of Nonnos, Alexandrian audiences were becoming a bit bored with the usual sort of poetry, especially ancient dramas and played-out myths. If they were going to put up with this sort of stuff, they demanded more and more detail, mystery, and real substance. The situation resembled the Hollywood scene in modern America, where scandal and secrets whet the appetites of the devotees. Thus, the late Alexandrian poets were put to the pin of their collar to come up with the most remarkable research into ancient myth and obscure and little-known esoteric fact supported by well-written and dramatic storylines. It is in the context of Alexandria that the *Dionysiaca* became one of the most revealing documents ever to be written about the ancient world and its viewpoint. The *Dionysiaca* effectually reveals a way of looking at things that only a few of the most select people are ever allowed to see. Just as the era of dark antiquity was shutting its doors, Nonnos brought forth the hierophant's dream, a display of sacred knowledge only discussed within the circle of the exalted cosmologers of the Inner Temple. His work became the tell-all novel of antiquity that binds together religion, history, myth, astronomy, science, and culture into one revealing tableau.

Helping to expose the secret knowledge of the past were the book burnings that occurred during the early formation of Christianity. Coptic converts in Egypt openly exposed the sacred temple texts and in Luxor actually defaced the holy triad of that city into a botched mock crucifix. Anyone who wanted the teachings of the Inner Temple could easily lay their hands on the sacred mystery texts of Egypt. The exuberance of Christianity promoted an era of "out with the old, and in with the new."

Triad of Luxor defaced in an attempt to create a crucifix. Author photo

It was in this milieu that Nonnos became the leading light of the post-Alexandrian poets who vied with one another in the display of their repertoire of ancient knowledge. His pronouncements about the movements of the stars, astral myth, prophecy, religion, and obscure fields of cosmology are not to be found anywhere else in the record of the past. His *Dionysiaca* is a treasure house of specialized information. And even today, there are many arcane and unusual facts to be discovered in his works. The works of Nonnos demonstrate that he had not only accumulated ancient knowledge but that he had mastered its content. Nonnos the poet was the center of the intellectual community of Alexandria, a beacon of refined wisdom which did not suffer fools or pretenders.

The Astro-mythological Format

The hunger of the Alexandrian audiences prompts Nonnos to get off his mark quickly and not waste a moment of time. In the very first paragraph, Nonnos rehearses the birth of Dionysos, where Zeus:

> Cut the incision in his thigh, and carried him in his man's womb... and well he remembered another birth, when his own head conceived, when his temple was big with child...until he shot out Athena scintillating in her armor.

In these first 10 lines, Nonnos has connected the birth of the first Dionysos with the cosmic era of Sagittarius (the cosmic thigh) by repeating the tradition that Dionysos was born out of the thigh of Zeus. The cosmologers envisaged the universe as the body of God the Creator. The Milky Way Galaxy was also a body, and so on down the line through all the cosmic cycles. Therefore the yearly course of the sun was through the cosmic body represented by the signs of the zodiac, where certain parts of the body were assigned to each particular sign of the zodiac. Man was made in the image of God (the universe) so that the human body resembled the body of God. This is one of the secret codes of the zodiac, in that one could say "the head of the cosmic body," which meant "the sign of Aries." Nonnos relates that Athena was born from Zeus's head (the sign of Aries) in order to bring home the point to the audience or reader that many of the illusions of the *Dionysiaca* will have a cosmic meaning and an astronomical theme.

Also, over extreme periods of time the zodiac signs and constellations change their shape as the Milky Way spins around and changes the Earth's perspective toward the universe. The reference of zodiac signs to the parts of the body helps to clarify changes over long periods by having several names identifying the same region of the universe. These changes in the star pictures caused by the twirling of the Milky Way is exactly what creates monumental changes on Earth such as moving the fractured continents of Pangaea around.

The reader will not have read further than line 46 before Nonnos begins the story of the rape of Europa on the beach of Sidon, hometown of the ancient Phoenicians. Zeus has assumed the form of a Bull in emulation of the zodiac region of Taurus:

> ...and while he lifted her at his side, the sea-faring bull curved his neck downward, spread under the girl to mount...High above the sea, the girl throbbing with fear navigated on bull-back...

Nonnos has set a cosmological tone to his storytelling. Here again, the chronology of a myth is enfolded in the hinted reference to a position of the zodiac contained in the story. We can now easily guess that the rape of Europa occurred in the cosmic time of the zodiac sign of Taurus, the bull. The cosmic time of these events would be read as follows:

- Milky Way cycle (galactic rotation) = Zeus = Pisces (astrological house of Zeus)
- Precessional cycle = Bull = Taurus

The Reports of Natural Disasters in the Dionysiaca

The simple clue of placing myth into an astronomical context provides a scientifically accurate chronology. This becomes a golden asset to better understanding larger compilations of myths, even those from diverse cultures. This finally gives us the correct key to the reconstruction of ancient universal history.

The premier chapter of the *Dionysiaca* begins with the conflict between Zeus and Typhon, who is also called Seth. Nonnos immediately makes the connection between the destruction of the mantel of the Earth and the movement of the stars and constellations from their accustomed positions in the heavens:

> Then Nature, who governs the universe and recreates its substance, closed up the gaping rents in earth's broken surface, and sealed once more with the bond of indivisible joinery those island cliffs which had been rent from their beds. No longer was there turmoil among the stars. For Helios replaced the maned Lion, who had moved out of the path of the zodiac...Selene took the Crab [Cancer], now crawling over the forehead of the heavenly Lion, and drew him back opposite cold Capricorn, and fixed him there. (2.650)

Nonnos introduces the idea that—long ago, *at a time when* Leo and Cancer occupied different positions in the heavens—great natural changes occurred upon the face of the globe. These changes are personified in the myth of the battles between Zeus and Typhon. These dramatic myths seem to contain a scientific record of past changes, catalogued into an astrological and cosmological context and time period. The escapades of Zeus occurred during the galactic period when our solar system was in a perspective toward Pisces. During this long galactic period, the cycle of precession continues to revolve, presenting many subthemes and dramas to the main galactic theme of Pisces. Once understood and decoded, Nonnos' poetry may be seen as accurate scientific data (which it once was, before it became transformed into the secret and protective cocoon of myth).

There are many fragments of information offered under the name of the catastrophic deeds of the god Typhon, patron of hurricanes, earthquakes, desert storms, and tsunamis. Typhon is described as ripping off cliffs of land at the edge of the continents and throwing them into the sea, joining islands together, and raising the waters of the oceans up to the heavens:

> The bloodstained cave of Arima when the mountains had moved from their seats and were beating at the gate of inexpugnable Olympos, when the gods took wing above the rainless Nile...(I.140)

Changes in our celestial position over immense periods of time coincide with natural changes here upon Earth. The battles between Zeus and Typhon represent the interplay of celestial and terrestrial forces as our spinning galaxy changes its perspective to the universe. Nonnos' redaction of the astromythological format gives us a clear and simple view into the far-distant past. Without his cosmological overview, we would remain ignorant of the wealth of ancient information that has been patiently gathered and transmitted to us. Our ideas about the past would remain insubstantial, flawed, and incorrect. Nonnos absolutely stands out as a scientist, astronomer, cosmologer, historian, philosopher, and antiquarian. He has preserved the cosmological worldview of the ancient high priests. Without a doubt, Nonnos is our inspiration; without him, this book could not ever have been conceived.

Nonnos continues to cite the changing of the constellations:

> The many [serpentlike] hands of Typhon…throttled Cynosuris [constellation]…one gripped the…Bear's mane as she rested on heaven's axis…another caught the Oxdrover [constellation] and knocked him out; another dragged Phosphoros [Venus], and in vain under the circling turning-post [the Sun]…held the Bull [Taurus]…with a long arm he grasped…Aigoceros [Capricorn]…he dragged the two fishes [Pisces] out of the sky…he buffeted the Ram [Ares]… (I.163)

This rendition continues on with statements about the crest of the Atlas Mountains and the depths of the ocean. Peace in heaven is restored by the moon: "The unshaken congregation of the fixt stars with unanimous acclamation left their places and caught up their traveling fellows."

Nonnos shows us that ancient people created an astromythological format to support history and natural events in eras that occurred so long ago that a tally of years would no longer have any scientific validity. The cosmologers had their own clock right there in the heavens—the common clock face of the zodiac—where all the cosmic cycles were in evidence. Therefore, if something occurred in the precessional time period of Taurus, then they would refer to that epoch in terms of "the bull, cow-eyed, cow-headed" or as pertaining to "the neck" of the zodiac.

This astromythological format was even used by the modern astronomer Bayer (1564–1617) in his *Uranometria* (1603), where he lists historical and mythological personages under specific signs. Apparently these examples have been handed down over long periods of time from cosmologer to cosmologer. Therefore, even the scientific Bayer feels he should carry on this tradition:

- Andromedia: Abraham, Judazo
- Aries: Jupiter Ammon (*Princeps signorum coelestium*—
  the premier sign of the heavens)
- Aquarius: Deucalion, Ganymedes, Cecrops
- Capricornus: Pan, Pelagi
- Centaurus: Chiron, Minotaurus
- Corona: Ariadnae, Minos
- Draco: the custody of the Hesperides
- Eridanus: Oceanus, Mauritanis
- Hercules: Nixus, Nilus, Promethus, Orpheus
- Leo:Hercules
- Libra: Mizan Hebraeis
- Pisces: Veneris Mater, Venus, Cupid, Goddess of Syria
- Sagittarius: Chiron, Croton
- Triangula: Aegyptus, Nilus
- Taurus: Io, Isis
- Virgo:Erigone, Fortuna, Ceres, Pax

In the above catalogue, Bayer has transmitted astral chronology (just like the information from Nonnos), where history is directly related to a constellation or a zodiac sign.

Again, it must be said that our galaxy is both spinning and moving ahead in the universe, changing the Earth's perspective of the stars that surround us. One may begin to see why cosmology is geocentric in relationship to the universe at large.

Burning of the Library of Alexandria

It was Alexander's dream to bring together the East and the West in a union of culture, science, and information, the midpoint of which was a library—a center of learning in his city at the hub of the world. His motivation was the product of his tutelage by Aristotle, his mixed Eastern-Western parentage, and his megalomaniacal delusion that he was the new savior and prince of the world, who was meant to bring peace and prosperity to the world. His name and spirit were to be ever celebrated in the city of his name.

One fragment of Alexander's dream was the establishment of a mighty learning center dedicated to the muses, which would eclipse anything from the past. This was eventually carried out in 283 BC by the descendent of one of his generals. According to Preston Chesser (*ehistory* and *The Vanished Library* by Luciano Canfora), the Museum of Alexandria was modeled upon the Lyceum of Aristotle in Athens. The Alexandrian version held half a million documents from Assyria, Greece, Persia, Egypt, India, and elsewhere around the world. The complex included study and lecture areas, delightful gardens, a zoo, and, of course, shrines for each of the nine muses. The campus was manned by 100 scholars, who were in residence full-time performing research, writing, lecturing, translating, and copying. Though the library was quite large, it became necessary to transfer a large amount of the material overflow to the Temple of Serapis, which became a daughter library.

Other sources have stated that the Library of Alexandria was actively engaged in copying manuscripts to be sold to other great libraries around the world. Indeed, it was one of these warehouses of books-for-export that was burned in the skirmishes between Caesar and Anthony. In addition, literary scouts were sent out to various countries to buy and collect interesting material that would further the glory and reputation of Alexandria.

It may be stated that Alexandria has captured the distinction of being the most burned library in all of history:

> 48 BC: Burned in the conflict between Julius Caesar pursuing Anthony. The burning ships helped set fire to the district around the library. In another report, the fire only consumed warehouses of copied

documents. In any event, Marc Anthony afterward presented Cleopatra with 200,000 scrolls to make up for the destruction.

391 AD: Theophilus, Patriarch of Alexandria, converted the Temple of Serapis and its library into a Christian church. While most of the library documents were lost or destroyed, it is estimated that this library contained only 10% of the total Alexandrian literary treasury. Shortly afterward, his nephew Cyril became patriarch. During his tenure, the renowned Hypatia, said to have been the last head of the Library of Alexandria, was slain in partisan street battles between Christians, Jews, and followers of the older religions. It can only be assumed that the library suffered greatly during this revolution.

640 AD: The Moslem caliph Omar captured the city of Alexandria. He was informed that the city had a wonderful library that contained all the knowledge of the world. The caliph replied that if this library contained knowledge contrary to the Koran, it was heresy; if it contained knowledge in accord with the Koran, then it was superfluous. It took six months to burn the texts in the furnaces of the bathhouses. However, these reports were written 300 years after the fact by Bishop Gregory, who also denounced many other Moslem atrocities.

It may be inferred from the information above that a goodly portion of ancient information did survive, and that the destructions of the libraries of Alexandria did not constitute the utter disappearance of ancient reports, as many popular writers like to report. Indeed, there were several world-class institutions that did survive and preserve information down to modern times. These collections were the Library of Pergamum in Turkey, and Ugarit in Syria, and those of Ashurbanipal in Mosul and Bagdad in Iraq. Another formidable destruction of manuscripts took place during the Fourth Crusade with the burning of the Library of Constantinople. Finally, the earthquake, fire, and tsunami of 1755 AD in Lisbon annihilated important and irreplaceable libraries of that ancient port upon the Atlantic Ocean.

In the main, it may be seen that Nonnos was fortunate to live in times when many ancient and secret temple documents could be collected by those interested in such things. And indeed, it was Nonnos' profession as a leading poet and writer to collect and assemble pertinent and scientific information from the past. Scholars are in agreement that Nonnos was in possession of extraordinarily advanced cosmological knowledge interweaving the nature of the universe, human history, science, and religion.

A Final Note on Nonnos

The world, and especially the Near East, was alive with the expectation of the coming of the messiah or even a great king who would bring peace and order to the world. When the cosmologers and astronomers calculated the inception of a new cosmic age in the cycle of the Milky Way, they propagated the news of the birth of a new son of God, which accompanied these great cosmic changes. This son would set the new cosmic theme by his example and inform the people of the Creator's latest message. Of course, everyone expected a revelation in terms of their own culture. The Hebrews expected a great and powerful king who would bring peace to the Middle-east. Greek-Egyptian culture expected the appearance of a new Dionysos. Nonnos is a trusted reporter of ancient tradition, which is the love of his life. He will not contrive or falsify the facts to fit into some current religious movement. Therefore, Nonnos tells us that, according to his research, the New Dionysos will be born at Beirut, not Jerusalem. Nonnos is writing in the fifth century AD and has also composed a poetic version of the Apocalypse of St. John. We do not know the religious conviction of Nonnos, but if he were a Christian, he would most certainly have written Jerusalem in preference to Beirut.

The most amazing part of the revelation of Nonnos is that he affirms that the new son of God is not a son of Zeus-Jupiter, Saturn, or Uranus. Nonnos says the unexpected, namely that the new Dionysos will be the son of the most ancient of all the gods: the god Ocean.

Many people are repulsed by this kind of discussion because of their own steadfast religious convictions. But this is where the science comes into play. The rise of the Sun Kings, the warrior sun god Huitzilopochtli, the sun infant in the Coricancha Temple in Cuzco, the shepherd and lamb images surrounding Christ—all testify to the fact that a new epoch in time had taken place. Indeed, all the excitement in the world had been driven by the astronomers and cosmologers, who had propagandized this turnover of universal time. The key to abstracting science from religion, myth, and astrology is to absorb what tradition is saying and to translate it into scientific fact. Nonnos reports that the new king will be the son of Ocean, the most ancient of all the gods in human memory. Ocean belongs to the epochal time of Libra in the cycle of the Milky Way. And Libra lies directly across the circle of the heavens from Aries, the new cosmic era of the cycle of the Milky Way. Having the god Ocean to be the father of the new Dionysos does not make sense in the context that Nonnos has developed concerning the various apparitions of Dionysos. But in Mexica-Maya-Andean astronomy the zodiac signs in opposition to one another are linked together in art to show that they are closely interrelated. Only a master cosmologer would have had such knowledge. Nonnos has confirmed himself to be a true historian and accurate reporter. The cycle of the Milky Way has now entered the region of Aries, which is affected by Libra the region in opposition to Aries.

Part 3

Cosmic Myth at Opposite Ends of the Earth

The ultimate goal of this work is to show the existence of a global cosmology that existed in the far-distant past. The following chapters concern an ancient Mexican and an Egyptian cultural goddess of the Milky Way. It is almost unthinkable to imagine the close resemblance of character and cosmic context of these great feminine icons, whose cultures existed 120° apart on the surface of the globe and across an ocean that is supposed not to have been crossed until 1492 AD.

CHAPTER 3.1

Coyolxauhqui, Goddess of the Milky Way Galaxy

The mixture of the thin cool air at the mile-high altitude of Mexico City in combination with the heat of the equatorial regions provides such a balanced combination that temperatures are nearly the same year round, irrespective of the seasons. Modern inhabitants, even the wealthy, do not require heating or air-conditioning for their homes. The sheltered aspect of the Mexico City valley was a boon in ancient times. However, in our current time, the sheltered aspect of the surrounding ring of mountains traps the smog and pollution in the valley, making it one of the most polluted places on the planet.

The Aztec were foreign conquerors of the ancient people of this once-blessed region. Aztec culture revolved around the same story that Nonnos was writing about, namely the advent of the new era of Aries of the cycle of the Milky Way. The Aztec story relative to their geography concerns the story of the cosmic succession of the male Aztec warrior-god Huitzilopochtli, who overcame his stepsister, the very most ancient female goddess Coyolxauhqui, patroness of the earliest traditions of the geography of Mexico. The Aztec themselves depict and honor this succession from Coyolxauhqui to Huitzilopochtli because it substantiates their legitimate and divine right of kingship over these regions of the Earth.

The point has already been made that Coyolxauhqui is among the wide variety of bare-breasted goddesses whose milk supplies the Milky Way Galaxy. It is time to present the intimate details of Coyolxauhqui's story where it will be interesting to follow how ancient people wove astronomical knowledge into their folklore.

Courtesy of Karl Taube

Coyolxauhqui is also identified with every possible sort of female deity: as a very ancient Earth mother, moon goddess, and the goddess of the planet Venus. Coyolxauhqui even appears to have assumed one of the characteristics of the ancient cosmic monster, Tlaltecuhtli, because she also has gnashing mouths on her elbows, knees, and other joints. These multitudes of identifications—especially the terrifying maws of the cosmic monster at her joints tell us that Coyolxauhqui is a goddess of the Milky Way cycle of the epochal age of Pisces (astrological house of Jupiter; exaltation of Venus; and triangle of Mars, Venus, and the moon). Unfortunately her cosmic epoch is now passed and another god is waiting in the wings to initiate a new cosmic theme for the universe. Exactly like the head of Coyolxauhqui's mother, the head of Tlaltecuhtli is formed by two serpents, traditional symbols of the Milky Way Galaxy where the souls of the dead are recycled. This concept of the Milky Way as the "avenue of the dead" is portrayed by the skull and bones ornamenting the creature's body.

The Story

The story of the overthrow and replacement of Coyolxauhqui is recorded in *El Templo Mayor De Tenochtitlan en la Obra de Fray Diego Duran* (p. 69):

> One day Coatlique was sweeping the temple, when a ball of feathers magically appeared and fell from the sky. Coatlique put the ball of feathers underneath the folds of her petticoat, but afterwards could not find it. Thus a magical union was consummated between the ball-of-feathers and Coatlique.

The 400 stars ask their pregnant mother, Coatlique, who has put you in this condition? Their mother could not give them an answer. Then Coyolxauhqui tells the 400 major stars of the sky that they must kill their mother who has committed this infamy. Before they can attack her, she gives birth to Huitzilopochtli who is born as a fully-armed mature warrior. He defends his mother against Coyolxauhqui and the 400 stars; kills and cuts off her head, arms, and legs—and throws Coyolxauhqui down the pyramid-temple staircase to her death.

Handcarved granite image of Coyolxauhqui by the author

This is a very shocking story, indeed. But the story of Jesus is equally shocking to others—that he was tortured and nailed to a cross and that his flesh and blood is ritually symbolically consumed. Even in classical Greek myth, Saturn attacks Uranus, and the gods kill gods. This is so all over the world.

The legend of Coyolxauhqui is really a wonderful and beautiful story, as well as an accurate cosmological tale. The little ball of feathers signifies the heavens as all feathered objects do. Even the feathered headdresses of the native peoples represent "a spiritual halo" like that of the portraits of European saints and gods.

The story is about a celestial union on a higher plane than we may understand. Coatlicue is the faceless mistress of the entire Milky Way Galaxy. Coatlicue is she who is covered with snakeskins, and her face is made up of snake heads. She is the Great Snake of the Milky Way and, as the legend tells us, the mother of the 400 major stars as well as the cosmic deities Coyolxauhqui and Huitzilopochtli. Both of her children are epochal gods of the Milky Way but of successive epochal periods (Pisces followed by Aries).

Illustration of the Coatlicue sculpture by León y Gama, first published in 1792.

Coatlicue, goddess of the entire galaxy, mother of Coyolxauhqui & Huitzilopochtli. Her head is formed by two serpents just like the ancient cosmic monster. Courtesy of Karl Taube, *Aztec and Maya Myths*

Coatlicue, as the goddess of the Milky Way, receives the ball of feathers from the universe (the Creator Father). She sequesters the ball of feathers in her bosom, the astrological house of the chest. The chest, breast, rib cage is related to Cancer on the cosmic human. Cancer represents the moon's control over the zodiac. This is the same symbolism as the creation of Eve from the rib from the chest of Adam (who stands next to Cancer in the sign of Gemini). This myth is illuminating the fact that the galactic epoch of Coyolxauhqui (Pisces) is ending and that a new galactic epoch (Aries) has been born from the twirling and movement of our galaxy within the universe.

Mary Miller writes (p. 68), "Although it has often been stated that Coyolxauhqui represents the moon… Coyolxauhqui may actually be a goddess of the Milky Way." Taube (p. 47) also cites Carmen Aguilera who says that this goddess represents the Milky Way.

Coyolxauhqui shows herself to be the goddess of the former epoch of the cycle of the Milky Way because she has the power to command the *Centzon Huitznahuas*, the star gods, her 400 brothers and sisters. It is an unexpected coincidence that even today some astronomical studies limit their catalogues to the 400 major stars of the celestial globe. The name Coyolxauhqui means "golden bells" or, more precisely, "face painted with bells." Usually long, complicated names are common to newly emergent cultures. Short, hacked-off names are indicative of older cultures that have repeatedly shortened their frequently used appellations. In ancient Ireland, the name for the moon is Aine. In Sardinia and Rome the names are quite similar in form and pronunciation, Jana and Diana. In the Mexico City Valley, the names of ancient gods are very long because they are in the form of a descriptive sentence: "She with golden bells painted on her cheeks" and "She with the skirt of serpents." This could mean that we are dealing with a brand-new culture. It could also mean that an ancient culture was adopted by a new conquering people that imposed its own language upon the original inhabitants and their ancient gods.

Tenochtitlan and Templo Mayor

Before the arrival of the warlike Aztecs from the north, this special valley belonged to the Otomis, Nahua-Chichimecs, and Olmec. This unique mountain valley was also the home of the people of Xochimilko, a Venice-like island city dedicated to fruit and vegetable production. The people of this island paradise were gentle and kind. They developed the science of flowers, cultivating and investigating their psychological, medicinal, culinary, herbal, holistic, color, and aromatic virtues and essences. These "flower people" knew nothing of the warlike sun god of the later Aztecs. Their primary deity was the sun god Xochipilli, a gentle patron of colorful blossoming flowers. All in all, it may be said that this original culture of gentile refinement was most probably like a Garden of Eden or an image of heaven on earth. Their use of extraordinary brilliant colors, soft ribbons, and floral designs and patterns was adopted by the Aztec, and it continues to be one of the most striking features of Mexican culture today.

The Great Temple of Mexico City stood in the very center of the city of Tenochtitlan, which was regarded to be the navel of the world. Modern excavation of the Templo Mayor shows that it was refaced at least seven times and drastically renovated and added to on four occasions. This suggests an antiquity reaching far into the remote past. New excavations reveal refacing, restoration, and, in some instances, complete redevelopment of sites throughout Mexico, Yucatan, Belize, Guatemala, and the rest of Mesoamerica. New research continues to uncover advanced cultures farther and farther into the past. It is purported that the Aztec arrived in 1325 AD when they started to redevelop the magnificent city of Tenochtitlan. The Aztec burned the history books and claimed to have founded the city, which had existed long before their arrival.

The beautiful foundation legend of the eagle perched upon the cactus devouring the serpent suggests to all minds that the Aztec originally discovered the island city of Mexico. Yet it is admitted that the Aztec paid tribute for a long time to their new neighbors. It is also related that when the Aztec went out to view the great pyramids of Teotihuacán, they were utterly amazed at the sophistication and size of these structures. The Aztec called them the work of the supernatural gods and "the road to the gods." Another Aztec saying regarding the pyramids is that here is "the place where time began," which is another way of saying that here is the place where "the measurement of time began." It is now accepted that the Aztec were relatively new immigrants to Mexico, most probably warlike Cherokee from the North. It is likely that blood sacrifices should be linked to these tribes and not predicated upon the earlier and gentile inhabitants of these regions.

The magnificent Coyolxauhqui Stone and even the amazing Templo Mayor were only rediscovered in 1978 during the excavations of the new underground railway system. The funds for the award-winning Museo Antropologia were a portion of the redevelopment funding for the 1968 Olympics in Mexico City. There is a point to be made that Mexican and Mesoamerican research is still in its infancy. It is especially curious that underground caves were broached under the main pyramid at Teotihuacán. After brief and rudimentary excavations back in 1923, the site has been neglected and has remained basically untouched.

The great circular stone of Coyolxauhqui is several feet thick, 10 feet in diameter, and weighs eight tons! Coyolxauhqui is tied up with her own serpents and was cast down the great stairs of the Templo Major, which stands at one corner of the vast Zocalo square. The artwork suggests movement, action, and a multiplicity of meaning. It is truly one of the most unusual and astounding works of art that has ever been produced. The stone was found at the foot of the temple buried beneath the streets of the modern city. The megalith is unique in its complexity as a design that depicts such awful brutality and slaughter while, at the same time, attempting to represent an honored goddess.

The Templo Mayor is either founded upon the original Coatepec—"the Hill of the Serpents"—or built to resemble the original and mythical Hill of the Serpents. The temple is completely decorated with different types of serpents' heads, especially the Coatepantil, or the "wall of the serpents." It will be remembered that the defeated moon goddess was tied up with serpent ropes. Many snakes are also nocturnal and are therefore associated with the moon. She was defeated by a weapon called *Xiuhcoatl,* or Fire Serpent. It is distinguished from the other serpents by being emblazoned with stars.

Other rooms and features of the Hill of the Serpents are the area of penitence for the rite of self-mutilation with agave thorns, apparently one of the activities most practiced in the building (National Museum of Anthropology, *Great Temple of Tenochtitlan*, p. 19). Other areas are dedicated to the Eagle Knights, the elite soldiers of the sun god. There is also the wall of the skulls dedicated to *Mictlantecuhtli*, the god of the dead and lord of the underworld. Note that the great image of the moon goddess has a skull tied around her waist.

Huitzilopochtli is the god of the new galactic era. He is also often called the sun god because the zodiac sign of Aries, which is the new epoch of the cycle of the Milky Way, is the astrological-cosmological exaltation of the sun. Huitzilopochtli is said to have cut off the limbs of Coyolxauhqui and then tossed her head into the sky, where it became the moon, so that his mother would be comforted in seeing her daughter in the sky every night. It seems apparent that the transition from one galactic epoch to a new epoch and god is an agonizing and slow process. It would not do to abandon Coyolxauhqui so suddenly after such eons of service. She has been given a new position as matron moon.

The Blessed Virgin of Guadalupe

There is a side chapel dedicated to *The Virgin Mother of Ancient Times* in the National Cathedral on the great Zocalo square in the heart of Mexico City. The cosmic aspect of Coyolxauhqui is still worshiped in Mesoamerica through the image of the Christian Mother Mary, who is clothed in the ancient star mantle.

The Basilica of Our Lady of Guadalupe is located in one of the suburbs of Mexico City. Many miracles and cures have been performed upon this holy ground once sacred to another ancient virgin-mother goddess of the Mexican people, whose name was Tonantzin. The Basilica is said to be located at the ancient sacred site called the Hill of Tepeyac, which may have boasted a pyramid at one time dedicated to the goddess. The virgin-mother Tonantzin was associated with the moon and also with the snake, mother of the corn, grandmother, seven flowers, and the seven serpents. The ancient goddess is a partner to the transition of the old beliefs into the Christian Church. There are innumerable ancient mother goddesses of many costumes and aspects that have been adopted into Christian veneration throughout Mesoamerica.

When we look at the 15th-century *Annunciation* by Roger van der Weyden, now at the Louvre in Paris, we see a fine Dutch upper-class apartment of that period, with the angel (announcing to Maria that she has been chosen to give birth to the son of God) and Maria dressed in contemporary Northern European garb with the hairstyle of Holland. This particular icon is so flavored with the contemporary character of the Netherlands that it would not serve well as an icon recognized by the rest of humanity. It would be unsuitable as a universal picture to introduce other cultures around the globe to this concept of the Catholic religion. Yet, it is a common practice in religious art to portray divinities in contemporary garments and familiar locations. In the colonial art schools of Cusco, the young artists were told to find the most beautiful young girl in each village and to use her as a model of the Virgin Mary.

The image of the Virgin of Guadalupe at the Basilica in Mexico City is the subject of much controversy and wrangling. The icon has a very European appearance. Some people even claim that they have discovered the artist who painted the Guadalupe image. St. Augustine has put forth the idea that the Holy Spirit has never for one moment abandoned humankind, even in the darkest history of the past. In this light it could be imagined that Our Holy Mother, the mother of God, could never have abandoned her children even in the ancient past.

What harm if the Franciscan priests wished to dress her up in European garb featuring the classical star-clad mantel of the universe, with an angelic supporter, while standing upon the horned moon as a token to the zodiac constellation of Taurus, the exaltation of the moon. After viewing the image at the Basilica, most people come away with a wonderful feeling of exaltation and happiness.

After scrupulous examination, the picture turns out to be an extremely wondrous and sacred image. The colors and the cloak upon which it was painted should have disintegrated long ago. The eyes are very detailed and reflect the light of optical instruments that have looked into them. Other microscopic examination shows no brush strokes but reveals that a convex image of the office of the Bishop Juan de Zumarraga, Saint Juan Diego, and other persons is perfectly reflected in the Virgin's eyes. Many inexplicable features were discovered during several inspections of the miraculous cloak. The image is smooth like a modern-day photograph.

According to ourladyofguadalupe.org (2008), the stars upon her mantle depict the stars in the sky on December 12, 1531, the date of her appearance in Guadalupe. The rose-colored garment under her mantle shows a contour map of Mexico and the exact place of her appearance.

One need only travel out to the great pyramids of Teotihuacán to appreciate the significance of the veneration of the moon. Here the Pyramid of the Moon occupies the place of honor at the very north end of the great north-south axis of the long Avenue of the Dead. It is in front of the Pyramid of the Moon that the reflections of the stars and planets were recorded by the astronomers looking into the water pool centered in this plaza de luna in front of the pyramid. Anthony Aveni says (p. 223) that, according to recent excavations, the Pyramid of the Moon may be among the earliest of all the Teotihuacán edifices.

Finally, the story of Coyolxauhqui and Huitzilopochtli presents the idea that our galaxy revolves and goes through cycles over great periods of time. These cycles bring forth specific new themes, cosmic and earthly drama, and unique gods and individuals. Though Coyolxauhqui reminds us a bit of the Amazons, the warrior women of the ancient world—unfortunately her time is past. Pisces is the geography of Mexico, and Pisces is a triangle of Venus and Mars, the combination of which would certainly produce warrior women. But now, Huitzilopochtli is the new cosmic god of the new and emerging galactic epoch of Aries. Huitzilopochtli is born fully formed as a mature warrior and fully armed with weapons—precisely like the birth of the fully armed Athena. The warrior goddess Athena was born from the cosmic head (Aries) of the cosmic body. It is difficult to gainsay that myth and classical astrology have been used to identify cosmic time. And the proof of this assertion is the indisputable fact that the bare-breasted heaven goddesses of the Pisces cycle of the Milky Way became a universally recognized and accepted icon around the entire sphere of the globe. Again, myth and astronomy were combined with science to promote icons of a universal philosophy that contained everything in one image and one idea. The idea that the universe supplies energy and spirit to the galaxy, which in turn transfers it onward to the solar system and our planet, is a highly sophisticated philosophy that is absolutely true today in the sophisticated world of modern science. The heaven goddesses transcended all nations and colors, demonstrating one unity of cosmic belief.

CHAPTER 3.2

The Circular Zodiac of Dendera

The cultural goddess of the Milky Way, according to the Egyptians, is found nearly 120° triangular to the Mexican homeland of the goddess of the Milky Way, Coyolxauhqui.

The cosmo-vision of the Egyptians shows a comfortable and friendly picture of the celestial sphere populated mainly by human figures and domesticated animals. The composite figures like Sagittarius are joined by lions, scorpions, and fish in a pleasing aspect. These are surrounded by about 36 *decan* figures, which are of a mythic-historical and thematic importance. "Decan" comes from the number ten, because they each occupy 10° of the circle of the zodiac. Therefore there are three per each sign of the zodiac which support and amplify the myth and history of each sign.

The Circular Zodiac of Dendera from *La Description De l'Egypte.* 1838

The celestial hemisphere is viewed from outside the rim looking in toward the North Pole. The heaven-holders who support the sky are a curious combination of the eightfold directional and geographic system and the twelvefold celestial system of 12 x 30 = 360°. It should be especially appreciated that the heaven supporters are orientated contrary-wise in opposite directions. The interpretation of these images is that this contrary facing is intended to show that the great cycles of the universe are counterpoised (which they are). The chevron patterns are water symbols emblematic of the cosmic ocean of the universe. The giant figure to the right of the circle of the heavens is the sky goddess Hathor, whose breasts replenish the Milky Way. She is outstretched from hands to toes from Sagittarius to Gemini across the zodiac, exactly like the Milky Way. In Egyptian cosmology, she gives birth to the sun every day from her birth canal in the east, and she swallows the sun every day with her mouth in the west. She is the ancient sky goddess called "the sow who eats her piglets"! What does this strange epithet mean? It means the same thing as the account of the Greek god Cronus, "who eats his children." Hathor and Cronus are sky gods who produce celestial phenomena (children or pigs) in the east and who devour their creation in the west. The celestial goddess Hathor is portrayed eating the sun in the west and giving birth again to the sun in the east through the passage of her womb. As with all cosmological ideas this symbolic imagery mixes scientific and childlike concepts into metaphoric concepts from which different levels of intellect can derive appropriate meaning, leading to a general human understanding. Every culture affirms that, "Truth will come out of the mouths of children."

The celestial scene is such that Hathor's vagina is positioned directly opposite the border of Pisces and Aries, showing the current chronological position of the cycle of the rotation of the Milky Way. Christianity adopted this Egyptian demarcation of the cycle of the Milky Way by calling the region of the borders of Pisces and Aries the "Keys of Saint Peter." Aveni writes (p. 35) that, "On medieval European maps the constellation of St. Peter included all of the zodiacal constellation of Aries and parts of Triangulum, Cetus, and Pisces."

The Circular Zodiac of Dendera is an expert assemblage of astronomical information, presenting much more information than obviously appears to the untutored eye. The Egyptians populated their universe with familiar human and animal figures to symbolize stars, planets, and constellations and also tell of natural and human history through the relationship of heaven, humans, and earth. The planets appear as human and composite figures near the zodiac houses of their exaltation.

The Circular Zodiac of Dendera is a multifaceted image of the Egyptian worldview. It represents their philosophy, their science, their religion, their portal of communication to their ancestors, and their myth and history of the past. The Zodiac of Dendera is special because it demonstrates the counterpoised physics of cycles flowing in different directions, which create, harmonize, and also destroy life on Earth. The ultimate goal of the piece is to indicate the cycle of the rotation of the Milky Way Galaxy—a celestial fact of the highest astronomical caliber.

There is no culture that can match the purity of iconic representation of Egyptian artisans. Egyptians were masters of communication. Whether it is an image of an owl, hawk, or the judgment of the heart against a feather, Egyptian pictures directly and economically convey their meaning. The proof of the precision of their images is that they are recognized across almost all cultural borders. But that which looks so simple is also fraught with deep meaning and nuance. Everything in Egyptian art means something very particular. The Egyptians even divided their language into sacred and common. Everything in Egyptian art also conveys many levels of meaning, encapsulating math, numbers, geometry, divine proportions, and countless other themes and sciences. Egyptian symbolism required a special genius to penetrate its meaning. In *The Temple in Man* (Ch. 7), Schwaller de Lubicz explains Egyptian symbolism in regard to the human body:

> The parts of the body with symmetrical organs [features] are shown in profile. The parts of the body with asymmetrical organs [features] are shown full face...the arms...are sometimes represented with two left hands, or two right hands. The left hand receives the right gives... The legs are joined...to express the idea of fixation, death, or inertia; they are placed one in front of the other to indicate a state of life. Thus, the seated, standing, or running personage has its particular meaning which—like its gestures, attributes, costume, and color—

> must be interpreted...personages issued from the Divine principle and not procreated through woman—have no navel. The figures are the primary, secret writing.

Thus the images are perfectly clear, but one needs a guidebook to fathom all the intricacies of meaning. Without the proper guide, Egyptian thought is esoteric, existential, and magic because we do not grasp their fundamental cosmological philosophy, a worldview that looked at all things from the vantage of the universe and its many cycles. Egyptian gods were not fantasized concepts. Their gods were actual historical persons whose being and story revealed true examples of real life. They were "gods" because they typified an aspect of the divine. They were avatars of "natural science" because they expressed the force of chemistry and science in their life story. Egyptian gods were examples of history, science, and religion. Humans became the paradigms, icons, parables, and revelations of the Egyptian experience and their worldview of the universe.

The astronomical ceiling of the Temple of Dendera is so beautifully carved and harmoniously balanced that it actually distracts our attention because of its apparent simplicity. We subconsciously imagine that we have understood what we have seen. It would be better if it failed in some respect by having a prominent mole on its face like the false patches worn at the court of Louis XIV to draw attention to the beauty of the wearer behind the outrageous imperfection of a cosmetic black spot.

The smooth harmony of the Dendera image distracts our attention from the disharmony of the counterpoised human- and falcon-headed images looking into one another's faces outside the celestial circle. We should notice their power, indicated by their size, which is less than the giant Hathor but much greater than the constellations of the heavenly sphere. Therefore, they appear as majestic intermediaries between Hathor (the goddess of the galaxy) and the celestial sphere that we humans may observe. These counterpoised male and female figures suggest the power of cosmic physics and the inevitability of cosmic law and fate directed by the constant flow of formal cycles of the cosmos.

The Circular Zodiac of Dendera was cautiously chipped and blasted from its stone ceiling by Napoleon's engineers and noted savants. This quixotic campaign once again introduced Egyptian wisdom, science, and beauty to the entire world. The Egyptian cosmological worldview believes that all things are interconnected. Every part of the universe is essential to the whole. Every aspect helps to define every other aspect. Sir J. Norman Lockyer (*The Dawn of Astronomy*, p. 135), speaking about the Zodiac of Dendera, remarked, "It is impossible to disconnect Egyptian mythology from astronomy." The Zodiac of Dendera is truly an amalgamation of myth, science, history, geometry, and religion.

The 12 "heaven-holders" prompt a suggestion of a connection to Atlas, the greatest astronomer of all time. Atlas made his observations in the Atlas Mountains upon the Atlas Ocean in Fez-Morocco—the place of the origin of Greek culture, the birthplace of the gods, where history, science, mythology, and genealogy had their beginnings. Morocco was a colony and a nautical culture descended from Atlantis. Greek genealogy attests that the ancient branch of the Egyptians came from the stock of Atlantic peoples in Morocco. And indeed it must be wondered that the classical Egyptians continued to portray their celestial gods—and the sun and the moon—piloting ships that ride across the cosmic ocean. This is highly significant because land-based cultures show their solar and lunar deities driving in chariots. Greek genealogy tells us that the astronomer Atlas was in the line of descent from the gods Ocean and Uranus, from whom he most probably received his science. Greek myth tells us allegorically that Atlas passed down these important traditions to Hercules when he traveled to Spain and Morocco in search of the Golden Apples of the Hesperides. This Hercules, who fought the giant Antaeus near Lixus (Larache) in Morocco, is identified with the Egyptian Hercules-Shu, showing that there is a connection between Fez-Morocco and Egypt.

The Zodiac Clock

The Zodiac of Dendera is a giant clockwork representing the exact astronomical position of multiple astronomical cycles. The Egyptians loved to parade their knowledge, and this intricate icon certainly gave them the opportunity. It also afforded them the satisfaction of expressing the most complex secrets of the universe in plain view of those who could see and obscured the mystery of the cosmos to those who could not fathom its meaning.

On the very edge of the heavenly disc, a band of heavenly forms (the decan figures) are walking in a counterclockwise direction. Meanwhile, halfway inside the circle, the sun's annular path through the signs of the zodiac (the ecliptic) proceeds in a clockwise direction, yet most of the figures face counterclockwise, except Taurus and Aries, whose faces are purposely turned away from one another to mark the significance of the new position of the galactic cycle of the Milky Way having entered Aries. Directly opposite to Taurus and Aries is another lion figure whose head is averted.

The cycle of the precession of the vernal equinoxes flows in a counterclockwise direction on the Dendera Zodiac precisely in the direction in which the zodiac figures are facing. Were the signs of the zodiac based upon the annular movement of the sun, or were they based upon the precession of the wobbling of the Earth's axis? Every anomaly should direct one's attention toward the correct indicator of the current position of a major cycle. The sun's yearly course is a common reoccurrence that is not significant or remarkable, while precession is of considerably longer duration (25,920 years), and therefore its unique correspondence to specific regions of the globe would be seen to have long-term effects upon our planet.

The direction of the five cosmic cycles as seen against the clock of the zodiac is as follows:

- The day (diurnal movement):clockwise
- The year (annular movement):counterclockwise
- Precession (vernal equinox):clockwise
- Rotation of the Milky Way Galaxy:counterclockwise
- Movement of the Milky Way in the universe:clockwise

For a very long time the Mid-East was alive with the prophecy of the coming of a messiah, a great savior, possibly a mighty king who would bring justice down from heaven and restore peace to the Earth. It is undeniable that the Book of Revelation and the fathers and bishops of the new religion used astronomical icons such as the zodiac signs of Pisces and Aries as powerful emblems of the new revelation. In the *Dionysiaca*, Nonnos affirms that we are currently in the galactic time of Aries, "the Ram, the center of the universe, the navel star of Olympos." Aries and Pisces were: the ram, the lamb, the wrath of the lamb, the good shepherd, the sign of the fishes, and the ceremony of humility in the washing of the feet (Pisces) of others.

History of the Temple of Dendera

The Zodiac of Dendera is said to have been carved in Ptolemaic times around 100 BC during the renovations to the temples at Dendera, sacred to the great sky goddess Hathor. It has been proposed that the current image is a copy of a very ancient zodiac portraying high cosmological knowledge from the far-distant past. The authors of *Ancient Skies* (p. 269) cite Pogo, who concluded that the sky map on the ceiling of Senmut at Thebes represented a much older image of the skies than was contemporary with Senmut, adviser of the famous Queen Hatshepsut. This is evidence that copying ancient stone zodiacs is not exceptional in Egypt.

Peter Tompkins, in his *Secrets of the Great Pyramid*, reports that Sir Norman Lockyer asserted that the Temple of Dendera was previously orientated to the North Star, gamma Draconis, at about 5000 BC, and then at Dubhe at about 4000 BC. Because of several sight lines of orientation—numerous additions and renovations—it was Lockyer's opinion that the astronomical temple of Hathor was rebuilt in 3233 BC, then in 1600 BC, and again by the Ptolemys in 100 BC. Egyptian inscriptions confirm these dates concerning some of the remodels. At this period in the dark ages of archaeology, the Egyptologists actually objected to Lockyer's dragging in astronomy to straighten out the difficult chronology of the temple's history. They unanimously dismissed his theory and his book *The Dawn of Astronomy*. In 1964 Giorgio de Santillana of MIT and others showed that Lockyer's work was correct and true.

Franz Boll, in his *Sphaera* (p. 159), reports that Teukros, the Babylonian astrologer, claimed that astrology was taught by the gods themselves to two holy people—one who lived by the Tigris/Euphrates and one who lived by the Nile. Boll contends that the images on the zodiac show many Babylonian influences, especially the image of Sagittarius. He imagines that the work is a mixture of two cultures. Boll further says that the zodiac was conceived under an astrologic viewpoint because it shows the five planets personified as gods standing near to the zodiac houses of their *exaltation*.

The universal astronomical images—such as the sky dragons and winged serpents; cosmic turtles; topless Milky Way goddesses; and the many common usages, such as the reckoning of the seven days of the week—are evidence of a worldwide community of astronomers who certainly traveled and attended scientific symposiums as we do today. Boll admits that the Dendera Zodiac is an amalgamation of some of the most ancient as well as contemporary images of that time of the Ptolemaic reconstruction of the temple (p. 163). The French archaeologist Auguste Mariette noted that the foundations of Dendera were sunk 20 feet into the ground. This is quite unusual, because Luxor, Carnac, and most temples are founded directly upon sand trenches, encased by bricks to prevent seepage of the sand (Wilson and Flem-Ath pp.167–172). The sand-trench method appears to be a seismic safeguard. This radically different form of foundation (the deep trench) may support the idea that the temples at Dendera are from an extreme antiquity as some others have inferred.

Latrone, Bally, and Dupius dated the stone zodiac anywhere from 15000 BC down to the time of the Emperor Augustus. Lepsius identified the image of Osiris as the constellation of Orion and the central leg of beef as our present day Big Dipper. He also picked out the five planet images placed in their house of exaltation. Lepsius likewise identified the 36 decan figures around the rim of the zodiac that divide the zodiac into segments of 10 degrees. Helene Hagan, in her *The Shining Ones* (p. 80), says that Egypt was divided into 36 nomes, each corresponding to a constellation, giving these nomes a spiritual and personified character or pedigree. She also mentions that the stars represent enlightened ancestors. Herodotus has told us that the nomes had their special and separate culture and god and that many of the nomes identified with a foreign family, tribe, or nation. For example, the town of Sais was a Greek-friendly colony or ghetto. There were also Babylonian ghetto towns, and so on. Perhaps Egypt endured for such a long period of time because of its segregated cultural mix, carefully unified and respected under one nation. Similar examples of multinational and cultural respect under one unifying nation were found in Spain and Ireland, to some extent in Babylon and Rome, and in modern times in the United States of America.

In conclusion, the Circular Zodiac of Dendera presents multiple planetary and astronomical cycles upon one clock face, the zodiac and the celestial sphere. Also, many of the 36 decan figures on the rim refer to mythological and historical personages and natural and divine events. The Zodiac was created to depict the scientifically correct position of the major great cycles like that of the rotation of the Milky Way. All in all, the Zodiac of Dendera remains as the most dynamic image of the heavens ever created. It undoubtedly is the most important ancient scientific instrument and artifact in our possession.

The height of the giant Hathor figure equals the diagonal of the celestial square to her left. The height from soles of feet to top of head of each the four female heaven-holders is the radius of the heavenly circle that they support. The height of the four pairs of Horus falcons holding the sky appears to be the radius of the ecliptic of the constellations of the zodiac. Eight Horus figures divided by the total of all the 12 figures gives us the sexagesimal astronomical matrix (8 ÷ 12 = .666).

Chapter 3.3

Cosmic Symbols—Snakes, Dragons, Turtles, and Goddesses

All ancient people regard the galaxy as our supportive mother, who provides material and spiritual sustenance to her children here on Earth. The sky goddesses transmit the wisdom and intelligence of the cosmos to inspire us here below. Western culture is not generally familiar with the symbols of the Milky Way represented by the sky goddesses, the dancing dragons of Asian culture, the feathered serpent of the Maya, or the winged solar serpent above the temple entrances of Egypt. Modern people are not aware that the ancients predicated many more things upon the Milky Way than upon the vital course of the sun around the ecliptic of the zodiac. The idea of a celestial mother who provides all things is equivalent to the statement of science saying that our galaxy transmits energy from the universe to our solar system and to our Earth. The ancients were not sun worshippers; they were galaxy worshippers, in which the sun only serves as an integral part of the cosmic mechanism. The kings of the Maya at Tikal actually dressed up in a ceremonial costume—not as a sun king but fashioned to resemble the stars of the Milky Way. The ruler of the Maya derived his legitimacy and power from the galaxy, because our beautiful garden planet is the creation of the Milky Way, which is our intermediary with the Creator God residing in the temple of the universe. This is the ancient worldview we wish to uncover and explore. It is a fascinating perspective combining science, humanity, religion, and God. According to Schele and Freidel, the main icon of the Maya is their Tree of Creation, the

Maya symbol of the upright Milky Way wrapped in the double-headed serpent that represents the sun's path along the ecliptic (Aveni, p. 37).

Along with cosmic snakes and dragons, there are also celestial turtles, one of the best-known of all cosmic images around the globe. This icon represents countless aspects of astronomy, such as the World Tree and the equinoxes. But in actuality, the turtle represents the Earth in a cosmic context, as a hemisphere of the globe, like the curved shell of the tortoise.

Several cultures represent the moon as a speedy rabbit, whose superprolific constitution allows her to breed up to seven times a year. Aesop records a fable of the tortoise and the hare, which may be one of the oldest surviving cosmic stories:

The Tortoise and the Hare. One day, the hare ridiculed the tortoise because of his slow movements. In response, the aggravated tortoise challenged the speedy hare to a race. The hare quickly outdistanced his opponent and filled with confidence decided to take a nap halfway through the course. Suddenly waking-up, the hare saw the tortoise slowly ambling across the finish line to win the race. The moral is—*slow and steady wins the race.*

The story is peculiar in the sense that a hare is always swifter than a turtle. Why does this turtle win the race? In Maya, Hindu, and global cosmology, a hemisphere of the Earth is thought of as a giant turtle's shell. Giant turtles gracefully bob and swim through the ocean. The Earth emulates the sea turtle because the Earth turtle swims through the cosmic ocean of the universe experiencing every possible form of creation that exists in the entire universe. This is the mystery of the sacred Earth. The turtle image is a very beautiful and cogent simile based upon the observation of nature and the heavens. The turtle is very special because it is amphibious and is comfortable on both land and water. This makes turtles a transcendental symbol combining the material nature of the Earth and the divine nature of the cosmic ocean. Many cultures also honor caiman, crocodiles, and alligators because of this ability to exist in the dual worlds of water and land.

Ancient people loved this kind of symbolism, in which the many attributes of a creature elevated it to an almost sacred status. The slow-moving turtle was sometimes also associated with the slowest-moving planet, Saturn/Cronus—the master of time. The tortoises occasionally carry small frogs and young turtles on their backs and are like the Earth, which carries all of creation upon its orb. The tortoise shell is also divided into sections like maps of the Earth divided into longitude and latitude. Eleanor Mannikka (*Angkor Wat*, p. 33) reports that the turtle was an incarnation (avatar) of Vishnu and described as a hemisphere, or half a globe.

In the Maya cosmology, a rabbit appears in the orb of the moon and is the moon's companion and totem animal. The race concerns astronomical phenomena. The moon-rabbit appears to move rapidly as it circles the Earth-tortoise but occasionally slows down dramatically at apogee (the farthest distance in its elliptical orbit from the Earth). The moon-rabbit imagines that she is swifter than the Earth-tortoise, who follows a slow course around the sun. The precocious young rabbit can never win the race of the Earth's orbit. No matter how fast the moon-rabbit thinks that she is, she is obtuse to the fact that she is a satellite being dragged along by the Earth. Even modern science admits that moon tracking is full of countless nuisances and perturbations. Rationally, the rabbit is only a passenger and not a competitor. The Earth is a symbol of the wisdom of age, a tortoise who knows the paths through the great cosmic ocean.

Kelley and Milone, in *An Encylopedic Survey of Archaeoastronomy*, devote an entire subchapter (15.3.2) to the worldwide phenomena of the cosmic turtle, which is found in Mesoamerica, North and South America, Mesopotamia, Ireland, Africa, India, Tibet, China, Korea, Japan, Southeast Asia, Cambodia, Oceania, New Guinea, and Polynesia. They say that the concept presents sophisticated astronomical conceptions but is of extreme antiquity in time. The Earth-tortoise is associated with complex astronomical phenomena that range from the movement of the world axis, the equinoxes, solstices, the planets, the 12 signs of the zodiac, the 28 lunar mansions, Orion's belt, the Pleiades, and the spinning of the Milky Way. In the traditions of Angkor Wat ,the cosmic turtle is involved with the rotation of the Sea of Milk, where opposing daemons pull upon a snake wrapped around the World Tree. It is also involved with the flood, five- or seven-headed dragons, and the sacred lotus that appears as a pillar upon the turtle's carapace.

Again, the band of the Milky Way crosses the path of the sun on the boundary of Taurus/Gemini on one side of the zodiac and crosses through the boundary of Scorpio/Sagittarius on the other side of the zodiac. Aveni (p. 312) quotes Urton, who relates that, "Andean people take the Pleiades [in Taurus] and the tail of the Scorpio to represent two opposing groups of stars, which they employ in the ordering of terrestrial space." They call the Milky Way their "Mayu, the celestial river, a continuation of the river system which flows through the sacred valley of Cuzco."

Ancient cosmologers were aware of the black hole at the center of our galaxy which they marked with the tip of the arrow point of the constellation of Sagittarius. It was only in the year 1997 that modern astronomy discovered a strange form of ultraviolet light coming from the M42 Nebula on the other side of the sky below Taurus/Gemini. The M42 Nebula, diametrically opposite to the black hole, is anciently referred to as "the smoke from the fire of creation". The belt of Orion was called the "hearthstones of creation" and often portrayed in the image of a turtle. Every culture on Earth has recognized the belt-stars of Orion and the nearby Pleiades as sacred places of extraordinary energy and power in the heavens. It is evident that ancient astronomy knew a considerable amount of information about our galaxy which we are only beginning to rediscover. Hopefully this may lead to a renaissance and revival of ancient astronomy and cosmological wisdom.

One of the most famous astronomical serpents is Ladon, born of Typhon and Echidna—famous for composite monsters like the Chimaera of the Etruscans. Ladon is a 100-headed (with many eyes = stars) dragon speaking with 100 different voices. This dragon-snake resides in a great tree guarding the Golden Apples of the Hesperides (daughters of the astronomer Atlas on the Canary Islands). One of Hercules' labors is to get the Golden Apples. He slays Ladon, who becomes the constellation Draco, whose tail winds near the constellations of the bears of the North Pole. Ancient people have always portrayed the axis of the Earth as a giant World Tree, and therefore it is appropriate that Draco (Ladon of the Hesperides tree) is near the North Pole. Of course, Hercules went to Atlas to obtain astronomical knowledge when he shouldered the celestial sphere of his mentor, and the Golden Apples represent the orbs of the planets reflecting the light of the sun. But what is most remarkable about the story of Ladon is that, many cosmic ages beforehand, the tree with the Golden Apples was in the care of the daughters of the goddess Night, oldest of all the myths of Greek tradition. Diogenes Laertius, in *Lives of the Eminent Philosophers* (9:35), confirms that astronomy is always the oldest of all traditions when he records that Democritus (460–357 BC, founder of the atomic theory) declared that Anaxagoras' views on the sun and the moon were not original but of great antiquity and that he had simply stolen them.

The Egyptian Hercules being taught astronomy by Atlas in Morocco. Woodcut by Albrecht Durer

PART 4

NUMBERS OF THE UNIVERSE AND OF MAN

Humans are fascinated with numbers and geometry because they present a new way to organize and quantify the world. But who invented these numbers and geometry, and where did they come from? Numbers and geometry come directly from observation of the heavens, from astronomy.

CHAPTER 4.1

Vedic Super-Astronomy

The word "Vedic" means "sacred." The traditions of this astronomy originated in the Caucasus Mountains in the regions of Georgia, Armenia, and Azerbaijan. These were the homelands of the astronomer Prometheus, the brother of Atlas. These astronomical traditions were carried forward by Zoroaster and the Maga into Iran and Iraq, to the lands of the Chaldeans near Babylon. This astronomy was then brought to Hindu India and later to Southeast Asia. It seems appropriate to call the astronomy of Prometheus "Iran-Hindu-Vedic" or simply "Vedic" astronomy.

According to Koenraad Elst, in his *Update on the Aryan Invasion Debate* (Ch. 2), the earliest estimate of the date of the Vedas was made by the Scottish mathematician John Playfair in 1790. Playfair discovered astronomical measurements among the Indian Vedas texts that seemed abnormally refined and possibly surpassing the accuracy of modern standards. Playfair immediately informed the scientific community, who, as of this year 2011 AD, has still not gotten back to Playfair about these matters.

Playfair demonstrated that the starting date of the astronomical observations recorded in the tables still in use among the Hindu astrologers had to have been observed as early as 4300 BC. Vedic astronomers had recorded the great conjunction of heavenly bodies in Pisces on February 18, 3102 BC. Playfair noted that back-calculation of planetary positions is a highly complex affair requiring knowledge of a number of physical laws; universal constants; and actual measurements of densities, diameters, and distances of the planets. It is therefore nearly impossible that Vedic astronomers could have discovered such a precise date for such complicated data that is only verifiable by modern computers.

The French astronomer Jean-Sylvain Bailly wrote, "The motions of the stars calculated by the Hindus for some 4,500 years vary not even a single minute from the tables of Cassini (1648–1669) and Meyer. The Hindu-Vedic tables give the same annual variation of the moon as that discovered by Tycho Brahe (1546–1601)—a variation unknown to the school of Alexandria and the Arabs." Professor N.S. Rajaram, a NASA mathematician, comments, "Fabricating astronomical data going back thousands of years calls for knowledge of Newton's Law of Gravitation and the ability to solve differential equations...Two other elements of this astronomy, the equation of the sun's center and the obliquity of the ecliptic...fix the origin of this astronomy...4300 BC."

Count Bjornstjerna relates that King Louis XIV sent Ambassador Laubere to the king of Siam and that he brought back astronomical tables and tables of solar eclipses, which were reviewed by Bailly, Cassini, Gentil, and Playfair, who all maintained that, "Hindu observations were extant for a very long time" (*Hindu Superiority* by Har Bilas Sarda). The astronomer Bailly, who composed a *History of Astronomy*, inferred from certain advanced astronomical tables of the Hindu's that they, "not only advanced progress in science but a date so ancient as to be entirely inconsistent with the chronology of Hebrew scripture." Bailly also makes the astounding observation that Hindu astronomy was "the remains, rather than the elements of a science." This is Bailly's polite way of saying that Hindu astronomy is a degenerate tradition stemming from a far-advanced scientific culture from the distant past.

Richard L. Thompson (*Mysteries of the Sacred Universe, the Cosmology of the Bhagavata Purana*, p. 15) writes, "According to the early eleventh-century author Alberuni, the *Surya-siddhanta* was composed by Lata. According to the text itself, it was spoken by an emissary of the sun-god to the Asura (demon) named Maya at the end of Krta-yuga, over two million years ago... Indian system of world chronology...of 4,320,000 solar years." Thompson continues (p. 226), "The day of Brahma lasts 4,320,000,000 years, and this roughly matches the modern scientific estimate of 4.5 billion years for the age of the earth."

Berosus, in his history of Babylon and the Chaldeans, says that the Chaldean astronomer-kings ruled 432,000 years after the time of the great flood (Alexander Polyhistor: Berosus. *Cory's Ancient Fragments*, p. 60). It may be noticed that the number 432,000 is a multiple of the scale of the Great Pyramid at Giza in relation to the size of the Earth—1/43,200. Also, the sacred hexagram divides the circle into segments of 60° which are equal to 4,320 years of the precessional cycle.

We will continually come across important large astronomical numbers hidden and preserved in historical and religious texts. This tactic has been one of the most successful and fundamental means of preserving astronomical science among all cultures around the globe.

Myth and History of Iran-Hindu-Vedic Astronomy

Atlas of Morocco is recognized as the greatest astronomer who ever lived. The Egyptian Hercules came to him as his pupil and carried traditions back to the land of the Nile. Atlas had a brother named Prometheus who was punished by Zeus for giving fire to mankind. He was chained to the Caucasus Mountains above Iran in the present regions near Georgia, Armenia, and Azerbaijan. The astronomical traditions of Atlas were spread by Prometheus throughout the Near East, from Iran, Afghanistan, Iraq, and Chaldea to India and as far as Southeast Asia.

Greek mythology says that Prometheus had the gift of forethought and prophecy. Prometheus spoke concerning the coming of "a new Lord of Heaven" *(Apollodorus* III.13.5). This prophecy was adopted by the Maga, the followers of Zoroaster. It was Prometheus who struck the head of Zeus to give birth to Athena, goddess of wisdom. He made men out of clay and then gave them fire without Zeus' permission. Prometheus forewarned his son, Deucalion, to build an ark and thus survive the flood. It is reasonable to suppose that some great natural disaster took place in the region of the Caucasus that reduced humankind back into a primitive state. Otherwise

Prometheus would not have needed to give them fire, nor would Noah have grounded his ark on Mt. Ararat. This holy mountain is on the borders of Turkey, Armenia, and Iran. Ararat was considered to be "the home of the gods," like the Greek Mt. Olympus. Prometheus was released from his bondage on the Caucasus Mountains by Hercules, to whom he gave directions to find his brother Atlas and his daughters, who were the current custodians of the Golden Apples.

Later Prometheus accepted the offer to live the life of a god because Chiron was exhausted by immortality and wished to die. Chiron is the zodiac constellation of Sagittarius, which marks the location of the black hole, the vortex and center of our galaxy. This swirling matrix of the galaxy was known throughout antiquity from Peru to India and China and has always been respected and feared as one of the cosmic gateways to the underworld. Chiron practiced astronomy on Mount Pelion in Magnesia in northern Greece.

Vedic astronomy has always been regarded as a superastronomy. In 500 AD Aryabhata, the famous Hindu astronomer, transmitted ancient traditions that expounded the heliocentric theory. Aryabhata also discussed gravitation and expounded astronomical constants in scientific precision.

Zoroaster and the Maga

The Vedic texts have been preserved in India, with the admission that these traditions originated in Iran or Afghanistan among a people called Aryan. This particular treasure of astronomy was kept alive by Zadust, who is also referred to as Zarathustra and Zoroaster. His followers are called Magi, Magicians, and Maga. The Magi, of course, are referred to in the New Testament as the Three Wise Kings.

Fariborz Rahnamoon (*ancientiran.com*, 2007) tells us that the Persian Empire challenged the West, and, in return, Alexander of Macedonia annihilated Zarathustran shrines and destroyed the greater part of their ancient science and culture. In addition to this loss, the Arabs later conquered Persia, and their Muslims consigned books of Persian science and philosophy into the water and fire, saying that if they were relevant, then God would spare their destruction.

Zadust was a philosopher-astronomer born in ancient Bactria, which is now Iran. He was of the Aryan stock of the ancient Persians. Some accounts have him living 6,000 years before the time of the philosopher Plato. Diogenes Laertius (1.2) writes, "The date of the Magians, beginning with Zoroaster the Persian, was 5000 years before the fall of Troy [1194 BC + 5,000 = 6194 BC]."

Just to give an idea of the rarity of Zadust's science, it is said that he calculated a prime global meridian right through the city of Sistan (Nimrouz), located almost halfway between Japan and the western coasts of Africa, and at 33.5 degrees north latitude, halfway between the northern inhabitable climes. This prime meridian is 90° to the ancient Atlantic prime meridian by the Canary Islands.

The ancient Iranians always started the New Year with the vernal equinox. Here, Zarathustra calculated the rare appearance of the "New Day," when the precise point of the spring equinox exactly coincided with sunrise viewed from a point in Persia. His mathematical skills were so advanced that his predictions forecast the "New Day" of 1725 BC and 487 BC. The latter event was sighted upon a calibrated square block placed within the central hall of the palace of Tehran, in Iran.

There are several ancient maps that show this Iranian meridian calculated by Zadust. These maps still adhere to the genuine Atlantic prime meridian established by Atlas, which runs through the Cape Verde and Canary Islands, and show that Iran and the Caspian Sea are 90 degrees to the east, with Japan at 90 degrees to the west.

Some of the valuable remnants of Zarathustrian lore were preserved in Athens and in Spain by the 14th-century Abn Khaldun. Pythagoras may also have preserved some of these doctrines mixed into his philosophy. Zarathustrian scholars helped the Jews recalculate their expectation of the messiah after their chronologies were perverted by the megalomaniac Alexander.

Zadust typified the culture of ancient Iran. He never claimed to be a prophet or a minister of religion. He could best be characterized as a gentleman philosopher. Action and reaction was his cardinal motto—that good deeds beget good deeds, while a bad and ungenerous action encourages further evil in the world. He certainly did not originate the maxim, "Do unto others as you would wish them to do unto you," but he celebrated that principle and encouraged millions to live better by the idea of creating a perimeter of justice around themselves. It is also known that Zadust encouraged education and the study of the sciences as a foundation of a noble life.

It is said that the Chaldeans had their Maga astronomers. So we may assume that Chaldea was another historical point of the transmission of Vedic cosmology. The Chaldeans expressed large astronomical periods in terms of cycles from 473,000 years to 1,440,000 years. Not too much is known of the Chaldean astronomers other than that they were the scientists of the Babylonians. Even today, one of the sects in Baghdad is the Chaldean religion. The great patriarch Abraham was said to have been an astronomer and was born in the city of Ur in the land of the Chaldeans.

Astronomical Accuracy beyond Belief

Quite amazingly, the ancient Hindu values for the constant of precession, the sidereal year, and the tropical year disagree by only two seconds in the entire year when compared to modern scientific figures. This trifling inaccuracy may be merely because of tidal friction and other perturbations that have occurred in the meantime. It should also be noticed that modern India astronomy has deteriorated and is now vastly inferior to the Vedic science of the past.

Vedic astronomers must have observed the conjunction of Saturn, Jupiter, Mars, Venus, Mercury, sun and moon, and the southern lunar node near the fixed star, *Zeta Piscium,* on February 18, 3102 BC. This is an actual verifiable conjunction that, modern researchers say, had to be observed because it is too difficult to arrive at through a progression of calculations. The next great conjunction of these heavenly bodies happened on February 5, 1962.

Hindu cosmology began during the spring equinox, shown by the full moon being in conjunction with the star Sirius, according to Charles William Johnson in *Hindu Cosmological Cycles (webspace4me.net* 5/20/06). A full moon and Sirius below Gemini at the spring equinox means that the sun was in Sagittarius during the period from 17280 to 19440 BC. Johnson says, "When the mean vernal equinoctial point was last in its initial point on 25 November 18,532 BC."

The Vedic Super-Sexagesimal System

Charles W. Johnson continues, "Hindu science provides the origins of the sexagesimal system, and the most accurate solar calendar; because it recognizes three mean motions of the sun, which by inference include the exact solar year, and the constant of precession. It is hardly to be wondered that Hindus have regarded the cosmological time cycles as a revelation from the gods."

Johnson also admits, "The cosmological time cycles appear to be older even than Hindu civilization." The Hindu scientists also tell of a date in 147,108 BC as the last conjunction of the summer solstice with the initial point of the sidereal sphere (as recounted in the *Sury Siddhanta*), which points to Sirius as the true reference star. Their number units of Vedic astronomy are as small as 1/216,000 of a day and as large as 3.1104 x 10 to the 14th power in years.

Johnson writes, "In Hindu cosmogony, all things proceed to perfection in cycles of repeated incarnations. During the vast interval of one Kalpa, the god of our solar system manifests all sentient creatures out of himself. Hindus call this 'one day in the life of Brahma.' After this, the god of our solar system returns all sentient creatures to himself for the interval of one Kalpa. Hindus call this a 'night of Brahma.' Their chronological system and cycles are as follows:

- 1 Earth year = a day of the gods.
- 360 days of the gods = a year of the gods.
- 216,000 years cycle
- 432,000 years are the Kali-Yuga period.
- 864,000 years are the Dvapara-Yuga period
- 1,296,000 years are the Treta-Yuga period
- 1,728,000 years are called the Krita (or Satya)-Yuga Period.
- 12,000 years of the gods is a Caturyuga = 4,320,000 human solar years.
- 4,320,000,000 years = a Kalpa = a day of Brahma = the destruction of all things.

- A day and a night of Brahma = 8,640,000,000 solar years.
- Brahma's total life is 100 years = 864,000,000,000 solar years.
- Brahma's death is 100 years + 100 years of life = 1,728,000,000,000 solar years.

(Please note that the above numbers are all divisible by 216 and 6.)

We are currently in Year 51 of the life of Brahma. At the end of every Kalpa, or day of Brahma, a greater dissolution, called pralaya (or kalpanta) or "end of an eon" occurs when both the physical and subtle worlds are absorbed into the causal world, where souls rest until the next Kalpa begins. This state of withdrawal, or "night of Brahma," continues for the length of an entire Kalpa until creation again issues forth.

After 36,000 of these dissolutions and creations, there is a total universal annihilation, mahapralaya, when all three worlds—all time, form, and space—are withdrawn into the god Siva. After a period of total withdrawal, a new universe or lifespan of Brahma begins. This entire cycle repeats infinitely. This view of cosmic time is recorded in the *Puranas* and the *Dharma Shastras.*

The Hindu also believe (like the Greeks) that "Man is the measure of all things" and, therefore, human breathing reflects the cadence of the cosmos. Vedic cosmic cycles are based upon the numbers 6, 60, and 216:

- 10 long syllables (gurvakshara) =1 respiration (prana) = 4 seconds
- 6 respirations =1 vinadi = 24 seconds
- 60 vinadis =1 nadi = 1,440 seconds
- 60 nadis =1 day=86,400 seconds = 24 hours
- 86,400 seconds ÷ 4 seconds = 21,600 breaths over 24 hours

Students of art, ethnic studies, anthropology, religion, and science should be familiar with these concepts and numbers, which are an important basis of human culture. As may be seen, the format is simple, interrelated, and based upon the human respiration of breath and the life term of the patron god Brahma, who is the cosmos.

Comparison with Modern Science:

The number 108 is sacred in Vedic science, which says that 108 x the diameter of the sun equals the average radius of the Earth's orbit—our average distance from the sun (108 x 864,000 miles = 93,312,000 miles).

The *Surya Siddhanta* says that the diameter of the Earth is 7,840 miles. The modern estimate is 7,926 miles. The distance from the Earth to the moon in Vedic tradition is said to be 253,000 miles, while the modern estimate is 252,710 miles.

Modern science says that the big-bang universe is estimated at 10–20 billion years old. The Earth is estimated at about 4.6 billion years old. The *Puranas* say that the creation and destruction of the universe follows a cycle of 8.64 billion years (a day and a night of Brahma).

The 14th-century Rigveda of the sun says that there are 2,202 *yoganas* in half a *mimesa*, which equals 300,000 meters per second. This is the exact speed of light according to modern science.

The astronomer Aryabhata (b. 476 AD), laments, "By the grace of God the precious sunken jewel of true knowledge has been rescued by me..." But Johnson says that by the time the India astronomical works were compiled, only a small amount of the fragments of ancient Vedic-Hindu astronomical and cosmological time cycles remained or were understood well enough to be translated. Prior to Copernicus, Aryabhata argued for the plausibility of Earth revolving around the sun. He wrote upon mathematics, time, astronomy, and the celestial sphere. Units are defined using the consonants of the Sanskrit alphabet as numbers. The nine vowels indicate multiplication by powers of 100. Thus: a = times 1; i = times 100; u = times 10,000.

The Indian astronomer Brahmagupta (ca. 628 AD) used a 60-part circle and divisions and factors of 60 in the sexagesimal system. He spoke of the major Vedic and Hindu cycles of astronomy. The *Rig Veda* is a 12-spoke wheel including the lunar mansions as their major cosmic divisions. Written around the year 1000 BC, the *Rig Veda* says, "Twelve spokes, one wheel, navels three...three hundred and sixty like pegs...a seven-named horse does draw this three-naved wheel…Wise poets have spun a seven-strand tale around this heavenly calf, the Sun."

Indian astronomy was recorded in the works of al-Fazari, Islamic astronomer of the late eighth century. His material was in turn translated in 1126 AD by Adelard of Bath, who presented Vedic-Hindu astronomy to Europe.

It seems apparent that the poet of the *Rig Veda* is speaking about the 12 divisions of the zodiac and the circle of 360 degrees. The seven named horses are the sun, moon and visible planets. The wheel spins three ways: the zodiac seen from the spinning Earth, as seen advancing during the course of the year, and finally moving in the opposite direction following the precession of the equinoxes.

In a beautiful and almost lyric fashion Charles William Johnson pens his conclusion:

> A calendar for eternity so accurate that its formulations must be seriously considered as laws of nature, while at the same time a structure so simple, symmetrical, and orderly, that the best astronomers of modern times have completely failed to see the astronomical basis. It is hardly to be wondered that Hindus have regarded the cosmological time cycles as a revelation from the gods.

Johnson further admits, "The cosmological time cycles appear to be older even than Hindu civilization…human civilization must be far older and its secrets more profound than what is generally inferred from the available historical and archaeological evidence."

James Jacobs

James Q. Jacobs (*The Oldest Exact Astronomical Constant?* 1998 jqjacobs.net 4/17/05) quotes *The Aryabhatiya of Aryabhata, An Ancient Indian Work on Mathematics and Astronomy* (p. 9), translated by William Eugene Clark, professor of Sanskrit at Harvard University (The University of Chicago Press, Illinois, 1930):

> In a yuga the revolutions of the sun are 4,320,000, of the Moon 57,753,336, of the Earth eastward 1,582,237,500, of Saturn 146,564, of Jupiter 364,224, of Mars 2,296,824...

Jacobs says that if you divide the abovementioned Earth's revolutions by the moon's revolutions, you get an extremely accurate ratio for two fundamental cosmic motions (1,582,237,500 ÷ 57,753,336 = 27.3964693572).

Jacobs continues, "Given Jan. 1, 2000 astronomical constants and given the present day formulas to temporarily adjust the astronomical constants, I calculated that Aryabhata's ratio was exact for 1604 BC.... The date AD 500 is the approximate epoch in which Aryabhata wrote...his works include spherical trigonometry...algebra...sine tables:

Astronomical Constants	AD 2000	AD 500	1604 BC
Rotations per solar orbit	366.25636031	366.2563589	366.25635656
Days per solar orbit	365.25636031	365.2563589	365.25635656
Days per lunar orbit	27.32166120	27.3216638	27.32166801
Rotations per lunar orbit	27.39646289	27.39646514	27.39646936

The odds of preserving such scientifically accurate Earth and lunar rotations are incalculable. This is especially true when we consider that Aryabhata's figures may have come from more ancient Vedic sources. Jacobs says, "Aryabhata's ratio represents the earliest known recorded astronomic ratio with such incredible accuracy. It surprises me that this fact has gone unnoticed to this date." The same disregard was evident when Playfair attempted to bring these facts to the notice of the scientific community in 1790.

Aryabhata wrote that the apparent motion of the heavens was due to the axial rotation of our spherical planet and that eclipses resulted from the shadows of the moon and the Earth. Kumar (astrology-x-files.com, 2007) says that Aryabhata propounded the Heliocentric Theory of Gravitation, namely that all planets revolve around the sun due to celestial gravity (*Guru-tva-Akarshana*). He worked at the observatory of Khagola and studied at the University of Nalanda, which housed more than 9 million books.

Conclusion

Vedic astronomy is important on two fronts: First, it represents a truly advanced science handed down from former times that contains data equal or superior to modern calculations. Some of this material seems to be beyond the theoretical scope of modern thought. It is like a wondrous archaeological site where unbelievably precious fragments are scattered over its landscape. For this reason, Vedic astronomy has been purposely hidden in the dusty back rooms of the museum of scientific anomalies.

Second, Vedic astronomy reflects a mythological history that is stunning and, quite frankly, incredible. It features a connection of Atlantic tradition from the gods and goddesses Night, Ocean, and Uranus over the renowned Atlas himself. Then the connection continues through Prometheus (Atlas' brother) to the Vedic cosmologers, Zoroaster, the Maga, Abraham, and the Chaldeans, and finally on to the traditions of the Hindu sages onward to Southeast Asia.

The extraordinary science in Vedic astronomy is another instance of ancient science that does not fit into the false theory of constant human progress. It is therefore discarded upon the cultural trash heap—untaught, unrecognized, and unappreciated.

CHAPTER 4.2

Man Is the Measure of All Things

Ancient measuring systems come from the human body. An inch is the distance between the second and third knuckle of the pointing finger (middle phalange of the index finger). The human foot compares to the human hand (study by Oommen and Mainker). The most ancient cubit and the one preserved in English measurement is the cubit of 18 inches from the elbow to the tip of the middle finger. 18 inches is 6 + 6 + 6, while 6 x 6 x 6 = 216, which is the prime fractal in all of sexagesimal astronomical measurement. Because of this relationship to astronomy, the 18-inch cubit must reasonably be the ancient astronomical cubit.

The movements and cycles of heavenly bodies taught humans about numbers and geometry. The most influential motion is a relationship between the Earth and Venus. Over the course of eight Earth years, Venus draws a near-perfect pentagram in the sky. The number and geometry relation of Venus and Earth became the basis of Mexica-Maya-Andean astronomy. The motion of the planet Mercury draws a near-perfect hexagram in the sky. While Jupiter and Saturn in conjunction and opposition scribe double triangles upon the heavens. This "geometry in the sky" teaches mankind numbers, angles, time, measurement, and proportion. It is no wonder that Mercury and the other planets have been called the teachers and instructors of humanity.

Ancient natural philosophers detected geometric forms in the construction of the human body. They considered the idea that the human form was the product of the cosmos and a model and microcosm of the universe. A maxim from Greek tradition proclaims that before anyone can know anything, one should "know thyself." The actual complete wording of the maxim comes from the *Pythoness* of the Oracle at Delphi, which says, "Man, know thyself; and thou shalt know the universe and the gods." Another famous Greek proverb is from Protagoras of Abdera (490–420 BC), who said that, "Man is the measure of all things."

While the planets exhibit splendid formal regularity in their motions, nature here on earth is full of unique individuality and original specimens. The universe is a kaleidoscope of variety, full of objects of different shape and size that move at different speeds and in diverse directions. Survival is about managing and controlling energy, food, and resources. Humans are uncomfortable in a context that they do not understand and cannot control. They strive to discern logic and meaning in this jumble of events. But when humans look to the skies for help and inspiration, they begin to notice a symphony of events that reinforce the ultimate mandate of the universe—harmony and balance. This chapter is about humans and their position in the universe.

One of the first things that comes to our attention is that the human body is made to measure for this world and the cosmos. Physically, psychologically, emotionally, instinctually, and spiritually, we are a microcosm of the macrocosm of the universe. We are formed in the image of the Creator God. We are this cosmic model because we could not exist here, nor function here, if we were not a miniature traveling universe. And this is the law of the universe—every molecule carries the imprint of the universe. This is why we are not to kill or destroy without purpose.

The Bible also affirms that man is formed upon the model of the creators of the universe. The *Elohim* pronounce, "Let us make man in our image, after our likeness" (Genesis: I.26). This creation of man and woman was done on the sixth day, which is an important number in the cosmos.

"Man is the measure of all things" is a striking aphorism with a resounding ring of truth to it. This saying is familiar to everyone, and many philosophers have spent time ruminating, explaining, and speculating upon this pronouncement. Protagoras, the author of this phrase was a close friend of Pericles of Athens. The complete wording of the maxim is, "Man is the measure of all things, of things which are, that they are; and of things which are not, that they are not." Somehow, this does not seem to amplify its meaning but rather confuses the message. This is curious because Protagoras is credited with the invention of *orthoepeia*—the correct use of words. Perhaps Protagoras is saying that humans are the arbiter of reality—what is, and what is not—the idea that "the world is our impression of it."

A well-made athletic human form is absolutely the measure of all things: forms, proportions, and numbers of time and distance. This is true for the simple reason that the human form is *the* most sophisticated product that the universe has created. It is the high-tech wonder that is adaptable to every situation. The human body, male and female, reveals the measures and shapes of its origin. The cosmos is mirrored in the body, and this mirror represents a miniature version of the cosmos that created it.

Man was also "the measure of all things" at the other side of the world; Maya cosmology employed the 260-day calendar cycle as one of their fundamental chronologies. This timekeeper was also called the "midwife's cycle" because it is derived from the human birth cycle of nine moons, an average of 260 days. The nine-moon cycle also allowed the Maya astrologer to compute a possible date of conception. The disposition of the heavens nine months prior to birth was a valuable indicator of the prowess and conformation of both the body and the spirit.

Hunbatz Men, in *Secrets of Mayan Science/Religion* (p. 78), writes, "Philosophers in the Maya tradition...arrive at the conclusion that God, nature, and humans, are one and the same, a unity... The Maya classify the Supreme as Hunab K'u, the Only Giver of Movement and Measure, and proudly represent the concept with a square superimposed on a circle, a synthesis of universal geometry based on the human body." This reminds us of the image of the man in the square and circle drawn by Leonardo da Vinci.

The "Vitruvian Man" Drawn by Da Vinci

Everyone is familiar with the famous sketch of the man in the circle with his outstretched limbs drawn by Leonardo da Vinci. This diagram was based on a description by the Roman architect Vitruvius, who had transmitted it from more ancient sources.

The famous DaVinci figure of the "Vitruvian Man" is enclosed by a square and a circle. The square is formed from the height of the man, which is equivalent to the reach of his outspread arms from finger tip to finger tip. The man's outspread arms and his height are 6 feet. Six feet is also 18 handbreaths of 4" each. From the tip of his finger to the middle of his chest is a yard of 3 feet. The measures of a "span" and an "ell" are also to be found on this drawing. The square around the man can be further subdivided into 16 smaller squares, whose center is the material focus of the man, which is the genitalia. Da Vinci even left traces of his original construction lines, showing the height of the man to be composed of four boxes. The human genitals are located at half of the human height.

Nature can take any form and multiply it by .618 to create a division whereby the shorter length is in proportion to the longer, just as the longer is now in the same proportion to the entire length. Nature uses this formula abundantly in its creation of forms as well as the growth and development of all things from pine cones to mollusk shells to the overlapping of the petals of a rose. The seeds of an apple are arranged in a five-pointed-star pattern, which generates the golden ratio. The mollusk shell of the nautilus is constructed on the basis of the golden mean. This shell is held by the Hindu goddess Shiva as a symbol of creation.

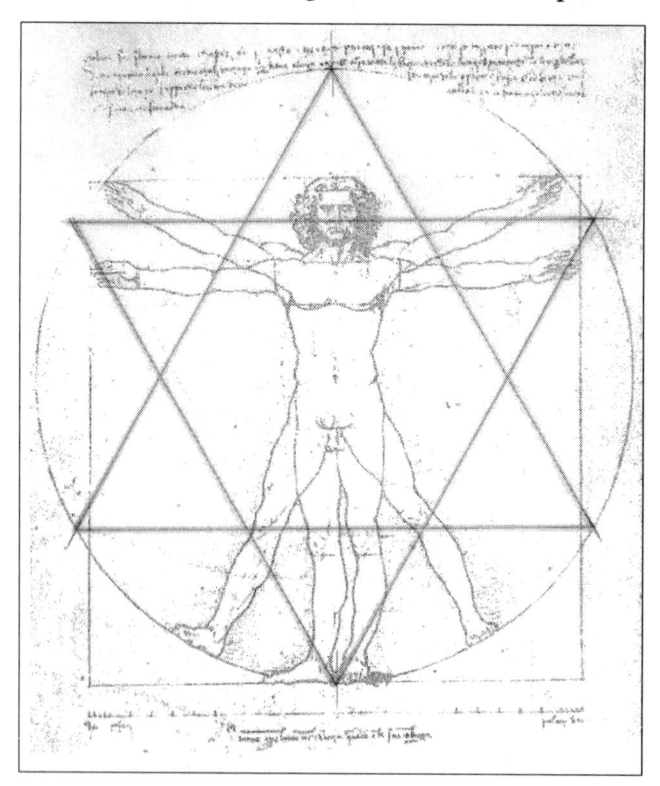

The Vitruvian man inside the circle, square, and hexagram. Author diagram

The man's navel is located near .618 (the golden mean ϕ) of his height. The navel is then used by da Vinci as the focus of the circle drawn around the human figure. The circle is the symbol of the spiritual nature of man. The radius of this circle (from navel to the soles of the feet) may be used to divide the circle into six equal arcs forming a perfect hexagram. This hexagram has been created from the golden mean measure of a man at his navel. The original genius who created the Vitruvian man has used this figure to relate the fundamental relationship of the square and the circle through the golden mean proportion. The hexagram became the basis of the sexagesimal system of astronomical calculation. The planet Mercury teaches us the hexagram, which it traces in the sky during its six conjunctions with the sun every year (three inferior and three superior conjunctions). The conjunctions and oppositions of Jupiter and Saturn also form a hexagram upon the heavens. The hexagram is sometimes represented in the three-dimensional shape of the dodecahedron. In this way, geometry and the hexagram are related to Mercury, Jupiter, and Saturn, and all are related to the human form.

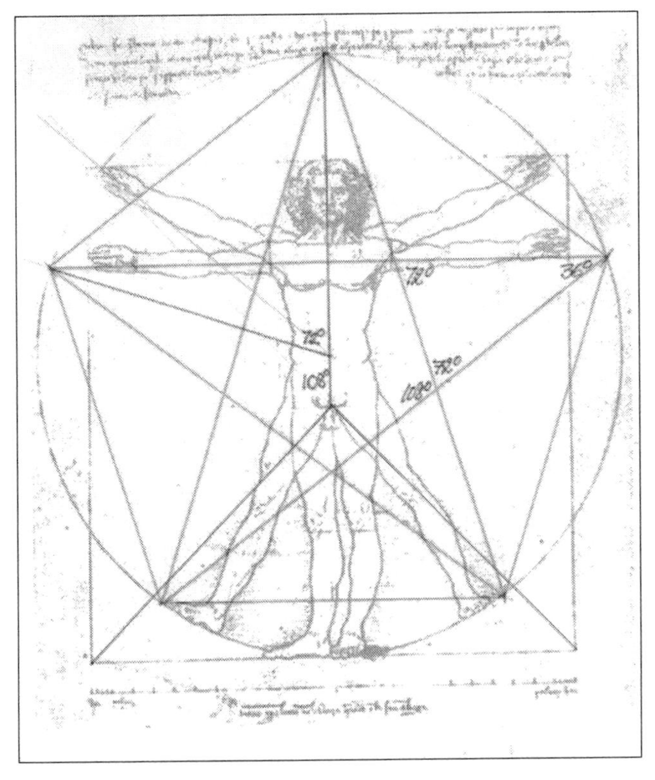

Another curiosity of the Vitruvian figure is that the line from the genitals to the circle above the man's head can cut five arcs on the circle at the points of a pentagram. This line is the same as the line from the genitals diagonally to the corner of the square. Later we will discover that the pentagram is the pattern of the standstills of the planet Venus in the heavens. The vertical division of the man down his center produces angles of 72° and 108° with the star point by his hand.

The pentagram is formed out of angles of 36°, 72°, and 108°. Again the heavens appear as the teacher to humankind. The planet Venus draws the pentagram, which produces angles that become sacred numbers in astronomical cycles. Man, geometry, numbers, cycles, and the planet Venus are related.

Da Vinci's construction lines are still visible below the knees, at the groin, and at the nipples. These marks suggest that the square around the figure was four boxes in height. Construction marks also appear at the elbows, which indicates that the square was also four boxes in width.

There has been much dispute about ancient measurements from different lands. However, the Vitruvian figure may demonstrate a cosmic solution to this problem. The cubit is the measure from the tip of the middle finger to the elbow, from the Latin *cubitum*, elbow. The Greek cubit is about a foot and a half (18 inches). The Vitruvian forearm and hand seem to equal one box, or a cubit equaling 1.5 feet. If the figure is four boxes tall (4 boxes x 1.5 feet), then his total height is six feet. The number of degrees in a circle (360) multiplied by the height of the "Vitruvian Man" (six feet) equals the number of miles in the diameter of the moon (360 x 6 = 2160 miles) as well as the number of years it takes the precession of the vernal equinoxes to proceed through one sign of the zodiac (2,160 years). The number 108 appeared as an angle of the pentagram. 108 + 108 = 216, the prime fractal, from which all the sexagesimal cycles are derived. Thus, the six-foot man is commensurate with the sexagesimal system and the measures of the cosmos.

Another curious incident is related by Dr. Emad Kayyam of the Jordan Medical Association and concerns the similarity of the human eye and the globe of the Earth (Philica.com, 9/1/08). Both the human eye and the globe receive sunlight from one side and are both set at a tilt of about 23 degrees. The shape of the eye also resembles the oblate spheroid of the Earth—wherefore, an eyeball sectioned horizontally describes the layout of Stonehenge.

The English Mile and the Greek Stadia Are Both Derived from Ancient Measurement

A.E. Berriman, in *Historical Metrology* (1953), poses the question, "Was the earth measured in remote antiquity?" He argues that ancient weights and measures were derived from measuring the Earth. He also says that land measure was based upon a decimal fraction of the square of the Earth's radius and that certain weights were based on the density of water and gold (Wilson and Flem-Ath, p. 250).

Abraham Ortelius tells us (Binding, p. 239) that early measurements of the circumference of the world were very accurate, namely 21,600 Italian miles, which are today called "nautical miles." Berriman points out that the Earth's circumference happens to be 216,000 Greek stadia. A Greek stadia is 600 Greek feet. One estimate (and there are many) of the Greek foot equals 1.0125 times an English foot. One degree of the Earth's circumference equals 600 stadia (216,000 ÷360 degrees = 600 stadia). And 600 is the same as the number of Greek feet in one stadium (600 x 1.0125 =607.5 x 216,000 = 131,220,000 feet ÷ 5280 feet =24,852 miles circumference). The current median circumference of the Earth is 24,883 miles.

Again, the human form is the measure of the world. In this instance it is the Greek, Roman, or English foot that is the measuring staff. The number 5,280 is convenient to use because it is divisible into whole rational numbers, moreso than 600 stadia:

1mile = 5,280 feet divided by:

- 2 = 2640
- 3 = 1760
- 4 = 1320
- 5 = 1056
- 6 = 880
- 7 = ***754.2857*** [600÷7=**85.71**]
- 8 = 660
- 9 = ***586.666*** [600÷9=**66.66**]
- 10 = 528
- 11 = 480 [600÷11=**54.54**]

- 12 = 440
- 15 = 352
- 16 =330 [600÷16=**37.50**]
- 20 =264
- 22 =240 [600÷22=**27.27**]
- 24 =220
- 25=***211.2*** [600÷25=24]
- 30 =176
- 32 =165 [600÷32=**18.75**]
- 33 =160 [600÷33=**18.18**]
- 40 =132

It may be seen that 5,280 feet equaling one mile is preferable to the measurement by the stadia of 600 Greek feet because more numbers can be divided into 5,280, giving a whole number as a result. It is therefore a wonderful vehicle for measurements of large global and astronomical distances. The English acre is defined as 66 feet x 660 feet, which, however, does not produce a sexagesimal figure. The Old English mile is probably derived from the Norman mile (640 acres in a square mile) brought over in 1066 AD by William the Conqueror. This 5,280-foot mile was confirmed by documents of the 13th century and in 1592 AD during Elizabethan times. It is based upon eight furlongs of 40 rods of 16.5 feet and a total of 63,360 inches (÷12 = 5,280 feet).

Dunn relates another coincidence of length and time in the size of the Great Pyramid. A pyramid inch is .001 inch longer than a British inch. There are 25 pyramid inches in a cubit, and there were 365.24 cubits in the square base of the Great Pyramid. There are, of course 365.24, days in a calendar year (Dunn, p. 132).

According to Wilson and Flem Ath (p. 92), the equatorial circumference of the Earth is 24,903 miles. If this figure is multiplied by the number of feet in the ancient mile and then divided by 360°, the number produced is a fractal of the number of days in a year (24,903 x 5,280 = 131,487,840 feet ÷ 360° = 365,244, a fractal of the length of the current year, 365.24 days). Cosmology appears to enjoy linking everything together, including proportion, geometry, the size of the Earth, and the length of the year.

Richard Heath claims that the Great Pyramid's south base of 756 feet multiplied by the height of 481 feet equals 363,636 feet, a curious repetition. But—irrespective of units of measure such as feet, inches, poles, cubits, or stadia—the perimeter (measured at the sockets) of the Great Pyramid is 1/43,200 of the Earth's true equatorial circumference. The circumference of the globe is 21,600 Italian or nautical miles.

Therefore, if the Earth's circumference is 21,600 nautical miles, the pyramid's perimeter is ½ of 1/21,600 of that size (= 1/43,200).

When the fractal 4,320 is divided by the magic 216 sexagesimal, the result equals 20. The number 20 is sacred from the land of the Maya to the Middle East and the Temple of Solomon (20 is the number of a human's digits, fingers and toes). The number 4,320 also divides the precessional cycle (25,920 ÷ 4,320 = 6) into the golden hexagram drawn upon a circle.

The Nautical Mile

As convenient as the 5,280-foot mile appears to be as a standard of global measurement, it had many competitors around the globe. The reason for different standards becomes apparent in Richard Heath's *Matrix of Creation*, where he cites John Mitchell's work on the Cosmic Temple, where he believes that the measures of astronomical sites and temples vary with their location in terms of latitude upon the Earth. The proportions are still according to the golden mean, but the standard of length is in proportion to a relationship between equatorial latitude and the latitude north or south of the equator, where the temple is actually built.

Crichton Miller reports that (p. 107), "In navigation, one degree is equal to sixty nautical miles, and one minute of arc is equal to one nautical mile." As said above, these nautical miles were formerly called "Italian miles." Therefore, 60 nautical miles x 360° = 21,600 nautical miles = the equatorial circumference of the Earth. Once again the magic number 216 makes its appearance. Obviously, nautical miles and nautical maps are connected with astronomy. The connection between accurate cartography and astronomy begins with the determination of the sight line of the equinoxes and the solstices to determine the positions of north, south, east, and west. These axes establish the main framework of place.

Most nautical charts are constructed on the Mercator projection, whose scale varies by approximately a factor of six from the equator to 80° north or south latitude. It is therefore impossible to show a single linear scale for use on charts on scales smaller than about 1/80,000. Since a nautical mile is, for practical navigation, the same as a minute of latitude, it is easy to measure a distance on a chart with dividers using the latitude-conversion scale on the side of the chart directly east or west of the distance being measured (educypedia.be/education/calculatorsge, 1/18/11).

It should be remembered that Mercator and Ortelius (16th century) were collectors of ancient maps who copied and refined the projections of such masters as Marinos of Tyre (c.120 AD), who also collected antique charts as all cartographers did. Nautical miles were therefore part of ancient cosmological systems employed by scientists from nautical cultures. Measurements across traversable seas are easy with a compass. Land measurements over terrain with adjustments for latitude prompted the 5,280-foot mile because this number divided by 6 (the height of a man) = 880 feet. The nautical mile is 6,076 foot divided by 6 = 1,012.66 feet, an inconvenient number to work with upon land. Again, the measure of a man becomes the ultimate standard. Also, the reappearance of the familiar 216 certainly shows that there was a complete scientific structure in place in ancient times. This structure comprehends time, speed, motion, the heavens, the oceans, the land, and the human form. Even the smallest to the largest elements of nature dovetail into the measure of a man.

The Lords of Time, Jupiter and Saturn

The Maya have a special veneration for the number 20, and every 20 years they celebrate a festival cycle. Richard Heath, in his *Matrix of Creation* (pp.

20–29), tells us that there are conjunctions of Jupiter and Saturn in the sky every 20, 40, 60 years, and so on. The human element is related to the cycles of Jupiter and Saturn both physically and psychologically. Humans count with their fingers and toes, which are 20 in number. Then the human drama unfolds through the basic stages of human development, which are youth until 20 years of age; early manhood and womanhood until 40 years; physical and intellectual maturity until the age of 60; and then wisdom after that.

One of the most important questions of astronomy is, "How did the circle become divided into 360°?" Once again, the planets of the solar system become the teachers of humankind. The time that it takes Jupiter to make a complete revolution around the sun is 12 years. Saturn takes 30 years to complete a revolution around the sun. In between these periods Jupiter and Saturn come together in the sky every 20 years. Therefore the regularity of their revolutions around the zodiac, and the regularity of their meetings or conjunctions, teach a chronological system where 12 years and 30 years will conveniently divide into 360° because 12 x 30 = 360. The period of 360 is also a close approximation of the number of days in the year. It is from this system that the zodiac of 12 houses of 30° was adopted as a paradigm for all astronomy. Also, the conjunctions of Jupiter and Saturn every 20, 40, and 60 years conveniently divide into 360°. Jupiter and Saturn complete 40 conjunctions during a full revolution of the circle of the zodiac in about 800 years. 360° divided by 40 equals 9, which is an extremely holy number in cosmological tradition.

These "moving together" or coincidences in their planetary orbits are called a synodic meeting or conjunction. Saturn is, of course, represented in Greek and Roman lore as the "Father of Time" (Saturn + Cronus = chronology). All around the world, the 20-year period of their conjunctions had a special scientific, social, and religious meaning.

Trigons of the Conjunctions of Jupiter and Saturn

Jupiter and Saturn trace an almost perfect triangle upon the zodiac after three conjunctions over the course of 60 years (3 conjunctions x 20 years = 60 years). After 40 conjunctions, the original conjunction that began forming all these triangles has revolved counterclockwise around the entire zodiac during 800 years (40 x 20 = 800 years). The next first conjunction will have moved about 9° further upon the zodiac. This 800-year cycle of 40 conjunctions was regarded as a very exact timekeeper by the ancient astronomers. And it is no wonder that, once again, the number 40 appears as a sacred time period of motion and human development. Astrologers also noticed that during the 800 years (modern estimate: 794.4 years) that the triangle of conjunctions of Jupiter and Saturn passed through the triangles of moist-hot-dry-cold (Cancer-Scorpio-Pisces = moist; Aries-Leo-Sagittarius = hot; Taurus-Virgo-Capricorn = dry; Gemini-Libra-Aquarius = cold). The triangle of Jupiter and Saturn conjunctions stays in the same triangle of elementary signs for a period of 66.6 years, producing a regular and noticeable climate variation for this period of time (66.6 years = 800 years ÷ 12). Again, the "mark of the beast" appears as one of the most important astronomical matrixes. The "beast" is the fundamental relationship between the geographical eightfold division of a square and the 12-fold division of the celestial circle (8 ÷ 12 = .666). At this moment in time (2011), the 800-year triangles of conjunctions are moving through Aries-Leo-Sagittarius, which would mean that there is a rise in global temperatures.

John Dee, astrologer to Queen Elizabeth I, figured a complete revolution at 960 years to 1,000 years and said that the Old Testament was divided into segments of 1,000-year periods from Creation-Enoch-Noah-Moses-Christ-Charlemagne. Kepler held to the ancient and correct 800-year period, which he said would repeat eight times from creation to the destruction of the world (800 x 8 = 6,400 years). The so-called "Greatest Conjunction" was during one of the many returns of the 40 Trigon conjunctions to the first point of Aries on the boundary between Aries and Pisces.

The astronomical numbers 20 and 40 produced by the revolution of the triangle of the conjunctions of Jupiter and Saturn have become ingrained in the cultures of Iran, Egypt, Babylon, Chaldean, India, and the Orient, as well as Mexica-Maya-Andean culture. Christianity, Judaism, and Islam all revere the number 40 as a specific holy period of self-denial and fasting.

Because of the relative positions of Earth, Saturn, and Jupiter, triple conjunctions of Jupiter and Saturn can occur in a single year. From our moving vantage point here on Earth, both the planets Saturn and Jupiter move retrograde, then forward, then retrograde again over the course of a 13-month period. A Babylonian clay tablet in the British Museum predicted such a triple conjunction in Pisces on May 27, October 6, December 1, 7 BC (iastate.edu/triple, 1/24/11)."

Man and Geometry

The "Vitruvian Man" drawn by da Vinci expresses the relationship of man with the geometry of the square and the circle, as well as many other geometric forms hidden in the diagram. Man is a key to the geometry of the universe.

Two superimposed equilateral triangles forming a hexagram star is an ancient mandala appearing in Hinduism, Buddhism, and Jainism. In the ancient south Indian temples, it symbolizes a perfect meditative balance between man and God (absoluteastronomy.com/hexagram. 1/18/2011). The symbol appears in a version of the Turkish flag and the Tibetian *Book of the Dead.* This symbol has been found in one ancient sixth-century BC seal and in one temple. The geometric symmetry has made it a popular symbol common to many cultures. In general, it seems to belong to Middle Eastern and North African culture, where it was a symbol for the infinity of the universe and the creation of the world through the joining of fire and water. The hexagram is also a sign of the joining of male and female forces represented by the upward- and downward-pointing triangles. Dr. John Dee, astrologer to Queen Elizabeth, claimed that these intertwined triangles originally came from the archaic Aryan temples and that the Aryans called the hexagram the mystery of mysteries. The Freemasons depict the interlocking deltas as one of black and the other of white, symbolizing the dichotomy and dual nature of the world.

Early Hebrew culture adopted the menorah, the candlestick of seven lights (seven stars of wisdom), as their main symbol. The hexagram became popular after the time of the French Revolution, when Napoleon legalized freedom of religion. In 1897 it was adopted as a universally recognized symbol of Judaism through the influence of Baron Rothschild and the Zionist Federation.

The *Olam Katan* in the kabbalah seems to express the notion of man as a microcosm of the universe. It is suggested that humans and the Temple of God are linked together through the act of the creation of the cosmos.

The Shield of Solomon is a five-pointed star (the sign of Venus), the pentagram, an amulet that protects against daemons and evil forces by the 72-letter name of God and the 72 guardian angels (360° ÷ 5-pointed-star = 72°). Again, the number 72 is common to many cultures, as it expresses the number of years that it takes for the precessional cycle to advance one degree. Most important is the fact that a pentagram can be formed by three triangles having interior angles of 36°-36°-108° (36° + 36° = 72°). While the number 108 x 2 = 216, which is the magical prime fractal number related to the true name of God according to TheBibleWheel.com (5/18/2009).

The Shield of Abraham is an eight-pointed star (360° ÷ 8 = 45°). The Shield of David is a six-pointed star, the sign of Mercury, Jupiter, and Saturn (chabad.org, 2/3/ 2009). Astronomy has taught us geometry, angles, number, measurements, and time. Humans have been receptive to these concepts because they have been formed from the very principles of the cosmos that have created all things.

The Number 72

The number 72 is celebrated in many cultures. It is a number that comes from astronomy and is related to man and nature through geometry (5 x 72 = 360; also, 3 x 72 = 216, the holy sexagesimal fractal). The *Shemhamphorasch* is the 216-letter name of God, composed of 72 groups of three letters, each triplet being the name of an angel or intelligence. This was derived by medieval Kabbalists from the Book of Exodus. Below are other instances of the astronomical number 72 (Ridingthebeast.com and Genesisveracity.com, 4/9/10):

- 72 disciples of Jesus Christ
- 72 disciples of Confucius
- 72 immortals of Taoism, and 36 hells and 36 heavens

- 72 conspirators of Seth-Typhon against Osiris
- 72 Seth cuts the body of Osiris into 72 parts
- 72 angels and 72 demons of the Kabbalists
- 72 races from Noah: 15 Japhet, 30 Cham, and 27 Sem
- 72 languages confused at the Tower of Babel
- 72 names of God in the Hebrew Kabbalah
- 72 is the number of 70 elders plus Moses and Aaron
- 72 old men of the synagogue in the Zohar
- 72 translators of the Old Testament at Alexandria
- 72 sicknesses according to Mohamed
- 72 virgins of Islam
- 72 Norse warriors of Valhalla
- 72 chapters in the old version of the Book of Revelation
- 72 members of the Convent of St. Bridgette of Sweden
- 72 malevolent stars in Chinese astrology + 36 benevolent =108
- 72 skulls on the necklace of Kali, the Hindu goddess of Destruction
- 72 linens of the Parsee
- 72 cardiac pulsations per minute
- 72 is the relationship between the mass of Moon to Earth to Saturn
- Hermes steals 1/72 of the year from the Moon goddess
  = 5 days added to the 360-day year = 365 days
- 72 x 360 = 25,920 years (Vedic precession of the vernal equinoxes)
- .7222 = 260 ÷ 360
- 7.2° Eratosthenes angle at Alexandria
- 720 = 2 x 360, or a circle divided into ½ degrees (c. Great Pyramid)

The Human Breath

Hindu cosmology also preserves the ancient tradition that the microcosm of the human body is related to the macrocosm of the universe. They affirm that correct breathing calms the mind and relaxes the body. One of their tenets is that there are 330 million gods who grant us 330 million breaths in our lifetime. If one can learn to control one's breathing, one can regulate how long one will live (University of Nottingham: su-web.nottingham.ac.uk/Hinduism, 8/30/08):

- 30 breaths per minute will equal 60 years of life
- 18 96
- 15 120
- 5 350
- 1 breath per minute will equal 1800 years of life

According to the *Chudamani Upanishad* there are six human breaths per one *pala* where 2.5 palas equal one minute. This equals 15 breaths per minute = 900 breaths per hour, and during the course of 24 hours human breaths = 21,600 (216 fractal). In this fashion, the Hindu relate that the breath of a human is the measure of the cosmological system. Kabalistic lore claims the 216 fractal as the creation hologram (6 x 6 x 6 =216; the true name of God). They also discuss the *Arun Elohim*, 343 (7 x 7 x 7). 21,600 breaths in 24 hours mean that there are 10,800 breaths during the day and 10,800 breaths during the night. There are 108 beads on the Hindu *Mala,* representing the 108 mantras. Some prayer beads have multiplication cords attached to the main ring so that 10,800 prayers are accounted for each night and day.

There is a time clock within humans that reflects the movements and pulse of the universe. Humans also have rhythmic fluctuations in their circulatory system in what has been found to be a 10-second cycle, or six times per minute. Again, this affirms the primacy of the number six as a universal cosmic factor. The rhythmic fluctuations of the human body beat a cadence of 360 in one hour (6 x 60 = 360, the number of degrees in a circle).

The human body is a model of the universe. It is half material (the square, symbol of the Earth) and half spiritual (the circle, symbol of the heavens). The Vitruvian man is 6 feet tall according to the square. The navel of the figure is in golden mean proportion (.618) to the square. This navel becomes the focus of the spiritual circle around the figure. In *Quadrivium* (p.76), Martineau says, "When these two shapes are unified by being made equal in area or perimeter we speak of 'squaring the circle', meaning that Heaven and Earth, or Spirit and Matter, are symbolically combined, or married." Therefore humans express the numbers 6 (material square) and .618 (spiritual circle). And it is these numbers which express all motion, speed, and size in the universe.

Geometry and numbers spring forth from the analysis of the human body: inches, cubits, feet, miles, phi, pi, the Monad, Dyad, Triad, the number four, circle, square, pentagram, hexagram, and the sexagesimal astronomical system. The human body beats out the cadence of the universe in the rhythm of its functions of heartbeat and respiration.

"Man is *truly* the measure of all things."

CHAPTER 4.3

Cosmic Numbers

It has been a common practice to preserve astronomical information among historical and religious works. *Cory's Ancient Fragments (Egyptian, p. 136)* states that gods, demigods, spirits of the dead, and 30 dynasties ruled Egypt over the course of 36,525 years. This is obviously a reminder of the correct length of the year as 365.25 days.

Christian documents based on Hebrew traditions use the same ploy. The Book of Revelation says that the antichrist will take over the world and that his number is 666. The same book says that the number of the good and righteous souls to be saved at the Judgment Day is a total of 144,000. It is so very curious that the white limestone casing stones of the Great Pyramid are also said to have been 144,000 in number. It may be remembered that 666 is also 6 x 6 x 6 = 216, the holy sexagesimal fractal of astronomy. The number of souls to be saved is 144,000 ÷ 216 = 666.666. These are obviously cosmic numbers placed within a religious document to ensure their preservation.

El Chaac Mo'ol de Chichen Itza

In cosmology the square represents the Earth and the material nature of the cosmos, while the circle represents the heavens and the spiritual energy of the cosmos. The circle can be drawn around the corners of the square or trespassing into the square so that the interior areas of both figures are equal. The square naturally subdivides itself into eight segments through its diagonals, which are then cut into halves. The circle naturally subdivides itself into 12 segments because its radius cuts its circumference into six equal arcs that are easily divided into 12 segments.

The relationship between eight and twelve is .666 (8 ÷ 12 = .666), otherwise known as "the Mark of the Beast." The Circular Zodiac of Dendera was set up as a combination of eight and twelve because it showed four sets of closely grouped falcon-headed gods along with four individual Hathor goddesses demarcating the directions of the eight winds. The eight winds are the cardinal directions of the map-making system for land and sea. "The Mark of the Beast" or simply, "the Beast," is a ratio between the 12 houses of the zodiac system and the eight directional geographic system. This ratio presents a medium between the celestial sphere and the globe. Imagine physicists of today discovering a number like 216 (6 x 6 x 6) that is so multifunctional that it handles an entire astronomical system, describes the precession of the vernal equinoxes, the ratio of the size of the Great Pyramid to the Earth, and enumerates the characters in the holy name of God. The Beast is truly a "beast" that can handle an enormous load of diverse numerical systems, complex measurements, and cosmic chronology.

C.W. Johnson has discovered that an ancient system of astronomy tied together size, speed, orbits, and time periods of the sun, moon, and planets of our solar system:

Again, it may be reviewed that *One Hundred and Eight* is a sacred number in many cultures. Twice this number (2 x 108 = 216) produces a fractal that seems to be born of the universe. Johnson says that 216 is a fraction (fractal) of the moon's diameter. Important astronomical numbers appear after 216 is added to itself—and then to each subsequent addition:

216—a fractal of the moon's diameter of 2,160 miles (This is also a vindication that the English mile stems from ancient cosmic measurement). The moon's true diameter is two extra miles. A fractal of precession: 30 degrees, or one zodiac house, equals 2,160 years of the cycle of the precession of the vernal equinoxes.

216 + 216 = 432—a fractal of the *sun's radius* of 432,000 miles and 60° of precession.

432 + 216 = 648—a fractal of precession of 6,480 years (three houses of the zodiac).

648 + 216 = 864—a fractal of the sun's diameter and precession. The sun's diameter is actually 864,900 miles. And incredibly, 864,000 x the holy number 108 = 93,312,000 miles, a value that is near to the mean orbital distance of the Earth from the sun (92.75 million miles). The reluctance of British engineers and scholars to abandon traditional ancient measure is based upon the idea that ancient measures are based upon the human body, the accurate microcosm of the universe.

- 864 + 216 = 1,080—a fractal of precession, 10,800 years (five zodiac houses).
- 1080 + 216 = 1,296—a fractal of precession, 12,960 years (six zodiac houses.
- 1,296 + 216 = 1,512—a fractal of precession, 15,120 years (seven zodiac houses).
- 1,512 + 216 = 1,728—a fractal of precession, 17,280 years (eight zodiac houses).
- 1,728 + 216 = 1,944—a fractal of precession, 19,440 years (nine zodiac houses).
- 1,944 + 216 = 2,160—the moon's diameter in miles and the number of years for precession to complete one zodiac sign of 30 degrees (1 zodiac house in 2,160 years x 10 zodiac houses = 21,600 years).
- 2,160 + 216 = 2,376—a fractal of precession, 23,760 years (11 zodiac houses).
- 2,376 + 216 = 2,592—a fractal of the complete cycle of the revolution of the precession of the vernal equinoxes around the entire zodiac in 25,920 years. As far as we know this is one of the

best scientific estimates of a complete precession, sometimes called the "platonic great year" and the Pleiades Cycle of the Maya.

- 2,592 + 216 = 2,808—a fractal of precession, 28,080 years (13 houses of the zodiac).
- 2,808 + 216 = 3,024—perimeter of the Great Pyramid at Giza (4 x 756). The perimeter of the Great Pyramid at Giza is truly 3,024 feet (4 x 756 feet = possibly 440 royal cubits). Irrespective of any standard of measurement such as feet, cubits, or stadia, the Great Pyramid is exactly 1/43,200 the size of the Earth.
- 3,024 + 216 = 3,240—a fractal of precession, 32,400 years (15 zodiac houses).

Skipping ahead in the count…

- 3,240 + 5 x 216 = 4,320
- 4,320—a fractal of the scale of the Great Pyramid compared to the size of the Earth (1/43,200 scale). Also, 43,200 years (20 zodiac houses).

The 216 fractal is truly amazing. It is a holy cosmic factor that gathers together so many different aspects of space, time, even size and motion.

In the previous chapter, it was said that the equatorial circumference of the Earth is 216,000 Greek stadia, and 21,600 nautical miles.

The fractal number 216 even makes an appearance in Ireland in *The Book of Fenagh* composed by St. Caillin around the time of St. Patrick. On pages 4–8 the pedigree of the saint is given as 36 generations of 30-year periods =1,080 years (1,080 ÷ 216 = 5, a reference to the pentagram star of Venus). On page 14 of St. Caillin's book, it says, "Eight score [8 x 20] cakes, nine times [160 x 9], was Caillin's feast, fact without falsehood. Three persons to each cake of these [8 x 20 x 9 x 3 = 4,320]…was the usual number of Church people with Caillin was 4,320 [216 x 20] men, together with all other guests." Why would St. Caillin have precisely 4,320 people at his church? These special sacred cosmological numbers tell us that St. Caillin was using Irish history to store and transmit astronomical, geophysical, and sacred numbers.

4,320 years equal the passage of time that it takes precession to pass over two house of the zodiac. Why two houses? Because the division of the zodiac by every two houses forms the holy six-pointed star, the hexagram, Star of Mercury, also called the Star of David in modern Hebrew tradition. The hexagram division of the zodiac is associated with points and geographies of divine incarnation and revelation, which are separated by 60 degrees of equatorial geography. The stone spheres at Costa Rica, the ancient Atlantic prime meridian, and Jerusalem epitomize the past history of a special sixfold division of the globe. Jerusalem is the seat of three of the great religions of the world. The Atlantic prime meridian was the seat of the birthplace of the classical Mediterranean gods. The stone spheres of Costa Rica must have marked some important sacred geography of the far-distant past.

Above, it was said the number 4,320 is related to the hexagram division of the equator of the globe and the proportion of the Great Pyramid in relation to the globe, as well as being the sixth part of the cycle of the precession of the equinoxes (6 x 4,320 = 25,920). It is also true that 4,320 ÷ 216 = 20. The number 20 is an exceptional number among the Maya as a basis of their calendar system. In Hebrew tradition, 2 x 20 = 40 is the number of days of fasting and Lenten time. During the great flood it rained 40 days and 40 nights. The Israelites ate manna for 40 years in the desert. Moses was 40 days on the mountain. Joshua, Saul, and David ruled for 40 years. Jesus fasted for 40 days. The Temple of Solomon is 40 cubits long and 20 wide. There are 40 stones at Stonehenge—30 stones in the Sarsen Circle and 10 trilithons in the center. Jupiter and Saturn in conjunction take 20 years to come into conjunction and 40 years to form the second conjunction, marking the intellectual maturity of a man and woman.

The Book of Revelation

The magical number of 216 from Iran-Hindu-Vedic cosmology is formed from the product of 6 x 6 x 6 = 216. This is the dreaded "Mark of the Beast," the number 666 from Revelation (Rev:17–18):

> And that no man might buy or sell, save he that had the mark, or the name of the beast, or the number of his name. Here is wisdom. Let him that hath understanding count the number of the beast: for it is the number of a man; and his number *is* Six hundred threescore *and* six [600 + 3 x 20 +6 =666, and 6 x 6 x 6 = 216].

It seems unusual that the Book of Revelation denigrates the 6 x 6 x 6 =216 number, because it uses the sexagesimal system in most of the numbers employed in its descriptions: "We have sealed the servants of our God in their foreheads...and there were sealed a hundred and forty and four thousand (Rev.7.3-4)." There were 12,000 of each of the 12 tribes (12 houses of the zodiac, 12 x 12,000 = 144,000 ÷ 216 = 666.666.).

The New Jerusalem had twelve gates with the names of the 12 tribes written upon them. There were 3 gates for each of the 4 ordinal directions: north, south, east, and west. The length, height, and breadth of it were all equal and were 144 cubits. And the Tree of Life bore 12 manner of fruit (Rev:21.1–22.2).

The Book of Revelation is full of astronomy and cosmological allusions: "The mystery of the seven stars which thou sawest in my right hand, and the seven golden candlesticks (Rev:1.20)." The Seven stars are the Sun, Moon, Mercury, Venus, Mars, Jupiter, and Saturn.

> A throne was set in heaven...and round about the throne were four and twenty seats...four and twenty elders...round about the throne were four beasts full of eyes...a lion...a calf...a man...a flying eagle (Rev:4.1–11)." The 2 elders per each of the 12 signs of the zodiac = 24 hours of the night and day. A lion = Leo, a calf = Taurus, a man = Aquarius, a flying eagle = Scorpio. Thrones, seats, principalities, and houses are terms used in astrology.

"And they sung a new song, saying, Thou art worthy to take the book, and to open the seals thereof: for thou wast slain, and hast redeemed us to God by thy blood out of every kindred, and tongue, and nation (5.9)." All cosmological cultures practiced some version of a blood sacrifice. "The new song" means a new epoch in the cycle of the Milky Way.

"These are they which came out of great tribulation, and have washed their robes, and made them white in the blood of the Lamb...they shall hunger no more, neither thirst any more; neither shall the sun light on them, nor any heat (7.14–17). The redeemed are no longer in the solar system of the sun and have attained a higher place in heaven

The Numbers and Geometry of a Mnemonic Universe

God speaks to us on our own human plane. Yet, he reminds us that he is speaking to us from the celestial sphere of heaven. It is recorded by the prophet Isaiah:

> "For my thoughts are not your thoughts, nor my ways your ways," says the Lord, "for as high as the heavens are above the Earth, are my thoughts above yours, and my ways above your ways" (Isaiah 55:8).

Manetho's *History of Egypt* (p. 11) tells us that the *Egregori*, the "Watchers" or angels, came down and had intercourse with the daughters of men. These angels (planets) taught men about the sun, moon, planets, and the 12 signs of the zodiac of 360 degrees. The first gods of the Egyptians clearly bear the names of the sun, moon, and the planets.

Astronomy is the premier science because it lays bare the work of the Creator. Isaiah says that God's thoughts are in the heavens high above the Earth. The drama of God visiting with Isaiah and the Egregori coming down to humankind is an expression of the concept that heaven is teaching us its science. It is simple for heaven to teach humanity because everything in heaven and earth is interrelated, congruent, and easy to remember:

The moon and the sun teach us about gravity, the pull on the tides of the oceans, and the changing seasons and cycles of the year.

Humans, Venus, Earth, and all of astronomy and nature are united through the golden mean proportion. Every line that forms the Venus pentagram stands in phi relation to other lines. The movements of Venus and Earth fit the Fibonacci sequence (5 + 8 = 13). The former chapter demonstrated that humans are cosmic creatures, and microcosms of the universe. Humans, Venus, and the Earth form a core expression of the universe, a matrix in microcosm, a seed kernel from which life can unfold according to sacred proportion.

From 5 + 8 = 13, the Maya followed these numbers to create one of the most amazing astronomical systems that the world had ever seen. Lucky 13 is a special holy number among most cultures. 13 + 13 = 26 is the fractal of the Maya 260-day midwife's gestation cycle of human birth. 26 + 26 = 52 is the Maya festival of the Calendar Round, when the 260-day and 365-day cycles melded together. 5,200 years is the great cycle of the Maya Long Count, which is $1/5^{th}$ of the 26,000 years of the precessional cycle, which the Maya call the cycle of the Pleiades. The numbers and equations of 5 + 8 = 13, and 5 x 8 = 40, as well as 4 x 13 = 52 are all special holy numbers still used in today's modern religions. But what should be firmly understood is that these "secret, sacred, and mysterious" numbers *are the plain facts of astronomy.* Secret societies and clandestine organizations have used these holy numbers and geometry as part of the atmosphere of veiled information divulged only to their initiates. In reality, these numbers are pure astronomy.

Mars also synthesizes into the above system because 3 x 260 days form 780 days, which is the synodic period of Mars. Astronomy does teach itself to every observer in ways that are easy to recall and remember. We should call the cosmos a "mnemonic universe," a science of the heavens that unfolds itself through paradigms that are simple to remember and evolve out of basic addition of one number to another. This addition mimics basic cell division of one cell into two like parts.

The planet Venus is our teacher. We see that the pentagram of Venus is formed by three overlapping triangles whose interior angles are 36°, 36°, and 108°. An equilateral triangle with two equal sides of 8 and a base of 13 creates the 36°-36°-108° triangle. The numbers 36 + 36 add up to the number 72. Venus is an absolute paragon of an astronomical teacher, covering geometry, chronology, and astronomical cycles. The pentagram of Venus also contains the interior angle of 108°. And again, 108 + 108 = 216, which is a respected holy number worldwide, a cosmological fractal used from the Mediterranean to India to Cambodia to the American continents.

The pentagram is a very special geometric design in which four different sections of the lines forming the pentagram all stand in perfect golden-mean relationship (.618 phi) to one another. If a pentagram is inscribed in a pentagon, the relationship of the lines is in the proportion of 1.618:1. The Earth-Venus relationship is close to approximating the golden-mean ratio (5 ÷ 8 = .625, which is within .007 of phi).

Another memory device is that if we know that 365 days x 8 Earth years = 2,920 days, then 2,920 ÷ 5 (Venus pentagram) = 584 days, which is the exact mean synodic period of Venus from one conjunction with the sun until the next conjunction.

It is amazing that 5, 8, 13 can lead us to 20, 26, 36, 40, 72, 108, and 216, which all combine to express so much information about our cosmos. In ancient times, education was transmitted by the word to the ear. Education did not involve books or notes. A person had to remember what was said. The teacher had to formulate a multidimensional story that contained many useful elements—such as vocabulary, science, and history—all bound around an educating tale that could be remembered. One such example was a story about Sir Isaac Newton sitting in his garden underneath the apple tree during a full-moon night. This tale, the name of Sir Isaac Newton, and the principle of gravity were never forgotten by the scholars who heard the story. Astronomy was ever the perfect science. It required no books or chalkboard. Astronomy taught itself upon its own canvas in the heavens—a permanent record book that could be consulted anytime and anywhere. Such a system was more reliable, superior, and global than our concept of the Internet.

CHAPTER 4.4

Calendars and Sacred Sites—*the Social Culture of Astronomy*

Most of the ancient megalithic sites around the world have astronomical sight lines directed at the solstices and equinoxes of the sun in order to keep track of the times and seasons of the year. This relationship between a site and specific movements of the heavens was one of the factors that made a site "holy and sacred." Astronomers became the "masters of time" who arranged the vital matters of every community around an astronomical context. On the principle of "on earth as it is in heaven," astronomy served to bind together the culture and the society of a community. Astronomy served as the foundation that gave legitimacy to social gatherings and meetings for such matters as:

Regulation of agriculture, planting, harvesting, preserving food, navigation, fishing, sailing for trade, sending the young population off to piracy, making war, religious observance, anniversaries of the dead, festivals, rituals, government, general meetings, speeches, councils, deliberations on policies and war, amusements, songs, saga telling, social celebrations, marriage and divorce, courts of legal disputes, judgment and settlements, new legislation, the election of kings, payment of taxes and wages, climate forecasts, history, prophecy, healing, and magic.

What is also remarkable is the number of solar devices in any one locality. It seems as if every megalithic village wanted a clock of its own. Time-keeping was taken over by the churches of the new Christian religion, whose giant steeples sported clocks and whose belfries rang out the important hours of the day for prayers, lunch, and the beginning and cessation of labor. The new religion took over from the old by becoming the new "master of time." Modern time is divided into three 8 hour periods: work, recreation, and sleep. In the ancient world time was a function of astronomy to synchronize events here on Earth with those of the heavens. These events are natural and beautiful and evoke sentiments celebrating the harmony and regularity of the cosmos of which humans are an integral part.

The winter solstice celebrates the return of the sun from its lowest angle on the horizon to ever-increasing light, warmth, and length of day as the sun ascends to a higher position in the sky. But more importantly, the precise instant of the winter solstice sunrise (or sunset in some places) is a momentary instance symbolizing "a flash of resurrection" to remind us of the rebirth of the universe, humanity, and our relationship with God the Creator. This moment is sacred—celebrating the bond between our planet and the universe and the continuity of a divine covenant reenacted through cosmic physics.

Bauval mentions R.W. Stoley's remark that, "Our clocks are really timed by the stars. The master-clock is our earth, turning on its axis relative to the fixed stars." Bauval also writes that we compute our calendar in a linear manner, starting from the birth of Christ. But to the Egyptians, time was not linear but cyclical (*The Egypt Code* p. 39, 47). The Egyptians introduced a 365-day calendar shortly after the unification of Upper and Lower Egypt in about 3000 BC. With this change, the year was divided into three seasons (whose lengths were three, four, and five months) with five special holy days added to the end of the years. (12 x 30 + 5 =365). Again the number 72 comes forward where the god Hermes-Mercury wins 1/72 of the year from the moon goddess to create the five extra holy days at the end of the year for the birth of the gods (360 ÷ 72 = 5).

Sacred sites were founded above powerful springs and water spirals, as the carved images of spirals on the stones so readily proclaim. Brú Na Bóinne in Ireland was so famous throughout antiquity because its underground water line sprang directly from the chamber mound and continued exactly along the path of the winter solstice sunrise. This mystical bond expressed a unique concord between the land and the sky. Courts and elections were held in the presence of these sites, hoping to absorb and participate in the gift of right judgment in a magical place between water, earth, and stars. Very often these sites were specially arranged around stone markers that served as stone clocks and calendars of astronomy that sought to synchronize the heavenly truth with our stage here upon Earth. The movements of the heavens were always considered to be the absolute representation of unalterable truth.

Astronomy has served as a global language for humankind. Astronomy also served as a binding social force among people and kingdoms that shared stone clocks and calendars. In this fashion, dolmens and standing stones were not just timepieces but icons of unity among people of a common cosmological worldview. This would explain their overabundance in many areas. Astronomy became the embodiment of the wise and comforting mother. It was also predictive in forecasting climate and crop cycles and when to be prudent and resourceful for long winters and possible agricultural failures and droughts. Astronomy provided a realistic drama of life full of hopeful anticipation as well as disappointment. As much as people enjoy their individuality and "freedom of choice and will," they also feel secure in the regularity of those annual feasts that are prescribed by tribal, social, state, and national calendars. The calendar of life appeared in the skies above. Most ancient people knew the lunar mansions and the solar zodiac and were able to identify the planets and the meaning of their position and relationships. Life was not a repetition of the days but a genuine personal and sincere communion with the cosmos. The world can sometimes be a lonely place without this special relationship with the heavens and their Divine Creator. Ancient people have always referred to the heavens as their mother and father.

The Seven Days of the Week

It is incredible that the exact order of the seven days of the week is found throughout the globe:

> Thomas Barthel was the first to recognize that seven of the symbols in the so-called "planetary band" on the coffin of the Maya king Pacal,

> King of Palenque, were the symbols of the "seven planets" of the ancient world in their modern weekday order (Kelley and Milone, p. 362).
>
> Mannikka (p. 186) writes about the identical order of days of the week in Angkor Wat in Cambodia: Surya-Sunday, Candra-Monday, Yama-Tuesday, Varuna-Wednesday, Indra-Thursday, Kubera-Friday, Agni-Saturday

The global agreement of the arrangement of the seven days of the week is really quite amazing. The arrangement does not come from the planets' distance from the sun or the Earth. One possible explanation is based upon the balance of male and female and their correspondence to numbers where the odd are male and the evens numbers are female:

Sunday Monday Tuesday Wednesday Thursday Friday Saturday
Sun Moon Mars Mercury Jupiter Venus Saturn
1 2 3 4 5 6 7
male female male common male female male
(Mercury can apply to either sex)

The male Sun and planets are odd numbered. The female planets and the common-natured Mercury are even-numbered. Asian and Mesoamerican numerology attribute lucky and generative powers to the number four. Classical astrology recognizes that Mercury assists and acts in agreement with whichever planets or forces he aligns.

The Astro-Calendar of the Zodiac Celebrates Anniversaries of History

The calendar seeks to synchronize events in the heavens with events on Earth. This helps humans feel comfortable and at home in the cosmos. The constellations and zodiac images present a human history in the form of mythical characters. They also designate events of natural history as well, such as that Capricorn, the sea goat, represents the epochal age of the cosmic flood in the cycle of the Milky Way.

Every year, as the sun moves through the zodiac cycle of the months, it touches upon birthdays and anniversaries of ancestors as well as the cultural gods and heroes of universal myth and history.

When the sun entered Pisces, the entire month could be dedicated to the anniversaries of Zeus and Hera, Isis and Osiris, Coyolxauhqui, and the gods from the epochal time of Pisces; that is when the cycle of the Milky Way was in Pisces. These gods and goddesses are still characterized in the signs of the zodiac in the epochs during which they first made their appearance. The special influences, themes, and natures that created these particular heroes, gods, and goddesses are still evident and present in the body of the Milky Way, even though the cycle itself has moved on to mark a new region of the Milky Way. Zeus and Hera are now the gods of the underworld, as their position has slipped below the current horizon of time and reality to become myth in the land of the former heroes and most ancient of all the Greek gods: the goddess Night (Nyx), Sleep, and Dreams.

The Cosmic Physics of the Calendar

The creation of the calendar was important in organizing and directing society to specific tasks in fishing, hunting, farming, and religious, social, and legal observations. The calendar helped to impose and cement structure and security in the community. Dates of new moons, eclipses, and planetary positions helped the astrologers present and paint forecasts of the coming year for the attention of the kings, their advisers, and the military.

The notion of time is abstracted from astronomy. The cycling hands of the clock have been modeled directly upon astronomic movements and cycles. Twenty-four hours is the time of one day and one night as our Earth spins once around. A month is the period from one new moon (or one full moon) until the next new moon (or full moon). A year is the time from one winter solstice to the next. The solstices and equinoxes became the cardinal divisions of the year. Half of the space between these cardinal divisions became the "quarter days" of the year. The combination of all eight positions became holy days of religion and the days of administration of government.

The position of the moon relative to the Earth affects the height and strength of the tides. New moon and full moon are the most powerful positions. As anyone who works in hospitals, hotels, fire departments, and police departments will testify, human activity and drama are heightened at the time of the full moon. This is because this heavenly body not only shifts the tides of the oceans but also activates and arouses the fluid content of the human body. Calendars are founded upon the extremes and standstills of cosmic physics, such as the solstices and the new and full moons. Therefore religious festivals are exhilarating and enhanced through extremes of astronomy. And most celebrations feature racing or dancing modeled upon the cosmic hijinks of the sun, moon, and planets.

The solstices, equinoxes, and the four quarters halfway between became the eight sacred places of the calendar that regulated the agricultural, nautical, religious, social, and legislative calendar of events of every community. In Irish and British tradition, servants were hired and paid and rents and rates were due on the quarter days. In some places, local laws are still in effect reflecting these quarter days. The British tax year still stands on "Old (time) Lady's Day." The 1990s' Term and Quarter Days Act redefined the old days in terms of modern official use around the 28th of February, May, August, and November. Some of the oldest feasts are recorded in the Celtic calendar of Coligny (second century AD).

<u>The Olden Eight High Days of Ritual during the Solar Year:</u>

- Lady Day, March 25th.....................spring equinox.
  Easter, the first Sunday after the Full Moon in Spring was substituted for the olden Oster fertility celebrations.
- Midsummer Day, June 24th............summer solstice.
  Christianized as the feast of John the Baptist.
- Michaelmas, September 29th..........autumn equinox.
- Christmas, December 25th ....winter solstice.

Christmas feast was the substitution for the Roman Saturnalia and the European Yule. Rituals included making images of an old woman and a ceremonial feast for the house fairies, spirits, and elves.

The Ember Days (adopted by the Roman Church) derives from Anglo-Saxon: *ymbren* = a circuit, a cycle of the year. These are probably of Celtic origin because Ember days are unknown in the Eastern Church. The ordination of priests is usually set on these days.

The Four Cross-Quarter Days between the Solstices and Equinoxes:

- May 1st, Beltane, May Day, and Walpurgis Night: A fertility and purification ritual commemorated by walking between two lighted fires. The Church condemned this as reminiscent of witchcraft.
- August 1st, Lughnasad, Lammas Eve, and Loaf Mass: Harvest celebrations and contests of strength and skills, such as the Scottish Highland Games from Aug. 1st–15th.
- November 1st, Samhain, Martinmas, All Hallows and All Saints, and the Day of the Dead. The dead are honored and walk among the living. The beginning of a New Year in Mesoamerican and Rabbinical tradition.
- February 1st, Imbolc, Candlemas, and the ritual purification of the Blessed Virgin Mary. Protestants in America instituted Groundhog Day to obscure the abovementioned celebration. Celtic fest of the "quickening" and the lactation of the ewes for the spring lambs.

Sacred Sites, the Cosmic Connection between Heaven and Earth

The ancient sacred sites served as a cosmic mandala (model), a stage upon Earth where the interaction of cosmic physics (timed by calendars) and humans could take place. Most often these sacred sites were founded over powerful underground water streams and spirals in order to further heighten the effects of the cosmic physics. This additional stimulus from below would place humans within a special energy field between the waters of the Earth and the cosmic waters of the heavens. This magical equilibrium would inspire the participants and speakers with a special gusto and rare power. Decisions made under these conditions at holy sites and special times of the year would seem to be binding and remembered with a stronger force than general pronouncements in other places and at insignificant astronomical times.

In many places in the world, there occur multiple underground water spirals that are arranged in geometric patterns and golden-mean proportions that accentuate the power of the underground water spirals when they act in unison with the heavenly bodies. Examples of these places would be complexes such as Brú Na Bóinne, Stonehenge, Karnak, the pyramid plateau at Giza, the Wailing Wall and Temple Mount at Jerusalem, Cuzco, Teotihuacán, Tenochtitlan, Tiwanaku, and many other places around the world.

Sacred sites are often called "navels of the earth"—that is, passageways to communicate with other planes of the universe. The magic of these special places lay in the special coiled patterns of their underground streams and aquifers, which permitted humans to enter into one of the most powerful force fields of the universe—the "cycle of changes." The cycle of moist-hot-dry-cold mimics the original act of creation followed by degeneration, destruction, and rebirth.

Professor Burl has fashioned a wonderfully expressed comment on the subject of the Cumbrian stone circles regarding the ancient people's use and intention about their holy sites (*Ancient Skies*, p. 182):

> A place to which the bodies of the dead were brought before burial, but, above all, a place that was the symbol of the cosmos, the living world made everlasting in stone, its circle the circle of the skyline, its North point the token of the un-changing-ness of life, a microcosm of the world in stone, the most sacred of places to its men and women.

Burl's definition could be expanded to say that a sacred place is a meeting of heaven and earth in a synthesis and harmony of the elements of water, fire, air, and earth.

The Ancient Assemblies called Things

From the descriptions of the Scandinavian conferences called "Things"—which were still enacted in recent historical times—we are informed that these convocations occurred at specific astronomical times and quarter days in the spring and fall. The name "Thing" derives from Old Norse and Old English. It means an assembly at an appointed time.

The Things occurred at ancient stones and stone circles that were erected to serve as calendars for marking the important festivals of the year. The holy sites functioned to commemorate and observe specific significant times of the seasons of the year, so they were located in places that had vistas of important and very specific astronomical phenomena. For example, a site may have been somewhat constricted but presented a perfect view of the summer solstice sunset in the notch of a far-distant mountain range. But the main function of the Thing was to draw together the worldview and culture of a community into one unifying event containing all matters of life. The Thing acted as a catalyst of astronomy, social order, government, law, religion, and ritual. The Thing was an event that bound everything together.

Regular assemblies were presided over by a law-speaker and a chieftain or a king. At one of these, the law-speaker informed the king that it was the people who held the power, not the king. Things were intimate parts of Scandinavian and Germanic culture held in such places as Gothland, Isle of Man, Iceland, Scotland, the Orkney Islands, Shetland, and the Danelaw areas of England, such as Yorkshire. There was an organized hierarchy of Things from the local village, to hamlets, ridings, and provinces.

The system of the Things was possibly the oldest fully developed democracy in the world and very like the usages set forth in the original democracy of the United States of America. Things were decided by majority vote of freemen who were landowners. The term "landowner" means that only one sole legal owner could vote, but not his sons or relatives. "Democracy" actually means a *demos*, a tribe—or one vote per family within a tribe. It should also be remembered that the ancient Scandinavians originate from ancient Atlantic sea kings and that democracy is the political system of nautical societies, especially pirates. Furthermore, landowners were required to be knights and to carry arms in the service of the king. At the Thing meeting, a defendant in a trial could challenge jurors, who would be replaced by others. Appeals from a lower court could be taken to a higher Thing court. A very plausible case could be made that Western democratic institutions did not originate in Greece and Rome. Democracy originated in the nautical societies of the ancient Atlantic.

Paul B. Chaillu (*woden.org*, Jan. 2008) reminds us that, in olden times, Things were assembled near holy sites and temples and opened with holy ceremonies and convocations of a solemn peace under the protection of God. Things were not to be sullied by feuds and bloodshed. Representatives traveling to and from Things were under the protection of the peace of the Thing, where all weapons were put away and only taken up again at the conclusion of the Thing. Weapons were demonstrably shaken as a mark that the Thing was concluded. Violators of the peace of the Thing committed a sacrilege and were called "wolves in the sanctuary" and "outlaws." They were then strictly placed beyond the pale of the assembly.

Prophecy at Calendar Sites

It is evident that many sacred sites served as oracles. Sites like Delphi in Greece, Filitosa in Corsica, Quenco above Cuzco in Peru, and numerous sites in Ireland had their resident pythoness or prophetess. Throughout many of the lands of the ancient world there were innumerable oracles of the Sibyl, a Greek word—*sibylla*—meaning "prophetess." Many of these places are associated with the powerful actions of the moon upon the subterranean springs below these sites. The standstills and the cycle of regression of the lunar nodes also affect the amplitude of the moon's light and power.

There was a Persian Sibyl said to be of the family of Noah. There was a Libyan Sibyl at the remote Oasis of Siwa that Alexander wished to visit, the Oracle of Ammon. The Erythraean Sibyl opposite the town of Chios predicted the Trojan War. There was a Sibyl at the island of Samos. The very famous Cumaean Sibyl at Naples forecast the coming of a savior. The Trojan Sibyl held forth at Dardania. The Tiburtine Sibyl reigned at the ancient Etruscian town of Tibur, later called Tivoli. She also made a prophecy of Christ. There were also collections of some prophecies collected at Gergis (*futurerevealed.com/* 4/20/2008).

PART 5

HANDBOOK OF COSMOLOGY

Classical astrology, as described by Ptolemy (the noted Alexandrian geographer, astronomer, and scientist), is indisputably a part of the culture of astronomy (archaeoastronomy). There are countless fragments of important cosmology hidden within classical astrology. Archaeoastronomy cannot advance to a higher stratum of understanding without an examination of classical astrology.

CHAPTER 5.1

Introduction to Cosmology

There are some tribes in South America that firmly believed in a stellar origin of humans, animals, and all earthly forms. Even today, the link between the stars and us is occasionally put forward.

Mankind's first perception of the link between the heavens and the earth is the moon's pull upon the tides of the ocean. The tides determine the livelihood of those who voyage, trade, fish, and gather food from natural and artificial tide pools along the ocean. The correct understanding of the tides opens the doorway to a rich abundance of sustenance, which in turn allows the luxury of time to think and to develop philosophy and science. All philosophy, law, science, and religion has been taught to us by the sun, moon, planets, and stars.

The second great discovery in astronomy is that everything is related, interwoven, and balanced. In 1787 Laplace and Lagrange showed that if the orbit of one planet increases its eccentricity, those of others must decrease in eccentricity sufficiently to strike a balance (Asimov, p. 210). It is said that tidal friction slows the Earth's rotation, which in turn increases the moon's distance from us. But extreme heat or cold would transfer water mass into humid, hot atmosphere or ice-cold glaciers, which would reduce tidal friction. There is no such thing as isolated change.

The first skywatcher saw the strongest tides (flood or spring tides) occur when the sun, moon, and Earth were all lined up during either new moon (conjunction 0°) or full moon (opposition 180°). This created the highest ocean bulges on two sides of our globe, and consequently two of the lowest bulges at right angles to the highest. Therefore the time of the alignment of sun, moon, and Earth creates the highest and lowest tides. During the moon's first- and third-quarter phases, the moon works at right angles (90°) to the sun and Earth, and the difference between the high and low tides (ebb or neap tides) is much less pronounced. There are extreme tides when the new or full Moon is at the extreme ellipse of its orbit at perigee, nearest the Earth. Less powerful geometric relationships (30°, 60°, and 120°) of the moon and tides have also been adopted into astrology, a science that in ancient times inquired into astronomic cause.

Astronomy tracks and names the movements of the sun, moon, planets, stars, and cosmic cycles. *Astrology* investigates the effects of astronomy upon the Earth, nature, and humans. *Cosmology* considers the big picture of counterbalanced harmony that pervades the entire universe.

The Irregularity of Nature

Seamus Murphy, the renowned Irish sculptor, proclaimed, "Look at any group of people, or the leaves from the same tree; and you will see that no two of them are alike. All of nature blossoms forth individuality, diversity, originality, and irregularity." Indeed, to the eye of observation, nature seems to enjoy displaying what appears to be chaos and discord. This diverse plurality of form serves the true beauty, the relish and drama of life itself.

Ancient Peruvian cosmologers recognized that each star in the universe was the patron of some ideal form. This perfect "platonic" form is communicated from the universe to the galaxy, to the sun, and lastly to Earth. Our planet is not the center of the solar system but rather is in an offset position, as third rock from the sun. This makes the Earth subject to numerous cosmic cycles, churning clockwise and counterclockwise from diverse perspectives and thereby producing a cosmic frappe of the pristine ideal and perfect forms. Perfection is therefore scrambled and sculpted into unique individuality through time, geometric angles, and the counterpoised cosmic cycles. Therefore, a perfect universe is able to create imperfection, change, and the cycle of life, death, and resurrection. All of this confusion belongs to the challenge and drama of life.

Every culture on the face of the globe reenacts these convoluted astronomical rituals through the swirling dervish of motions and countermotions simulating the great back-and-forth dance of counter-opposed cosmic rotations. It must have been the greatest intellectual achievement to have penetrated this confusion and to have arrived at the underlying laws of symmetry and perfection within the cacophony of discord.

The skywatchers looked at the cosmos and saw that it was moved by spinning cycles, such as the day, the month, the year, and even higher cycles above these, such as precession, the cycle of the Milky Way, and universal revolution. All these cycles had one thing in common: a revolution from moist-hot-dry-cold or a mirror image of cold-dry-hot-moist repeating over and over again. Upon this common ground, the astronomers were able to relate the common cycles of nature to the most enormous and complex astronomical cycles.

The Great Cycles of Precession, Galactic Rotation, and Galactic Revolution

The Cycle of Precession of the Vernal Equinoxes: Every 72 years the spring equinox moves 1° clockwise along the zodiac. In 2,160 years, this equinox moves from one zodiac sign to the next sign. This cycle does not change our relationship to the sun, and therefore all solar alignments are unaffected and stay the same as they were originally made. Ancient monuments aligned to the equinoxes and solstices of the sun remain accurate for long periods of time because the inclination of the orbit of the Earth to the sun and the invariable plane only changes over 70,000 and 100,000 years respectively, while the change in the tilt of the Earth's axis is only 2.4 degrees over 40,000 years. Bauval, in his *Egypt Code* (pp. 216–229), gives a good discussion on this point, saying that precession does affect alignments to the *stars* within only a few thousand years.

Many astronomers have tried to equate precession of the vernal equinoxes with "cultural change." Precession moves clockwise through the zodiac and does not meld with the sequence of the Greek "generations of the gods" from

Uranus to Zeus. However, the *counterclockwise* movement of the cycle of the Milky Way perfectly melds with the Greek "generations of the gods."

Felicitously, however, the cycle of precession drives the world of politics, the short-term "rise and fall" of civilizations and empires from China to India, to Mesopotamia, to the Middle East, Greece, Rome, and to Europe. Such is the truth of history. There is no record of any civilization that has endured beyond the shallow limits of a thousand years because of the politics of deception, war, conquest, and greed. The benefit of this political cycle is the even distribution of power and wealth around the world in 25,920 years. This allows most nations the patience of endurance, based upon the certain knowledge that things will change, with the turning of the wheel of political power.

The cycle of the precession of the vernal equinoxes also has a general effect on the global climate as this cycle moves from zodiac houses associated with cold, to dry, to hot, to moist. This cycle moves clockwise through the zodiac and against the grain of most natural change which follows a cycle of moist, hot, dry, and cold.

The author of *Hamlet's Mill*, Giorgio de Santillana, wrote the preface to the reprint of Lockyer's *The Dawn of Astronomy*, saying that, the Precession was considered the basic mechanism of the universe by the Egyptians, controlling not only astronomical phenomena but all human and biological development...it was the mysteriously ordained behavior of the heavenly sphere...with one world-age succeeding another...each age bringing with it the rise and downfall of astral configurations and ruler-ships, with their earthly consequences. In the land of ancient Egypt scholars have found evidence that the Precession of the Equinoxes was precisely tracked in the proper and timely current use of astrological symbols and rituals synchronized with the cycles of the heavens. Schwaller de Lubicz has gone to great lengths to demonstrate that the symbols of the cosmic religion of the Egyptians exactly changed and corresponded to the movement of the precessional cycle. When the cycle was in Taurus, bulls and cows were revered. As the cycle moved into Aries, sheep and the ram were worshipped. Schwaller de Lubicz also points out that the history of Egypt is punctuated with the rise and decline of artistic and architectural achievement. As was said above, the precessional cycle does affect global climate which tended to be very cold from 6480-4320 BC (Gemini), and very dry from 4320-2160 BC (Taurus), after which there was a glorious temperate era of heat from 2160-0 BC (Aries). Kelley and Milone (p. 494) also concur, saying that cosmologers from around the ancient world from India to Mesoamerica regarded precession as a forecast of changes in the theme of the world ages, changes in society, and changes in government and the ruling houses. They called the wobbling Earth's axis the churning pivot, a spindle whorl, or a fire-drill that ignites the flame.

Equating the power of the cycle of precession with the power of the cycle of the Milky Way is totally wrong. All ancient astronomers observed the precession of the vernal equinoxes as a symbolic pathway to celebrating the great anniversaries of the cycle of the Milky Way. Precession *does not* create culture, gods, or global epochs of creation and destruction. Precession influences climate and also drives the flow of civilization and empire from east to west. It is this cycle that is spoken of as the "Fall of the Tower of Babel," where a great city had dominated many lands and their citizens into one empire and one universal language. The fall of that empire resulted in the dispersion of people and the confusions of the universal language back into their original native tongues.

The Cycle of the Spinning Milky Way: The science of the ancients held that the rotation of the Milky Way Galaxy brings culture to every part of the globe. This cycle moves counterclockwise (contrary to precession), completing a full rotation in about 216 million years. It is a curious coincidence that this period is equal to one full cycle of the expansion and reforming of Pangaea. As the Milky Way spins through the 12 regions of the universe, it engenders dramatic and epochal change upon our globe, including four episodes of creation and destruction through water, fire, drought, and ice. It is the most major factor in global climate change.

In the past history of our globe, the regions of Greece, Egypt, and Libya which are in the region of Pisces have been the beneficiaries of the cycle of the

Milky Way as it marked the celestial region of Pisces. The Milky Way cycle has now moved on to Jerusalem and the Middle East which is in the region of Aries. Past cycles of the Milky Way marked Algeria-Morocco-Western Europe (Aquarius), and prior to that existed Atlantis (Capricorn), and before Atlantis came Bolivia-Peru (Sagittarius), which was preceded by Mexico-Yucatan-Guatemala (Scorpio). The sequence of the "generations of the gods" from the traditions of Greece, Atlantis, and Egypt substantiate a history of the movement of the cycle of the Milky Way. The traditions of the Mexica-Maya-Andean culture likewise validate a history of the cycle of the Milky Way.

The ancients adored the Milky Way through their goddesses of Coyolxauhqui, Hera, Hathor, and Shiva. Franz Boll in *Sphaera* reports on the Babylonian Star catalogues of asterisms and constellations that have vanished from the view of astronomers. Several chapters of the *Dionysiaca* of Nonnos are about constellations being displaced from their positions. Modern man's knowledge of the Milky Way only began with the astronomer Halley (b.1656 AD), who observed that the stars Sirius, Procyon, and Arcturas had changed their position since Greek times and therefore concluded that stars have their own proper motions within the universe (Asimov, p. 145).

Carlos Milla Villena devotes all of Chapter 2 in *Genesis de la Cultura Andina* to the Andean astronomer's recognition and devotion to the Milky Way Galaxy. He speaks of the "dark constellations" in the Milky Way formed by huge concentrations of galactic dust that block the stream of starlight. Andean culture actually constructed the amazing El Amaru Orcco de Montesierpe—a gigantic geoglyph of tens of thousands of deep holes ascending up the mountain from the river Pisco. These holes depict the image of the Milky Way standing in the sky directly above the Earth. The Southern Cross, which is in the Milky Way, is used as the Andean clock and calendar. The Southern Cross also marks the position of the "Great Attractor" of the universe, toward which our galaxy and its neighboring galaxies are drawn. Carlos Milla Villena confirms that the El Amaru Orcco allowed for the study and analysis of the changing trajectory of the Milky Way (p. 45).

The Cycle of the Revolution of Our Galaxy around the Universe: While our Milky Way Galaxy is spinning on its axis, it is also journeying through the universe. Ancient astronomers were able to detect this movement, which they characterized in terms of a cycle of four seasons predicated upon the Milky Way.

Modern science states that the Milky Way and the Andromeda galaxies are the dominant members of the Local Group, which in turn is an outlying member of the Virgo Supercluster. Our Local Group is hurtling toward the center of the Virgo Supercluster. This center is hidden from our view by the masses of stars at the center of our own Milky Way Galaxy, but its location is in the general direction of the constellation of Centaurus and Hydra (dailygalaxy.com, 2009). The center of the Virgo Supercluster is called "the Great Attractor," toward which everything appears to be heading. Greek myth gives considerable information about the constellation of Centaurus. The other member of our Local Group appears to be heading on a collision course with our own Milky Way. Crashing galaxies, true "cosmic monsters" have been observed throughout the universe.

Astrology has served as a repository of ancient astronomical knowledge and data. The astrological division of the zodiac between Leo and Cancer (the houses of the sun and the moon) is the indicator of the position of our galaxy in the universe. The astrological idea of the "cosmic man," whose head is in Aries, represents the current position of the spinning cycle of the Milky Way. This idea is supported by the Circular Zodiac of Dendera, where the birth passage of Hathor (the cosmic womb and portal of the sun) is positioned by Aries.

The Underworld, the Land of the Dead

Some ancient people have associated the Underworld with caves and stream-filled caves that they called the "womb of Mother Earth." There were places in Italy and Greece said to be entrances to the Underworld. In the world of the Maya, there were caves such as Xibalba Actun Tunichil Muknal in Belieze and the flower-petal cave under the Great Pyramid in Mexico. But in reality, the Underworld is a concept taken from astronomy.

The cycle of the Milky Way creates and destroys cultures as it moves slowly along. The places of creation are rising, and the places of destruction are sinking below the horizon into the so-called "Underworld". Energy, spirit, and life cannot be destroyed; they can only be moved to different places. The spirits of the dead travel through the cycle of the Milky Way, returning to regions of the stars from where they came. The Underworld was the place where the former cycles of the Milky Way had elapsed and disappeared like a setting sun under the horizon. However the history and myths, and the spirits of the dead were still accessible when these regions of the sky came into view each day or night. Anniversaries could be celebrated when the yearly course of the sun touched the heavenly sphere at those places which represented the time when beloved ancestors had lived. Prayers and incantations could be directed to the spirits of ancestors who had returned to the heavens. Unfortunately this beautiful idea has been subverted by charlatans and so-called spiritualists. Aveni writes (p. 256) that the Mayan Underworld was an exotic plane of existence, through which rulers and diviners could pass only while in a trance. It was a real world with real, if supernatural, inhabitants, and every night when the sun set, the Underworld flipped over and became the sky dome.

In many cultures, psychotropic drugs were used to contact spirits and realms of the Underworld through their historical-contextual place in the heavens. This is the provenance of all diviners and soothsayers. Here in the Underworld, the shaman can travel to seek the knowledge and advice of former generations. Many adepts have claimed to have mastered "the force" (*shakti*), the matrix of galactic time, and the Maya *Zuvuya*—a cosmic consciousness; a surfing wave; an interdimensional thread; or a circuit that connects the future, present, and past. All of this shamanism is founded upon the understanding of cosmic physics, energy, and spirit.

Petrie tells us (pp.76–9) that the Egyptian *Book of the Dead*, *That Which Is in the Underworld, the Duat* and the *Book of Gates* describe the successive hours of the night, each hour fenced off with gates that are guarded by monsters like Cerberus, the dog of the Underworld. Aveni (p. 250) takes us through the main plaza complex of Tikal and its east and west twin pyramid group.

In Maya cosmology, north is up and south is down. The southern structure consists of nine doorways, the same as the number of levels in the Underworld. Ashmore describes the five cosmological components of a classical Maya city, which includes politico-religious statements and the dualism between the celestial supernatural sphere to the north and the Underworld in the south. All these elements must be balanced and work together to form a cosmic mandala and temple on Earth representing time and space, humans and the divine.

Ancient gods of the Maya carry skulls fastened to their belts, while temples in Mexico and Yucatan have walls of skulls within their temple complex. Skulls and bones are memorials of ancestors that suggest reverence and worship. But more importantly, the skulls and bones symbolize a belief in the cosmological context of a balanced and harmonious universe of cycles and resurrection, where death actually demonstrates life that continues on. Aveni writes (p. 297), "The message plays on the Maya fascination with cyclic time. Death is necessary to life: it is the ultimate creation force that produces birth..." The gods Xbalanque and Hunahpu search for their father in the Underworld, and Quetzlcoatl goes there to retrieve the bones of the previous creation to create the next world (Taube, p. 73). Here is the embodiment of the concept of "renaissance"—to combine the past with the future in order to create the present.

We read about the Inca mummy positioned to observe the annular spring equinox and then paraded through the streets of Cuzco after the mummy has been filled with new cosmic life. In the lands of the Mexican-Maya-Andean culture, the Day of the Dead is a joyously and elaborately celebrated at graveside encampments with food and drink. Petrie, in *Religion of Ancient Egypt* (p. 82), tells us that, in China and India, sacrifices were held for their progenitors; and in Egypt, both Copts and Mohammedans held family feasts and spent the night at the tombs of their ancestors.

The Underworld is a vibrant and living concept in cosmology. It means that ancestors and the historical and mythical past are not dead; but like the setting sun, this cosmic cycle has set below the western horizon (comparing the Milky Way cycle to the daily cycle of the sun). The Netherworld of every day is evident in the nighttime sky, where it fully and triumphantly still exists encapsulated in the heavens. The Tukanoan tribe of Brazil relates that a dualism pervades their culture (K&M, p. 469). The dead in this world become alive in the Underworld, where it is day when our world is in darkness.

Every culture proclaims that their dead ancestors and their history exist in the West, the land of the setting sun, night, and darkness. Many cultures bury their dead on the west side of their cities and rivers. Hadingham tells us (p. 116) that the California Chumash say and that the souls travel westward along the Milk Way, where Turtle is chief of the land of the dead. Their midwinter solstice ceremonies included dances that dramatized the soul's journey along the Milky Way to reach the land of the dead. The Chumash used star maps inlaid with constellation patterns of shell beads. They also had tally cords and threaded beads to keep track of astronomical cycles and kept information bundles grouped in periods of 512 years. They understood the appearances and disappearances of Venus and created the most beautiful astronomical rock art of the Americas. Hadingham says that these skills are totally at odds with the conventional picture of the limited intellects of the lifestyle of the hunter-gatherer.

The Common Clock Face of the Zodiac—Representing Many Cycles in the Universe

Cosmologers kept track of all the cycles of the universe upon the one clock face of the 12 signs of the zodiac. Every cycle from the smallest to the most august was marked like an hour hand upon this clock of 12 houses like the 12-hour clocks that we have inherited from the Egyptian astronomers.

The zodiac functioned as a veritable time machine, presenting a catalogue of portals to the future and the past. This ability to study data from all periods of time was an exquisite vehicle of comparing historical data and prognosticating future and similar events toward better understanding the nature of the universe. The cosmologer was no longer limited to the confined scope of his village and epoch but could investigate different lands and immense reaches of time. Now the cosmologer was at home among his scientific contemporaries from all other nations as well as being at home in the entire universe, irrespective of time, place, and condition.

Dancing rituals and images of twirling gods mimic the clockwise and counterclockwise milling and churning of the diverse cosmic cycles. Other images are the back-and-forth motion of the shuttle of the loom as the cosmic fates weave the destiny of the world. Another image is that of a fire stick, which is spun backward and forward by a bowstring or pulled by gods and daemons, as may be seen in the stone carving at Angkor Wat.

Every year when the sun enters into a particular sign, great cosmic events and myths related to that sign may again be celebrated through this portal. This is called "anniversary cosmology." Taube writes (p. 72), "Not only are creation events described in terms of calendrical cycles, but calendrical rituals frequently express creation episodes." Taube continues to say that the *Creation of the World* story is repeated every year as part of the New Year celebration.

However, this compacting of information into one zodiac sign has led to much misinformation by people who are not familiar with the entire cosmological system. As, for example, using the cycle of precession instead of the cycle of the Milky Way to express the idea that the great world flood occurred only some few thousand years ago when this event actually belongs to the cycle of the Milky Way in terms of millions of years in the past. Precession presents the opportunity to celebrate an anniversary of an event of the Milky Way cycle –but precession never caused such global catastrophic events.

The Rules of Astrology Are the Ancient Bones of Cosmology

Classical astrology should be regarded like an archeological dig, where the fragments are priceless and should be cautiously dusted off, catalogued, and preserved. This is because there really are no books and materials about cosmology. This highest of all sciences was passed down in oral tradition from master to pupil in order to safeguard its content. All that we really have are some folk traditions, ancient astronomical sites and images, and astrological rules. We will therefore now turn our attention to Claudio Ptolemy's *Tetrabiblios*, a pure and simple redaction of the rules of classical astrology. Ptolemy was a scientist who realized that astrology was founded upon important principles and ancient data.

The First Precept of Astrology

The astrological zodiac is divided into two half-circles between Leo and Cancer. The hemicircle of Leo is white like the light of the sun. The other hemicircle of Cancer is dedicated to the moon and is as black as night. Aveni writes (p. 310), that the Inca held a dualistic, vertical view of the cosmos with masculine nature, light, and the sun on the left side and feminine nature, darkness, and the moon on the right side. The identical division of the circle of the zodiac is common to Asia, Egypt, Greece, and the Mid-East. The Book of Genesis in the Bible also copies this cosmology. They all say that the first act of creation is the separation of night and day, darkness from light. All these so-called astrological rules and formats originate in ancient cosmology.

Light and darkness is the primary dichotomy of the universe. This dichotomy is synonymous with day and night, summer and winter, and the great seasons of the universe, which the Hindu call the life and death (sleep) of Brahma. From this duality springs the fourfold cycle of the elementary natures: moist, hot, dry, cold. These natures drive the cycle of life from birth, maturity, degeneration, death, and to rebirth, that no spirit or energy may be lost in the universe. The elementary cycles repeat over and over again—and so also the cycle of life and death is followed by resurrection and rebirth over and over again.

A single cell divides to form two cells. Then two cells divide to form four cells. The cosmos starts as a dichotomy of two things. Then the two become four things—like birth, life, degeneration, and death expressed by the classical cycle of moist-hot-dry-cold. These are the four great elements of the universe: water, fire, air, and earth—the primary pathway of all changes. The seasons of the year, the four divisions of the day, and the phases of the moon—all follow this cycle and succession of elementary natures.

From new moon to first quarter is moist like spring and dawn. First quarter to full moon is hot like midday and summer. Full moon to last quarter is dry like afternoon and autumn. And last quarter until new moon is cold like the depth of night and winter. All astronomical cycles—all natural, social, and human cycles—follow these four elementary periods in their sequence.

The Second Precept from Astrology

The astrological circle of the zodiac is sectioned into 12 divisions. And these divisions are catalogued into four elementary triangles: one triangle of moist, one triangle of hot, one triangle of dry, and another of the nature of cold (4 natures x 3 triangles = 12 divisions):

- Cancer, Scorpio, Pisces =Wet (Water) *Governors,* Mars, Venus, Moon
- Aries, Leo, Sagittarius =Hot (Fire), *Governors,* Sun and Jupiter
- Taurus, Virgo, Capricorn =Dry (Air), *Governors,* Venus and Moon
- Gemini, Libra, Aquarius =Cold (Earth) *Governors,* Saturn and Mercury

The Third Precept from Astrology

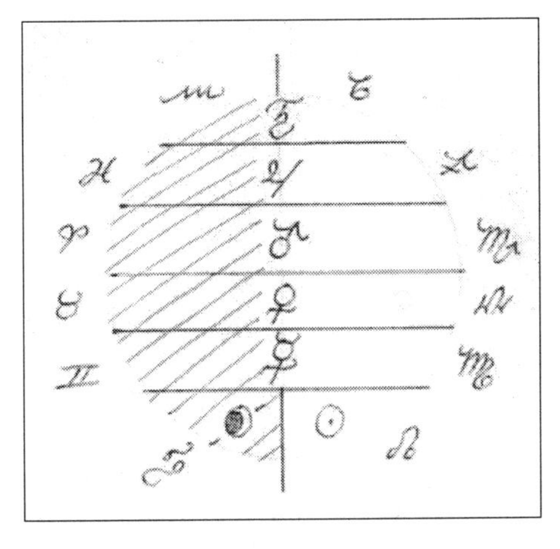

The zodiac is divided into 12 houses: one for the sun and one for the moon, while the remainder are given in pairs to the visible planets as their lunar and solar houses. Thereby, the 12 houses are divided into the seven days of the week. The five planets each get two houses, while the sun and the moon have their house as well as sovereignty over their half of the circle of the zodiac:

- Leo = Sunday, the Sun
- Cancer = Monday, the day of the Moon
- Aries & Scorpio = Tuesday, the day of Mars
- Virgo & Gemini = Wednesday, the day of Mercury (common)
- Sagittarius & Pisces = Thursday, the day of Jupiter
- Libra & Taurus = Friday, the day of Venus
- Capricorn & Aquarius = Saturday, the day of Saturn

The Fourth Precept of Astrology

Ptolemy discusses the lunar and solar houses of the planets. This presents a guideline to the mixing of the nature of each planet with the nature of the sun or the moon. Ptolemy continually exhorts us to remember that the sun and moon are the rulers of the zodiac. More importantly, the sun and moon are the marshals of every prediction. In every astrological event, the sun and moon must be involved in a strong geometrical relation, called an aspect, to the other planets and the geography of the Earth—or nothing will happen:

- *Saturn* in his solar house of Capricorn creates Dry. Therefore, whenever Saturn works together with the Sun the combination is Dry.
- *Saturn* in his lunar house of Aquarius creates Cold. Therefore, whenever Saturn works with the Moon, their combination is Cold.
- *Jupiter* in his solar house of Sagittarius creates Hot. Therefore whenever Jupiter works together with the Sun the combination is Hot.
- *Jupiter* in his lunar house of Pisces creates Moist. Therefore whenever Jupiter works with the Moon, their combination is Wet.
- *Mars* in his solar house of Scorpio creates Moist. Therefore whenever Mars works with the Sun the combination is Moist (in the sense of Hot and Humid).
- *Mars* in his lunar house of Aries creates Hot. Therefore whenever Mars works with the Moon, their combination is Hot.
- *Venus* in her solar house of Libra creates Cold. Therefore whenever Venus works with the Sun the combination is Cold (Crystal clear cold and dry air).
- *Venus* in her lunar house of Taurus creates Dry. Therefore whenever Venus works with the Moon, the combination is Dry.
- *Mercury* in his solar house of Virgo is Dry. Therefore whenever Mercury works in combination with the Sun, the combination is Dry.

- *Mercury* in his lunar house of Gemini is Cold. Therefore whenever Mercury works with the Moon, the combination is Cold.

The Fifth Precept of Astrology

Ancient cosmologies record the world flood and the world fire (Ekpyrosis) that consumed the globe. Seneca records, in his *Naturales Quaestiones* (vol. VII, book 3.29):

> Berosos [who translated Jupiter Belus, the Babylonian astronomer] says that these catastrophes occur with the movements of the planets. Indeed, he is so certain that he assigns a date for the conflagration and the deluge. For earthly things will burn, he contends, when all the planets which now maintain different orbits come together in the sign of *Cancer*, and are so arranged in the same path that a straight line can pass through the spheres of all of them. The deluge will occur when the same group of planets meets in the sign of *Capricorn*. The solstice is caused by Cancer, winter by Capricorn; they are signs of great power since they are the turning-points in the very change of the year.

The planets certainly assist in the great flood, the great fire, the great drought, and the great ice. But the real cause of these conditions is the astronomical cycle of the rotation of our own Milky Way Galaxy. Just as every day begins with moisture, then hot, dry, and cold—just as the seasons of the year also follow this basic cycle—so too does the rotation of the galaxy follow the basic changes from moist-hot-dry-cold.

Ptolemy speaks about the *Exaltations* and the *Depressions* of the planets. The Stoics and Seneca (following the traditions of Prometheus, Zoroaster, the Maga of Iran, and the Hindu) say that the great world-engulfing flood happened in the time of Capricorn—the depression of Jupiter. One could imagine that *depression* could mean greatest orbital eccentricity. Such wild elongated swings in Jupiter's orbit would account for a world flood. In terms of the galactic cycle, this world flood would come at the end of the dry galactic autumn and thereby refresh and save the Earth.

Regarding Jupiter's exaltation in Cancer, one would surmise that *exaltation* means Jupiter's most perfect circular orbit. This kind of an orbit almost nullifies the influence of Jupiter in Cancer, which is extremely important because Cancer is the galactic sign of the great world-consuming fire, the *Ekpyrosis*. The great fire is caused by the depression of Mars in this sign. *Depression* means greatest orbital eccentricity of that planet. The depression of Mars causes the great fire at the end of the extremely wet galactic spring, and this conflagration of fire serves to help dry out the planet. These are the exaltations and depressions that seem to refer to extreme orbital eccentricities:

	Exaltation (circular)	*Depression* (eccentric)
Sun (the Earth's orbit)	Aries	Libra
Moon	Taurus	Scorpio
Saturn	Libra	Aries
Jupiter	Cancer	Capricorn
Mars	Capricorn	Cancer
Venus	Pisces	Virgo
Mercury	Virgo	Pisces

Ptolemy also discusses the equinoctial signs of Aries and Libra; the solstical signs of Cancer and Capricorn which seems to define the revolution of our Milky Way through the universe. All in all, it seems very likely that these astrological laws about the planets derive from the influence of the cycle of the Milky Way.

The Sixth Precept of Astrology

Above, Ptolemy emphatically states that the sun and moon are the "marshals of every prediction." The sun and moon leverage the influence of the planets. Indeed, this is what makes life possible. For, if each planet had its own powerful influence, then the Earth would be torn asunder.

Astronomers concede that the two giant planets Jupiter and Saturn do exercise gravitation pull upon the Earth-moon system by minutely tugging upon orbits, inclinations, revolutions, and rotations. This admission came about when science needed an explanation for the Croll-Milankovitch cycles that so dramatically influence our climate on Earth. Astrologers attach great significance to the places in the zodiac where Jupiter and Saturn meet every 20 years, because this has an effect on global climate.

Other Precepts of Astrology

The signs are further divided into five pairs of *commanding* and *obeying* signs. This total of 10 signs is focused around the axis of Aries and Libra, the equinoctial signs. The sense of this division is to express the revolution of our galaxy around the universe. The signs are also divided into five pairs of *beholding* signs, which are focused around the axis of Cancer and Capricorn.

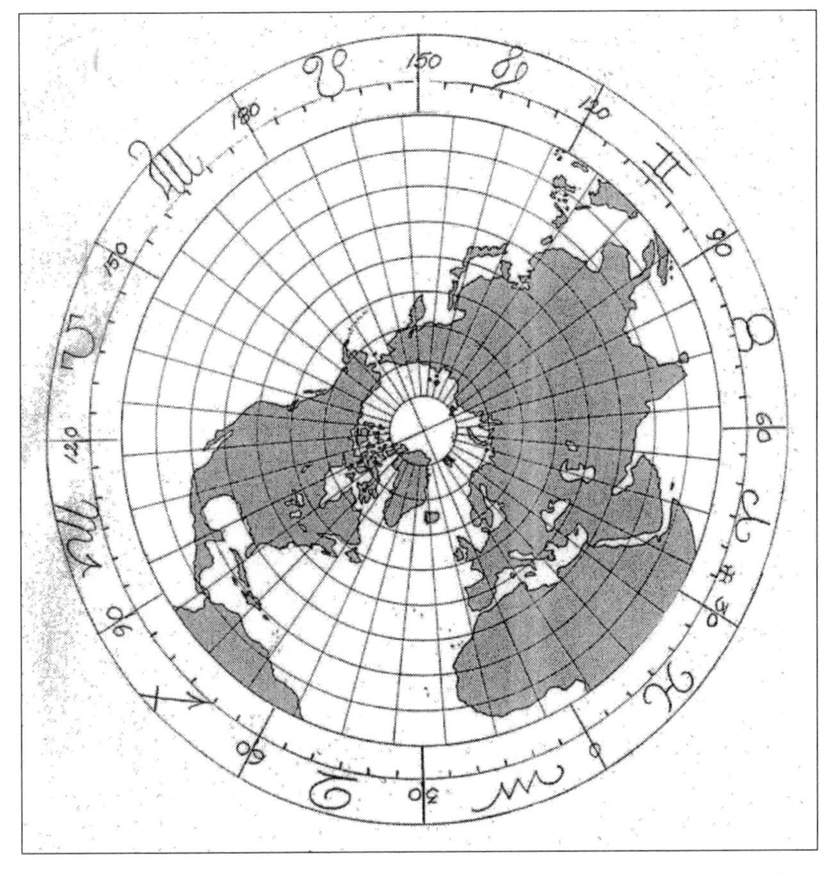

This map shows the relationship between the position of the cycle of the Milky Way and the current geography of the Earth. Author diagram

CHAPTER 5.2

Dichotomy and the Knowledge of Good and Evil

The universe teaches us that it is made up of matter and spirit. The first law of thermodynamics addresses the conservation of energy. This law states that energy cannot be created or destroyed. Einstein added that energy can only be changed from one form into another. Energy is just another word for "spirit." Matter needs *spirit* to attain form, shape, and movement. Spirit requires *matter* to be embodied, recognized, and appreciated by the senses. This is the basic dichotomy of the universe.

We could not call things "good" unless we had seen "evil." Ugliness allows us to perceive beauty. The universe is a giant clockwork of moving cycles of action and reaction. The cosmos is image and mirror image, and there are always two sides to every story. Matter and spirit represent the great dichotomy of the universe. The movements of the clockwise and counterclockwise astronomical cycles provide the *tension of flux* between good and evil and between being and non-being.

Mary Miller, in *The Gods and Symbols of Ancient Mexico and the Maya*, says that, "In ancient Mesoamerica, the sky was believed to have distinct levels, often cited as 13, particularly among the Classic and Post-classic" (p.154). The highest of these levels of the sky was called "place of duality." Dualism is a worldwide philosophy. It is spoken of among the Incas as binary oppositions and the dual organization of Inca society (Mann. *1491,* p. 377). The New Testament celebrates dichotomy in such sayings as, "The least among you shall be the greatest," "The meek shall inherit the earth," and "The humble shall be exalted, while the exalted shall be humbled." In the Book of Revelation it says (referring to those that are saved) that they have washed their garments clean in the blood of the lamb. In Ireland "the evil fairies" are referred to as "the good people." A "traveling woman" in our locality in Ireland allowed her livestock to graze the roadside grass, but they would sometimes break into the fields of the landowners, who occasionally made trouble for the woman and her family. Those who did so were horribly injured in accidents or otherwise humiliated. One day I asked her about her reputation in these matters, and she replied, "I don't curse them—I pray for them and leave them to God."

The Old Testament says, "But of the tree of the knowledge of good and evil, thou shalt not eat of it: for in the day that thou eatest thereof thou shalt surely die." But the serpent said to Eve that, "You shall not die, but your eyes shall be opened, and you shall be as gods—knowing good and evil" (Genesis 2.17). Originally, Adam and Eve lived with God in the Garden of Eden, a heaven-like place that was sheltered from the world of dichotomy and opposites. Once Adam and Eve had eaten of the apple, they attained the knowledge of good and evil because they were cast into the world of dualism, action and reaction. In the natural world, dualism splits into four stages of the basic cycle of life: birth, maturity, degeneration, and death. But, of course, death leads to regeneration and rebirth, and the cycle starts over again.

Duality Is Taught to Us by Astronomy

The reason that duality and dichotomy are part of every culture is because it is taught by astronomy. As we have remarked above, everything we experience is duality, which splits into four elementary natures:

> Darkness and light, night and day, split and produce moist-hot-dry-cold, spring-summer-autumn-winter, and birth-maturity-degeneration-death.

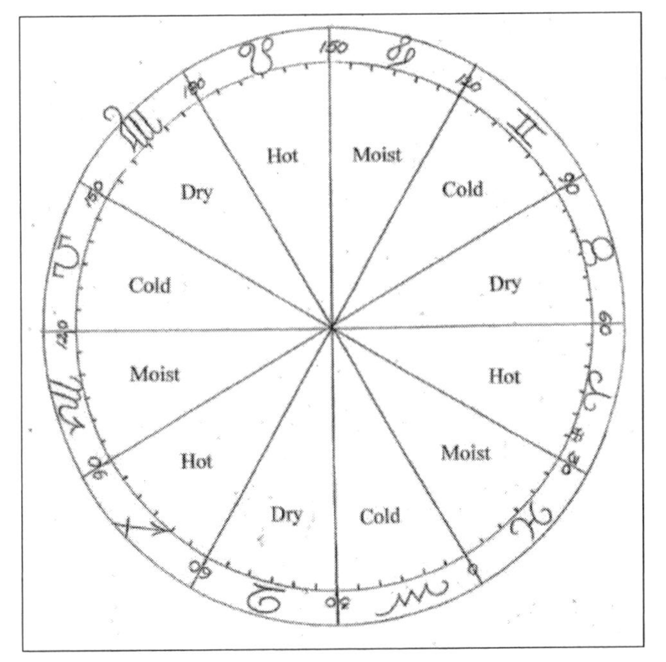

Duality and the quadrality of the four elementary natures are so much a part of the fundamental structure and being of the universe that they are an aspect of cosmic physics; they are cosmic law. Martineau in *Quadrivium* (p. 18) writes, "Four is the first born thing, the first product of procreation, two tows…Four is often associated with the material modes of manifestation, Water, Fire, Air, and Earth." The four natures are even discussed in religion. Wasserman writes that the first principle of reality is the divine name IHVH (Jehovah). Each letter of the name is assigned to one of the four elements: water, fire, air, and earth.

Dualism serves to illuminate and define the opposites. Dualism dispenses with fear of life and death by unfolding its meaning—not as two opposites, but as a cycle followed by rebirth. The symbol of death at the winter solstice is followed by the instant flash of regeneration when the light of the sun is reborn again and begins to increase day by day. This miracle of renewal has become the most important sacred festival to all of humankind around the globe.

There is a wonderful scene depicting the drama and tension of life and creation on a wall at Angkor Wat, where the *divas* and the *asuras* are using a great snake as the rope for the tug-of-war in order to create all things. This action is called "the churning of the sea of milk." This is their phrase for the spinning of the Milky Way Galaxy, which all ancient cultures regard as the prime source of creation. Good spirits and evil daemons participate in this act of creation—a cosmic frappe that allows the drama of life to unfold.

The cosmic cycles blindly dispense and promote truth, justice, equality, balance, and harmony. This is the sense of Karma, which is a cosmic principle: *That which is up will come down. That which is down will rise up. Slaves become masters, masters become slaves. The revered becomes abhorred, the abhorred becomes revered.* The Book of Job asks the question, "What is God doing right now?" The answer is given, "He is humbling the proud, and exalting the humble." The cosmic cycles teach us a real and an observable justice, enacted by the balancing cycles dispensing the cosmic order and the natural law.

Churning of the Sea of Milk by the *divas* and the *asuras* who are using the great snake (a symbol of the galaxy) as the rope above the Earth-turtle. Courtesy of Eleanor Mannikka and the University of Hawaii

Duality in China and the Orient

The cosmologer Moses uses male and female to personify the concept of good and evil. Adam is good because he listens to God, while Eve is cast into the role of evil because she wishes to exercise her free will to choose another direction. But really Moses has introduced us to the dynamic that creates the drama of life. The knowledge of good and evil is the understanding of the opposite forces of the cosmos—the yin and yang that propels life in its cycles.

There is a primal dichotomy that is so powerful that it moves the entire universe. In Eastern philosophy the symbol of the yin and yang wrap around one another and cling together, while also showing movement and direction. This contention between black and white is one of the clearest and most direct of all the great cultural icons. The image conveys a balance between conflict and harmony. The image shows that black and white carry the seeds of one another in their central being. The image of yang conveys the forces of male, white, good, and permanence. The yin represents the female, black, evil, change, and movement. Both confront each other and yet work together within the stability of the eternal circle. The yin-yang portrays the ultimate drama, tension, and electricity that move the cosmos. Once again, philosophy is taught by astronomy. The Chinese astronomers call the sun, Thai Yang, *the great Yang* and the Moon, Thai Yin, *the great Yin* (Kelley and Milone, p. 36).

The Yin Yang and the Trigrams.
Bing free image: ideonexus.com

Thomas L. Ogren, in *Safe Sex in the Garden*, explains that pollen is the essence of the male parts of the plant, the equivalent of male semen. The female part of the plant is called the pistil, where the male pollen settles and sticks. At the base of the pistil are the ovaries, where the seeds eventually form. Male trees produce pollen, while female trees produce seeds and fruit. In ancient times, marauding tribes would cut down and burn the "bull palms" in their enemies' date orchards, since the pollen could fructify up to 50 female palms. Slow-motion films show an incredible swift exchange of pollen between male and female plants like a bolt of lightning. The point is that the discharge from the *positive* male is accompanied by the equivalent powerful reception by the *negative* female. We are used to seeing pollen as lazy dust clouds because urban planners and nurseries have filled our landscapes with male pollen-producing trees. We have shunned the female fruit-producers because the fallen fruit leaves a mess on our fine urban streets and pathways. The tension between female and male, the yin and yang, weave a tapestry of dualism throughout nature and life.

It is said that the *I Ching*, the Book of Changes, was compiled by the first emperor of China, Qin Shi Huang. He certainly brought it back into prominence, but it has been resurrected many times. In 3300 BC, Master Fu Xi described an ancient binary code developed from the principles of yin and yang within the eternal circle. Yang was represented by a long, broad line. And in the like manner of the Egyptian-Pythagorean theory of the Monad, the yang split into two shorter lines to create the yin. The different shades and qualities of the yin and yang were expressed in a system of the trigrams. These trigrams are sets of three broken and/or solid lines arranged around the circle of the yin and yang that first represented eight conditions, later divided into 64 conditions, and with the addition of other lines conveyed thousands of variations and meanings. Like the original meaning of yin and yang, duality controlled this system by placing opposites in opposition to one another. The sign for heaven was three broad lines placed in opposition to Earth, represented by three pairs of two short lines. Fire was shown by the trigram of a broad line—two short lines—broad line. In opposition to fire, water was depicted by two short lines—broad line—two short lines. The element of wind was placed opposite to wood. The nature of marshland was put opposite to mountain. This is a most amazingly refined cosmological system founded upon sun and moon, day and night, heaven and earth, and all the elements of nature around us.

<u>*Duality in Egypt*</u>

Egyptian duality seems to have been expressed by Plato's ideal, divine forms that exist in heaven as the models of the shadowy forms that we see here on Earth. Our images are shadowy and fleeting because we live in the fast-flowing river of our experiences, driven by the cosmic cycles. Egyptian images of the human form are always full-front torso, even when they are walking in a particular direction.

Schwaller de Lubicz writes in *The Temples of Karnak* (p.13), "The Egyptian origin of the sciences and the main philosophical doctrines of Greece shall perhaps become still more evident through the interpretation of Egypt's monuments. The Platonic school is nothing but Egyptism that has left the sanctuaries of Sais, and the old Pythagorean sect propagating psychological theories that are developed in the paintings and sacred legends found in the tombs of the kings of Thebes..."

Schwaller (p. 74) expresses the Egyptian doctrines of polarities and concepts of action and reaction:

> The inscriptions and sculpture that are carved in sunk-relief signify *entering, penetrating,* while the same figures carved in high-relief denote *emerging,* or *coming forth*...as, for example, "opening and closing" may signify "to loose" and "to bind" with regard to the keys of Saint Peter. All activity provokes a reaction, and life is phenomenal only by alteration. Action and reaction, entering and emerging, and opening and closing: therein lays the entire esoteric story of the great temple of Amun.

Even the demigods of Egypt have their alter egos. There is night and day, black and white, male and female, positive and negative, finite and the infinite. Every statement has an alternative, because life is made up of opposites. Even the gods, or *neters,* are subject to the polarity and dualism. Schwaller de Lubicz writes (*The Temples of Karnak*, p. 35), "'The idea that a god might die is incompatible with our way of thinking,' remarks the great Egyptologist Erman, but he later acknowledges: 'The true sense of all the subtleties gathered here escapes our uninitiated minds.'"

In Egyptian philosophy, things that are far away (at the opposite ends of the poles) were actually related in the sense of being so far removed. Egyptian dualism really united the universe rather than dividing it. The very diametrically opposed forces became the warp and the woof, the fabric of the tapestry of life. Cycles that moved in opposite directions were in reality moving toward the same goal because they were part of the one universe. Dualism defines the oneness of everything, the holy monad of the Egyptians that was so celebrated by Pythagoras.

Dualism is common to all ancient cultures. But here is where the Egyptians seem to take a giant leap into discovering something new about our condition. They seemed to ask the question, "This is life, but what is the opposite of life;

is it death?" But death is inactivity without power, thought, and expression. From these thoughts and musings, the Egyptians came up with the idea of the afterlife, which is so eloquently expressed in the fine carvings in the *mastaba* of Mereruka in Saqqara. Here every aspect of life is carved into stone: There are stone images of men and women making beer, winnowing corn, butchering cattle, hunting, making offerings to the gods. Here is a perfect sacred life carved in stone, iconic images of the ideal and perfect life.

But *those who live* do not reside in fine stone palaces. Even the divine rulers of Egypt lived in humble mud-brick palaces. Stones were only used for the sacred temples of the gods. The images carved into the stones of the mastaba at Saqqara are the images of the perfect divine life, a form that only exists in heaven. These perfect images are like Plato's heavenly paradigms. We, however, live the opposite of the divine life. Our lives are imperfect and are like the upside-down images projected upon our retina that our brain must learn to turn right-side up.

Thus, death and nonlife are not the polarity to life. There is life, and there is "another life"—a perfect, divine, and ideal form of life. This perfect life is the life we wish to live, an ideal form of life in the highest and most sacred plane of the universe. Above, Schwaller de Lubicz said that deep engraved carvings meant "entering into through the gateway of a symbol." But, at the mastaba at Saqqara, the scenes depicting life were raised relief, representing that meaning was proceeding forth and projecting out of the images in order to instruct us in following the perfect life that we could attempt to attain.

Dichotomy presents both sides of a subject. This duality, or mirror image, serves to better define all issues. Mysteries, the efficacy of curses, and hidden esoteric truth are often nothing but dualism and dichotomy, principles that pervade astronomy and the universe.

The Doctors and the Medical Conditions

Today's medical practitioners smile at the times when doctors diagnosed the conditions of their patients as *sanguine, choleric, melancholic,* and *phlegmatic.* Here was another testimony to the dark ages and how science has advanced and triumphed over medieval thinking.

However, the doctors were only following the cosmic pattern. They reasoned that if the cycles of the universe operated through the conditions of moist-hot-dry-cold, then humans—as the microcosm of the universe—must also be susceptible to these cycles. This seemed plausible because a body is sick when it is assaulted by a preponderance of a particular elementary nature, such as moist-hot-dry-cold. It was the doctor's mission to restore balance and harmony in the human body. This system of diagnosis is still in use today. If a patient is too hot, doctors find medications, herbs, and a cold bath to cool down the patient.

Medieval physicians treated the *excesses* of the four elementary natures with their opposites or even their kindred natures. Shakespeare writes, "One fire drives out one fire, one nail—one nail; rights by rights do falter, strengths by strengths do fail."

- Moist = Sanguine .... humor = blood, organ = heart
- Hot = Choleric .... humor = yellow bile, organ = gall bladder
- Dry = Phlegmatic .... humor = phlegm, organ = lungs
- Cold = Melancholic .... humor = black bile, organ = spleen

Civilization has adopted the Greek caduceus as a symbol of medical expertise. The icon represents a staff of knowledge, the tree of life, or the Earth's axis, around which two serpents are twined (twined serpents represent the galaxy and also the equinoxes of the year in ancient astronomy). Snakes inhabit the bowels of the Earth and are privy to the natural sciences and the harmony of nature. The "Vitruvian Man" incorporates many geometric forms that have mystical meaning: square = earth; circle = air; triangle = fire; downward-pointing triangle = water. Balancing the elements is the key to life and survival. The function of the medicine man, medical doctor, and environmentalist is the same. They must first protect the body of the environment in which they live. Then they must strive to maintain the resources of the system so that they do not deplete or eat themselves out of their own environment. The human body may be likened to a complete environment of many balanced systems.

Heraclitus

Heraclitus was fascinated with the concept of change. His remark that "war is the mother of all things" is a play upon dichotomy because war destroys, but that very destruction in turn generates creation. Cycles create and destroy, and many cycles create and destroy in exquisite harmony. The end result is creativity and invention. The fruits of the two World Wars produced an absolutely amazing advance in technology, engineering, and production, vindicating Heraclitus' aphorism.

The works of Heraclitus of Ephesus (535–475 BC) are known to us only through the citations of other authors. Some of his notable sayings are:

- Everything flows, and nothing abides, everything gives way and nothing stays fixed…You cannot step twice into the same river…The sun is new each day…Immortals become mortals, mortals become immortals.
- War is the mother of all things…War is both father and king of all.
- We must know that war is common to all, and strife is justice, and that all things come into being through strife necessarily. Homer was wrong in saying, "Would that strife might perish from amongst gods and men." For if that were to occur, then all things would cease to exist.
- The universe changes according to a plan or logos (divine law).
- A change is the result of a change in balance. Cold things become warm, the warm grows cold, what is wet dries, and the parched is moistened.
- The death of fire is the birth of air, the death of air is the birth of water.
- Opposition brings concord. Out of discord comes the fairest harmony.
- This universe, which is the same for all, has not been made by any god or man, but it always has been, is, and will be…All things come

> in their due season...In the circumference of a circle the beginning and the end are common...It pertains to all men to know themselves.

The philosophy of Heraclitus focuses upon change. He says that no man steps into the same river twice, because both he and the river have changed in the meantime. Everything changes, and nothing remains.

Many scientists have credited the concept of the conservation of energy to Heraclites because of his assertions regarding the cycles of change and that strife is justice, in the sense that nothing is lost but only proceeds onward in the cycle of change. Heraclitus' philosophy is predicated on natural change driven by the forces of the cycles of moist-hot-dry-cold. Above all, Heraclitus has discovered the law of the cycle of cosmic change, namely that the laws of physics dictate that fire is born out of air, which in turn changes into water. There is no sluggish cause and effect. The very nature of one element in time is already transmuting along the cycle dictated by the physics of the universe. In the history of philosophy, Heraclitus is portrayed as a quaint primitive in the evolution of science examining nature. In a cosmological context, he is a veritable Newton or Einstein. He has examined the dichotomy of the universe in respect to the contrary natures of permanence and change: how can these opposites exist together as fundamentals of the essence of the cosmos? Heraclitus has come up with a unique solution by saying that the cycle of change is imprinted in cosmic physics. He explains that there really is not independent existence of moisture, fire, drought, and cold. Motion produces time, which reveals the constituents of matter. His saying that, "Fire is born out of air," confirms that "air" has no independent existence. *Change* is a prime constituent of the universe. Mexica-Maya-Andean cosmology says that the Creator God has instituted "movement and measure." According to Heraclitus, movement and measure *is* change.

Water—Most Magical

The cycles of moist-hot-dry-cold are the key to studying the natural sciences because they are a function of movement and measure. Heraclitus has given us the notion that fire does not really exist without air—something magical is going on here, something we do not fully understand. It should be noticed that water, which we always associate with moisture, is the most curious of the elemental natures because it acts differently to all other substances. Water is the only material that expands when frozen contrary to the reaction of all other forms of matter. Water is magic and can transform into a solid bit of matter, air, and then return to a liquid.

The magical quality of water is also revealed in a substance called "Brown's Gas." A section entitled "6,000 Degrees Celsius" in *Atlantis Blueprint* tells us that the inventor of Brown's Gas was Yul Brown, born in Bulgaria on Easter of 1922. While reading Jules Verne's *The Mysterious Island* (1874), he came upon the following:

> "Water decomposed into its primitive elements...by electricity, which will then have become a powerful and manageable force... Yes, my friends, I believe that water will one day be employed as a fuel, that hydrogen and oxygen, which constitute it, used singly or together, will furnish an inexhaustible source of heat and light...water will be the coal of the future."

It may be remembered that Edison did not invent the lightbulb until 1879. Yul Brown's discovery was to mix hydrogen and oxygen together in the exact proportions that they are found in water, H2O. Then, in these proportions—when the two gases are recombined with a spark—they do not explode but rather implode to create water, which occupies a far smaller volume. If the reaction takes place in a closed vessel, it creates a vacuum. When Brown passed these gases through a nozzle and applied a flame, it produced a colorless flame of about 130 degrees Celsius. However, when applied to tungsten and certain metals—and even detoxifying nuclear waste—it vaporized these substances. This reaction came about not through heating but by stimulating a chemical reaction, which joined into the combining of the hydrogen and oxygen molecules.

A modern-day chemical analyst would possibly conclude falsely that the elements that he saw had combined at 6,000 degrees Celsius, instead of in a simple chemical reaction. Also Brown's Gas is said to be able to produce 10 times more gold with the same amount of ore.

The authors of *Atlantis Blueprint* (pp. 119–131) tell us that the ancients used this alchemy in conjunction with the battery cell discovered by archaeologists in Baghdad, with which they were able to electroplate their amazing small figurines. At this moment, the Chinese Navy uses Brown's Gas generators to power their submarines, while many corporations are investing in this type of power to generate heat, and propel cars and other vehicles.

CHAPTER 5.3

Spinning Cycles—the Cosmic Blender

Charles William Johnson, in *The Aztec Calendar, Math and Design*, tells us that The Stone of the Sun, the great round stone calendar in the Museo National de Antropologia in Mexico City serves to depict numerous ancient cycles working and moving within one stone image. On the other side of the world, the Egyptian Circular Zodiac of Dendera is also a stone image that depicts many cycles moving in opposite directions, an impression that is manifested by the supporting figures facing in clockwise and counterclockwise directions.

Ancient scientists never denied a sun-centered solar system. They just tried to figure out why everything, including life, happens on Earth—as seen from the perspective of Earth. Many of the ancient symbols that look like sun symbols are actually representations of our spiraling galaxy. Ancient studies are not just about sun, moon, and planets but about a much greater field, namely the movement of our galaxy in the universe. The Earth is our platform of cosmic observation. In relation to the universe, our viewpoint will always be geocentric. For our viewpoint on Earth, the five great cycles rotate as follows in relation to the zodiac, the path of the sun:

The Day (Diurnal rotation .... clockwise
The Year (Annular cycle .... counter-clockwise
Precession of the Vernal Equinoxes .... clockwise
The Milky Way Rotational Cycle .... counter-clockwise
Orbit of Our Milky Way Galaxy around the Universe .... clockwise?

The cosmologers looked at the universe of God, humans, and nature. They concluded that what they saw was: A balanced order of repetitive hierarchical cycles forming a clockwork of cumulative, harmonious, and just effect.

Balanced cycles weave clockwise and counterclockwise through alternating positive and negative energy. Cycles of moist-hot-dry-cold produce a just harmony and balance throughout the entire cosmos. The cosmologers saw truth and justice in the stars where both *change* and *permanence* were counterbalanced and allowed to coexist in different segments of time.

Planetary Relationships in Geometry

Planets really only have power to leverage their energy and gravity when they are in a strong geometric relationship with the sun and the moon. Therefore, geometry and angles are of primary importance to cosmology. The astronomer Kepler added several new geometric aspects to the classic Ptolemaic astrology. It is also reasonable to suppose that there is a geometrical relationship of every number 1–12 within the context of the circle of 360 degrees:

- 1=360 degrees.
- 2=180°
- 3=120°—the Golden Triangles, 4 natures x 3 similar signs = zodiac
- 4=90°
- 5=72°
- 6=60°
- 7=51.42857143 degrees, or 51°25.7”
- 8=45°
- 9=40°
- 10=36
- 11=32.7272727273 degrees, or 32°43.6”
- 12=30 degrees

One may notice that the numbers 7 and 11 have always been held to be special and somewhat mysterious in numerology, because these do not produce whole numbers when 7 or 11 are divided into 360 degrees. Yet when two cubed dice, each of which have the numbers 1–6 on their faces (two dice are necessary to equal the number 12), are tossed in craps—the numbers 7 and 11 are the most probable and likely results statistically. Two dice of six faces each may represent the solar and lunar division of the zodiac.

The Cosmic Labyrinth

The ancient mystery schools copied the clockwise and counterclockwise rotations of the cosmic cycles in their initiation rituals. These were extremely successful because they copied the reality and truth in astronomy.

The journey into the Cretan labyrinth prepares one for the experience of mystic illumination on a journey through the cosmos. The classic labyrinth has five paths, like the five cosmic cycles, enclosed by seven walls.

The five paths represent the cosmic cycles: daily, annual, cycle of precession, cycle of the Milky Way, and universal revolution. As an aside, anyone who has ever visited the Greek isle of Mykonos is aware that the convoluted layout of ancient villages into small winding and circuitous lanes served to confuse and separate the forces of attacking pirates and give an advantage to small but well-positioned local forces. The labyrinth and maze are connected with Crete and Troy (where the treasure of the Palladium of Athena, the goddess of wisdom, was hidden). The dreaded beast named Minotaur was curiously called "Asterion," one who studied the stars. He was produced by Pasiphae, who had Dadaelus build a false cow so that she could be joined to the bull of Poseidon. In local tradition, Pasiphae is said to represent the moon, whose "exaltation house" is the zodiac sign of the bull Taurus. Seven male youths and seven maidens were sacrificed every year to the Minotaur. Again, all this reveals a cosmological context veiled in an extraordinary and strange folklore surrounded by the productive powers of the moon.

CHAPTER 5.4.

The Cosmic Temples of Angkor Wat and Jerusalem

Detailed examinations of holy sites by aerial and infrared surveys show them to be much larger than originally recognized on the ground. Many turn out to be a giant cosmic mandala; that is, a detailed and accurate model of the universe and its cycles. These are not only aligned to the solstices and equinoxes, as well as star groups and asterisms, but these temples exhibit cosmic numbers and the years in astronomical cycles through the multidimensional measurements of their circuit walls, heights, angles, and the shapes of their buildings. These holy temples are truly cosmic mandalas. The temples are an example of a heavenly city brought down to be viewed on Earth. The Pyramids at Giza as well as those outside Mexico City constitute a cosmic mandala and temple. The same may be said of Tenochtitlan (ancient Mexico City) and the *ceque* system surrounding the ancient city of Cuzco, focused upon the Coricancha, the Inca temple of the Sun.

Anthony Aveni, in *Skywatchers* (p. 222), writes that once an altar place or a holy site is chosen, it serves as a symbolic place of the reenactment of "creation." Aveni quotes Alfred Jeremias as saying, "On the one hand the building of the altar was conceived as a creation of the world. The water with which the clay was mixed was the same as the primeval waters, the clay forming the altar's foundation, the Earth...the altar fire is the year...the altar thus becomes a microcosm existing in a mystical space and time..."

Aveni (p. 235) calls Tenochtitlan (Mexico City), "One of the most convincing examples of an astronomically orientated city plan." Regarding the pyramids and the ancient city (Teotihuacán) outside of Mexico City, Aveni writes (pp. 223–44), "A planned community deliberately presented as a sort of paradise on Earth with a sacred geography...an ordered harmony and precision planning which surely finds its roots in the cosmos...once ordered every part of the environment seems forced to conform to the plan...One of the anomalies of the situation of the pyramids is that they are aligned 15°21' north of west, probably toward the Pleiades asterism, which arrived on May 18th in concert with the noonday Sun casting no shadows...an ideal sun-star timing device incorporated into the clockwork fabric of the city itself...The Sun sets along the same alignment on April 29 and August 12...a period of 260 days (like the famous 260 day calendar)...the east-west axis also marks sunsets 40 days after the vernal equinox and 20 days before the first zenith passage...the location of the Pyramid of the Sun was determined so that sunset observations made from its summit marked sunrises on the quarter days of the year...a thousand kilometers away the Maya city of Copan also expresses the 260 day calendar cycle found at the pyramids...this is why Teotihuacán is called the place where time began."

Bauval, in his *The Egypt Code* (pp. 55–61), tells of Jean-Philippe Lauer's *Le complexe calendaire de Djeser a Saqqara,* the calendrical complex of Djoser at Saqqara. Bauval writes that few researchers had paid attention to the 1,461 slender panels on the west side boundary wall and the 1,459 on the east side, "the uncanny similarity of these values to the Sothic cycle of 1,460 years was obvious." It has been said that this number has been associated with the return of the Egyptian phoenix bird in increments of 1,460 years cyclically for literally hundreds of thousands of years. Four x 365.25 = 1,461. It seems that the Sothic cycle synchronizes the length of the current year with the cycle of the star Sirius. The legendary Imhotep (2655–2600 BC) was chancellor to the king of Egypt, chief builder, chief carpenter, chief sculptor, chief maker of vases, demigod, astronomer, physician, and architect who designed the exceptional complex and step pyramid at Saqqara. Two of his titles were "chief of the observers" and "chief of the astronomers" who were represented wearing a mantel adorned with stars—the famous star mantel of the cosmologers. Imhotep designed the complex by the step pyramid to celebrate the anniversary festival of the king, who was obliged to race against a bull to confirm and display his good health and virility. Certain elements of this custom seem related to the Mediterranean bull culture of the gods Ocean and Poseidon and the traditions of the island of Crete.

Angkor Wat

In 1996 Eleanor Mannikka published *Angkor Wat: Time, Space, and Kingship*. This wonderful book explains the iconography and geometry of an Indochina holy site where images and architecture are exotic and utterly unique. Mannikka's achievement is to reveal that Angkor Wat is one of the amazing cosmic temples on our planet, a sacred shrine expressing astronomical constants to perfection. Just like other great cosmic temples from Peru to Chichen Itza and Chaco Canyon, the temple of Angkor Wat demonstrates several *hierophanies* or "plays of light" upon its walls during specific dates of the year.

In the prehistoric legends of Khmer, an Indian prince arrives by boat (bespeaking the nautical tradition of astronomy). Here he falls in love with Soma, daughter of the king of the *nagas*—serpents. Khmer culture was a matrilineal society where women had some control over the land, water, and power structures. Mannikka writes that this union mythologizes the marriage of indigenous beliefs and territorial sovereignty with Indian religions. Angkor Wat remains a historical enigma that is not referred to on any existing stone steles or other documentation. Also, its history ceased less than 100 years after it was completed, and the site became engulfed by jungle. In 1860 Henri Mouhot rediscovered Angkor Wat, which in 1901 was studied by the Ecole francaise d'Extreme-Orient.

Mannikka is credited with discovering the standard of measure used for the entire site based upon a cubit of .43545 meter. Once the meters were converted to the original cubits, "It was then that the temple began to demonstrate the ways in which the history of the king, cosmology, astronomy, the calendar, and the realm of the gods were all interrelated. All the information gleaned from inscriptions about the culture and architecture of Angkor was suddenly manifest in the temple itself" (p. 17).

The western entrance bridge over the shallow, wide moat yielded the key cosmological numbers of the sexagesimal astronomical system, namely:

54, 108, 216

Of course the number 216 is the product of 6 x 6 x 6, known as the matrix of the Vedic astronomical system. Mannikka says (p. 34) that 108 is the most auspicious number in all of Asia. It occurs in Buddhist and Hindu texts in many guises and forms. Vishnu has 108 names. Buddhist and Hindu prayer beads number 108. Mantras are often chanted with these beads 108 times and multiples thereof. The number is important in astrology and astronomy. For example, the maximum north-south arc of the sun can be as much as 49 degrees. The Croll-Milankovitch Earth-axis tilt shows a range between 22.1 and 24.5 degrees over a period of 40,000 years. So, 24.5 + 24.5 does indeed equal the above mentioned 49-degree arc of the sun from south to north of the equator. On the other hand, the moon's arc is as much as 59 degrees north-south. Then the average of the arc of the sun and moon together is 59 + 49 = 108. This seems an astonishing instance of ancient scientific knowledge and facts, which we are only recently beginning to rediscover.

Mannikka shows that the western entrance bridge is 54 units long, when one unit = 10 cubits. The bridge is divided into two sections of 54 columns and 54 balustrade supports covering a distance of 216 cubits to a central island staircase at the middle of the bridge. The other half of the bridge is again 216 cubits long and composed of 54 columns and 54 balustrade supports. The total of 216 + 216 is 432, which is a fractal of 432,000 years, the length of the Kali Yuga Age.

Fig. 2.7. Angkor Thom, south bridge across moat, view to southwest.
Over the five bridges into the site of Angkor Thom (ca. 1200), 54 *devas* and 54 *asuras* pull on a *nāga* railing. If the road in this view is followed southward and out, it passes just a few feet in front of the bridge into Angkor Wat.

The bridge built of cosmic symbols, numbers, and measurement at Angkor Wat. Courtesy of Eleanor Mannikka & the University of Hawaii

At the very beginning of her work (p. 3), Eleanor Mannikka proclaims, "At Angkor Wat the measurements of both parts and whole contain calendrically and cosmologically significant totals. The circumference of the fourth enclosure measures 1 lunar year expressed as 354.36 day-units." This same circumference has also been divided by the architect into a ritual path of 28 stations of the Moon. Angkor Wat is all about cosmic relationships and associations. The architecture expresses planetary orbits, cosmic cycles and sub-cycles through the collaboration of builders and astronomers (p.4). As an aside, the author mentions that Angkor Wat became a paradise supplying fish, chicken, rice, oranges, mangoes, coconuts, and other tropical fruit to the well satisfied Khmers of Angkor. In accord with the cosmological philosophy, the rulers accepted that their linage descended from the gods and demi-gods.

The author then quotes the 11th-century architect, Orissan:

> The Creator (Visvakarman) lays out the plan of the universe according to measure and number...the Creator is the architect, priest, and sculptor...this small universe (the temple) has to be situated with respect to the vaster universe of which it forms a part. It has to fall in line with the position of the earth in relation to the course of the sun, and also the movements of the planets...it incorporates in a single synthesis the unequal courses of the sun, the moon, and the planets, it also symbolizes all recurrent time sequences: the day, the month, the year.

Thus the axis that joined the temple to the city also joined it to the planets and the sky above. The gods that were gathered in the chambers of the temple not only represented regions of Cambodia; they also represented deities connected to the stars and planets, sun and moon, and who controlled the various seasons of the Earth. The temples of Angkor Wat were therefore spiritual, political, cosmological, astronomical, and geophysical centers. They embodied and encapsulated the world spheres through which Khmer culture and power structures moved, lived, and breathed. In their scope and conception alone, they were among the most spectacular of human achievements.

Personification of the Heavens and the Cosmic Cycles

Every culture populates the heavens with figures from their traditions in order to correctly chart the asterisms and to create a friendly and familiar picture of the cosmos. The great epochs of the cycle of the Milky Way were characterized by specific heroes and gods from the Atlantic-Greek culture.

Eleanor Mannikka presents the East Asian, or rather Khmer-India-China perspective of these personifications and incarnations by which the houses of the zodiac were made more real by using actual persons to build the images, which were then transformed into icons of culture and science.

The Khmer cosmology recognizes the following personifications and definitions:

- Avatar—An incarnation of a god, a personification of the theme of a division of a particular cosmic cycle.
- Asuras—The demons or antigods, servants of King Bali. These are muscular, corpulent, and tastefully bearded.
- Devas—Benevolent gods, thin and without beards. Indra is king of the Devas.
- Adityas—The 12 gods of the solar months.
- Apsaras—The celestial maidens.
- Vrah Guru—The main priest who interprets all these manifestations. (The modern Guru makes cosmological statements without revealing the source, which is astronomy and cosmology.)
- Mandala—A cosmic diagram or a model of the universe.
- Cosmic Temple—Angkor Wat is a mandala, a cosmic diagram of the universe and its many cosmic cycles.
- The sun is called "Surya," and the moon is called "Candra."

The Cosmic Temple of Angkor Wat as a Cosmic Mandala

Angkor Wat is built according to astronomical numbers such as the 27/28 days of the moon and the 108 and 216 fractals of precession and the cosmic cycles. Mannikka says (p. 21), "The architects were still able to provide all of the chambers, axis, and galleries of Angkor Wat with measurements that were cosmologically or calendrically significant." There are 12 staircases leading up to the central sanctuary, three staircases to each of the cardinal directions, whereby the seasons and the 12 months of the 12 *adityas* or gods of the solar months of the year are represented. Even the sanctuary door came to 13.41 cubits high, representing Angkor's 13.43 degrees north latitude from the equator.

Mannikka presents the temple as mandala, which was drawn on the ground prior to construction of the temples (pp. 55–58):

> Brahma resides at the axis of the earth, the North celestial pole right above the sacred Mount Meru at the center of the square mandala. This center is surrounded by the *adityas,* the 12 solar month gods. Following and surrounding this area are 32 *devas* sometimes called *naksatra* after the 28 *naksatra* (the lunar constellations, houses or mansions) plus four planetary gods: Yama, Soma-Kubera, Indra, and Varuna. Brahma is surrounded by 12 adityas plus 32 devas-naksatras which total 44 + Brahma himself = 45 total

Common mandalas are formed by squares of 7 x 7 = 49 squares; 8 x 8 = 64 squares, and 9 x 9 = 81 squares. The 49-square grid appears to be a Khmer invention.

Mannikka explains (p. 54) that Angkor Wat and its mandala also have a dimension of height as a model of the sacred Mount Meru. The surrounding galleries and towers, as well as the moat, can be understood as symbols for the seven concentric mountain ranges and seven oceans that circle the base of Mount Meru. The lower reaches of Meru include the mansions of the sun and moon, the summits of the concentric mountains, and four levels of minor deities on the lower half of Meru. The fourth and highest level houses the directional gods themselves, each on their appropriate side of the mountain. Their expanded realm constitutes the first heaven of the gods, and above that there are 24 heavens of gods in which form is still manifest. The heaven of Brahma himself is the seventh in this ascending list of 24. The central tower of Angkor Wat has seven levels. Above the 24th heaven are four "formless" heavens. The realms of the gods thus total 28, which is equal to the Devas or lunar mansions.

Mannikka offers a summary of her conceptions (p. 259):

> When the cosmos expanded outward from Visnu, when the mandala of the gods, time and space were set in motion, a newly created universe emerged from a center that could then be defined in terms of the cosmos around it. When Angkor Wat was completed, this mandala of time and divinity, and its center or creator, was built into

the periphery and heart of the temple, making it an image of the universe and its source.

Khamer and Vedic Cycles of Time

On pages 50–51, Mannikka discusses the great ages and cycles of time:

Yuga Age-Celestial years-Terrestrial years

- *Krta* 4800 *(x 360 =)* 1,728,000
- *Treta* 3600 *(x 360 =)* 1,296,000
- *Dvapara* 2400 *(x 360 =)* 864,000
- *Kali* 1200 *(x 360 =)* 432,000
- Time does not end with these Ages. 4 yugas = 1 *mahayuga,* 4,320,000 yrs.
- 14 mahayugas = 1 *Kalpa,* 4,320,000,000.
- 720 kalpas = 360 days and 360 nights of Brahma = 1 year of Brahma.
- 100 years of Brahma = dissolution of the universe at all levels, and Brahma merges again with the sleeping Visnu. It seems as if modern science has appropriated this cosmology into their Big Bang theory which is actually a cycle of explosion, implosion, and a specified dormant stage. In recent time, in 1933 AD professor G. Lemaitre invoked the mythical 'return of the phoenix' oscillatory cosmology once again promoting the Vedic theory of expansion and contraction of the universe.

The Temple of Solomon at Jerusalem

Another well-known temple said to have been built according to cosmic measures is the Temple of Solomon described in *The Book of Chronicles.* An excellent abstract of information has been composed by Jerome Bernard Frisbee in his *King Solomon's Temple* (2009), available at phoenixmasonry.org:

The design was composed by King David who left it to be executed by his son, Solomon with the wealth accumulated by the wars of David.

The Temple was a rectangular building 100 cubits long by 50 cubits wide.

The House of Jehovah had two large rooms: The Oracle was 20 cubits square and contained the sacred Ark of the Covenant. The Temple was 20 cubits by 40 cubits and contained a golden altar with 10 golden candlesticks and various other religious paraphernalia.

The ground-plan showed that these two large central rooms were surrounded by twelve small cubicles on each long side, plus 5 cubicles at the back making a total of 30 cubicles on the first floor, 30 on the second floor, and 30 on the third floor—all totaled 90 cubicles, each of which was 4 cubits long.

The front porch was open to the rising sun with two great pillars of brass.

The Temple stood in a square of 2.5 acres, surrounded by another square of 25 acres [The Venus numbers and the 12 signs or tribes of the zodiac = 25 = 5 + 8 + 12]. The entire complex modeled upon a magic square producing the number 15 which was the key to the lost word for God, YAH.

8 1 6

3 5 7

4 9 2

The above numbers are founded in the sacred Venus number 'five' related to her describing a pentagram in the heavens. The Hebrew Torah (teaching & law) represents the legal, ethical, and religious texts of the five books of Moses, called the Pentateuch (Gr. Penta =five & teuchos =tool, vessel, book). The Torah contains 613 commandments; of which 365 are negative, while 248 are positive commands. The number 365 is suggestive of the days of the year; while 248 years equals 13.333 revolutions of the period of the Lunar Nodes (248 ÷ 18.6 =13.333). The Cabbalistic Zohar says that the Torah existed prior to the world, and was used as a blueprint for creation. It is coincidental that the 800 year Jupiter/Saturn cycle divided by 60 also equals 13.333.

Frisbee claims that the measurements of the temple exhibit the true size of the Earth, the correct division of time, and a perfect system of weight and measures.

We notice that the 12 + 12 side cubicles + 6 end cubicles = 30 cubicles x 3 stories = 90 total cubicles as stated. Each cubicle was said to be four cubits long. Therefore 4 x 90 = 360, the degrees in a circle and the equator of the astronomical circle. Then 24 side cubicles x 3 stories = 72. The number 72 divided into 360 = 5 (the Venus number), which is the middle and controlling number of the magic square above. Ptolemy Philadelphus II (c. 282 BC) requested a Greek translation of the Hebrew Torah (the Pentateuch, the first 5 books). 72 scholars, or six translators from each of the 12 tribes arrived in Alexandria (6 x 12 =72). They translated the five books in 72 days (5 x 72 =360).

Seventy-two is an astronomical number reflecting the number of years that it takes for the precession of the vernal equinoxes to advance one degree along the equator of 360 degrees. 72 x 360 = 25,920 years total for the cycle of precession to complete an entire circuit of the zodiac according to ancient Iran-Vedic-Hindu cosmology.

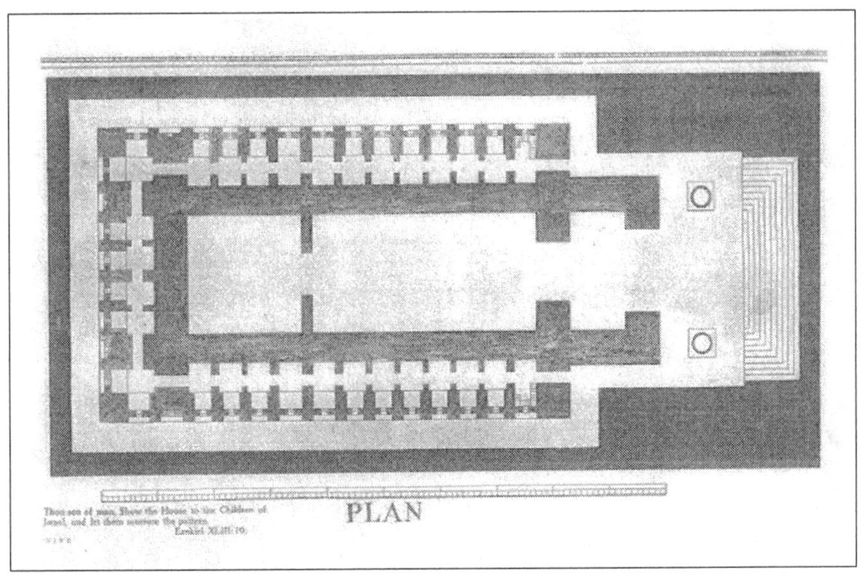

King Solomon's Temple by Jerome Bernard Frisbee.
By kind permission of phoenixmasonry.org

The Sacred Cubit

J.B. Frisbee states that the Ark of the Covenant contained the famous rod brought out of Egypt by Aaron. This rod was a specific measure of length—not the cubit of a man but "a Cubit and a handbreadth" (Ezekiel XL:5).

Both the Sacred Cubit and the metric system are a fractal of the size of the globe. Frisbee says that both systems are very old. The meter was developed by the prehistoric inhabitants of Central America, from where the Egyptians also derived much of their culture. The Old English system of weights and measures is derived from the Egyptian Sacred Cubit.

Old English measures derived from the Sacred Cubit:

- 2.5 Cubits = 1 Ell
- 4 Ells = 10 Cubits = 1 Pole
- 10 Ells = 1 Chain
- 4 Chains = 10 Poles = 1 Acre side
- 10 Chains = 1 Furlong
- 4 Furlongs = 10 Acre sides = 1 Metron
- 10 Metrons = 1 League
- 1,000 Leagues = Polar Radius

This Sacred Cubit of 25 inches in length was obtained by carefully measuring the distance from the center of the Earth to the North Pole and then dividing into 10 millionth part of a quadrant (25 inches x 10,000,000 = 250,000,000 inches divided by 12 inches = 20,833,333.33 divided by 5,280 feet in a mile = 3,945.707 miles in the polar radius of the earth). The modern figure for polar radius is 3,949.921 miles.

The Contents of the Ark

Frisbee now describes the size and contents of the Ark of the Covenant: 2.5 cubits in length, 1.5 cubits in breadth, and 1.5 cubits in height [1.5 ÷ 2.5 = 0.6—a symbolic approximation of phi (.618). Also, 2.5 x 0.6 = 1.5]. The Ark was the seat of Jehovah, for here the supreme architect of the universe kept the symbols of his power. From it emanated the *Shekinah*, the divine light. Here were preserved the sacred standards by which the universe was measured and the depths of divine mystery fathomed (Exodus XXXVII:1–9).

Beyond the second veil of the tabernacle was the holy of holies containing the Ark of the Covenant, wherein was a golden pot holding the measured Omer of manna—the spiritual food—and Aaron's rod that budded and the tables of the Covenant (Hebrews IX:4, Exodus XVI:33, 13. Numbers XVII:10, Deuteronomy X:5).

The Omer was the standard of measure and of weight. Aaron's rod was the Sacred Cubit of 25 inches and the standard of length. The Decalogue—the Ten Commandments engraved on the two tables of stone—was the standard of human conduct. The Ark itself was a perfect and just standard of length, weight, and measure, accurately proportioned to the size and weight of the Earth.

All was in terms of the number 25. The Sacred Cubit was 25 inches. The capacity of the Ark was 2,500 pints, equal to 2,500 pounds of water.

The interior of the Ark was 1.4 cubits wide, 1.4 cubits high, and 2 16/49^{ths} cubits long (2.326 cubits). This makes 4.56 cubic cubits, or 2,500 pints of 28.5 cubic inches each, the exact capacity of the stone coffer in the King's Chamber of the Great Pyramid of Egypt.

Hebrews VIII: 8–9: "Behold, the days come, when I will make a new covenant with the house of Israel and the house of Judah; not according to the covenant that I made with their fathers in the day that I took them by the hand to lead them forth out of the land of Egypt." And, from Hebrews X:16: "This is the covenant that I will make with them after those days; I will put my laws in their heart, and upon their minds also will I write them."

It may be remembered that the staff of Joseph of Arimathea bloomed just as the rod of Aaron. This may suggest that English weights and measures were connected to the Middle East—if "blooming" means acceptance. It may also be asked why the Hebrews took a sacred ark out of Egypt during their Exodus. Egyptian arks are certainly like boats. Egyptian gods, sun, moon, and planets travel the heavens by ship, which is a certain sign of a nautical culture.

An Egyptian Ark from the Temple of Luxor. Author photo

Finally there is the connection of the Ark's volume with the coffin in the King's Chamber in the Great Pyramid. That coffin is a rectangle of 2 x 1, which is the same as the floor plan of the Temple of Solomon, 2 x 1, or two 1 x 1 squares joined together. By bisecting either of these squares and placing the compass where the bisector cuts one side, and then placing the other leg of the compass upon the opposite side joining-line of the two squares, that leg can be swung down in an arc that cuts the other square exactly into the golden mean ratio of phi or .618 and .382. This ratio lies at the root of all creation within the universe.

The Numbers 8 and 12

We have noticed before that there is a conflict between 12 and 8 as a foundation of astronomical expression in dividing the circle. This difference is resolved through the number 666, because 8 divided by 12 =.666. Now, 12 divided by 8 =1.5, which is both the height and width of the Ark. Then 6 x 6 x 6 =216 x 12 houses of the zodiac = 2,592, a fractal of 25,920 years = precession of the vernal equinoxes. One of the great Vedic time cycles, 1,728,000 years ÷ 25,920 = 66.66.

Conclusion

There remains much fertile ground for research and discovery in the fields of cosmology, cosmic temples, and mandala. Thanks to the work of Eleanor Mannikka, the temple of Angkor Wat presents a complete cosmology and astronomy of ancient thought and science. Because of Anthony Aveni, Linda Schele, Karl Taube, Mary Miller, and Hunbatz Men, we have a clearer picture of Maya cosmology. Carlos Milla Villena is at the forefront of penetrating the secrets of Andean cosmic sites. But many intriguing questions still remain. Every mandala needs to be diagnosed and explained in detail. Cosmological knowledge must be gathered from the corners of the globe until the ancient universe is once again revealed in its magnificent totality.

Part 6

Concord of Cosmic Myth

Astronomical numbers are closely the same around the globe, because the Earth spins in one day, the moon takes 29.53 days to go from new moon back to new moon again, and the year is about 365.24 days long. While the numbers do not change from culture to culture, the astronomical constellations and celestial images do change dramatically because of the variety of peoples, environments, history, and traditions. Also, all cultures recognize the system of the cosmic cycles of moist-hot-dry-cold.

In addition to the unvarying systems of numbers and the system of moist-hot-dry-cold, there is another steadfast system common to all parts of the world. This system distinguishes the 12 signs of the zodiac as if it were a cosmic person. The head of the person is the current house of the zodiac that marks the correct position of the cycle of the cycle of the Milky Way. Therefore, Aries would be the "head," while Taurus would be the "neck," and Gemini would be the "shoulders" of the cosmic human body. With these three systems as tools it will be possible to the search for the concord of cosmic myth among the different images and traditions of the many divergent cultures of the world.

CHAPTER 6.1

Adam and Atlas

The date used for Adam and the creation of man continues to be a stumbling block for science, religion, and history. It is important to discover and understand the true facts about this tradition, which stands at the root of so many systems of belief. The current accepted rabbinical date for Adam and the creation of man is 3760 BC. Considering that there are Egyptian records of eclipses dated for 4867 BC, Native American astronomical sites called "Medicine Wheels" dated at 3200 BC, and that Brú Na Bóinne in Ireland is dated as 3300–3100 BC, it seems absurd to suggest that the first human lived only about four millenniums BC.

It is therefore imperative to find out when, how, and why the date for Adam was determined. The story of the original man comes from Hebrew tradition, from a people whose history is intimately connected with early scientific nations. Hebrew culture is connected to astronomy and cosmology through their affiliations with Phoenicians, Chaldeans, Babylonians, and Egyptians—nations who were all celebrated astronomers:

- Adam—himself is called a noted astronomer.
- Abraham from Ur of the Chaldeans—noted astronomers.
- Moses, half Jewish and half Egyptian—noted astronomers.
- Solomon and Hiram (the King of the Phoenicians)—Hiram gave his daughter to King Solomon. Hiram was the contractor who supplied cedars, stones, masons, carpenters, architects,

> and engineers in the building of the Temple of Solomon. Hiram also established Solomon in shipping and trade upon the Red Sea. The Phoenicians were the earliest cosmologers, astronomers, and, of course, noted cartographers.

The reason that the Jewish people are considered to be so intelligent and successful is that they are widely traveled in the world and have come into contact with most of the leading cultures. The Hebrew is also traditional in nature and has learned to combine the contemporary with the wisdom of the past, thereby developing a renaissance of ideas that utilizes the best from all worlds.

With this in mind, the myth of Adam may be connected with ancient cosmological knowledge of the highest importance. But first it is important to review some of the background material.

The First Cosmologers

All the ancient astronomers were versed in the natural creation and destruction cycles of the universe—caused by flood, fire, wind, and ice. And these traditions were passed along to subsequent astronomers. Among these were Adam, Thoth, Agathodaemon, Atlas, Promethius, Belus, Berosos, the cultural gods of the Mexica-Maya-Andean tradition, and Iitoi among the natives of Arizona and New Mexico. It is said that Earthmaker told Iitoi, the elder brother, that a flood would kill all the people (Saward, p. 68). These astronomers were recognized as the patriarchs and rulers of their nations as well as great scientists.

Josephus *(Jewish Antiquities,* 1.69–72) tells us that Adam and his children "discovered the science of the heavenly bodies and their orderly array…Adam having predicted a destruction of the universe, at one time by violent fire, and at another by a mighty deluge of water…" Seneca supports these statements by saying, "Flaming fires from the heavens once burnt up the Eastern parts, they say, in the time of Phaethon, and others gushed and spouted from the earth in the West." The Mormons declare that astronomical records were handed down from the patriarchs before the flood onto Abraham, Melchizedek, and Job (sacred-texts.com/mor/tboal/chap07, 1/24/11).

In Egyptian tradition, the cosmologer Thoth warned of the great flood and preserved the accumulated knowledge of mathematics and science, which he carved in stone as the inheritance for a later age. After the great world flood, the descendent of Thoth, named Agathodaemon, was able to decipher knowledge from the stones and rekindle the sciences. Some think, and it seems reasonable, that Thoth hid the measures of the Earth and possibly the universe in the proportions of the Great Pyramid. It was from these structures that Agathodaemon was able to recreate most of the cosmological science for the Egyptians.

The great galactic seasons caused by the rotation of the Milky Way might almost overwhelm the Earth with their prolonged periods of moist-hot-dry-cold. These extremes are cured by episodes of reaction, such as a world flood after the dry galactic season of autumn. Seneca says that the great world flood and fire is caused by all the planets joining together in one of the signs of the zodiac like Cancer and Capricorn. But Ptolemy gives a better explanation by saying that Jupiter has his depression in Capricorn, which we interpret as Jupiter's orbit being at maximum extreme ellipse and causing the world flood. Ptolemy makes the same assertion for the depression of Mars in Cancer, which we again interpret as the maximum extreme eclipse causing the world fire (ekpyrosis) by drying out the planet after the prolonged moisture of the galactic season of spring. The world ice episode is created by the depression of the sun and exaltation of Saturn in Libra, which cools the Earth after the long period of heat from galactic spring to summer.

Although all this sounds very "astrologic," modern astronomers have certainly considered significant changes in planetary mechanics, especially their orbit:

> There is a law generalized by Laplace (1749) and Legrange (1736) that says that the total eccentricity of the planets of the solar system had to stay constant, provided that all planets revolve around the sun in the

same direction. If the orbit of one planet increases its eccentricity, then the others must decrease in eccentricity sufficiently to strike a balance.

Adam in the Constellation of Gemini

It is extremely interesting that Adam, the cosmologer, predicts the destruction of the Earth by fire and water. Ancient images portray the zodiac sign Gemini as a man and a woman. Franz Boll in *Sphaera*, reports that the Circular Zodiac of Dendera has a young man and woman as the constellation of Gemini. He especially remarks (p. 235) that the icon of a young man and a young woman as Gemini must be from an ancient tradition, because he has found images in Germany, the Netherlands, France, England, and Italy. The works he mentions are the *Book of Hours* of Anna of Brittany, the *Missale Bologna*, and the *Psalter of Isabella of France*. Boll continues to say that (p. 342) the image of a young man and woman in place of Gemini is also found in India. Kelley and Milone report (p. 498) that the depiction of Gemini as "a male and female pair suggests the Egyptian version of the zodiac." Everything seems to accord since Genesis is the production of the half-Egyptian Moses.

Adam and Eve by Albrecht Durer. This is the constellation of Gemini in ancient times according to the cosmologers. A man and a woman appear as Gemini on the circular zodiac of Dendera

We notice that the serpent in the branches of the tree of life above Adam and Eve is reminiscent of the snake that guards the apples of the Hesperides, the daughters of Atlas. The Hereford map locates the island of Adam and Eve in the Far East beyond the Ganges Delta. If the 12 houses of the zodiac are placed upon the globe with the region of Aries attached to Jerusalem, then this island of Adam and Eve would be located by Gemini (the man and woman under the tree). This is as curious a coincidence as that of the land of India (the culture of the sacred cow) being under the sign of Taurus, the bull. Geography and the celestial sphere seem to coincide in many instances.

Adam and Atlas are named among the great cosmologers of ancient times. The solid marble image of Atlas holding the celestial globe on his shoulders was produced by the ancient Etruscans around 525 BC. This amazing work now stands in the museum at Naples. Atlas' daughters, the Pleiades, are in the region of the sky near to Taurus and Gemini. But, the homeland of Atlas is Fez and Morocco, which falls under the sign of Aquarius, which is nevertheless a member of the cold triangle of Gemini, Libra, and Aquarius. It appears that the ancient people recognized a relationship between the geography of the globe and the houses of the zodiac. And there is certainly a strong connection between Adam and Atlas, and Gemini and Aquarius.

Looking at Astronomical Numbers

Charles Francois Dupuis wrote *The Explanation of Myth through Astronomy* (1781). As a progressive child of the French Revolution, Dupuis was accused of attempting to undermine the foundations of the Catholic religion. One of his statements was that, "The philosophy of our days has made too much progress in order to be obliged to enter into a dissertation on the communications of the Deity with man, excepting those, which are made by the light of reason and by the contemplation of Nature." After this, Dupuis goes so far as to call Christianity "a solar fable"—meaning that it corresponds to all other ancient religions that worship the sun and the moon. Dupuis is noteworthy because he is extremely well read and exemplifies the modern attitude that everything must be in terms of science and reason.

Dupuis writes that the ancient Mithra worship—which was established in Persia, Armenia, and Capadocia—held that the world was the battleground between the forces of light and darkness, good and evil. The Maga (Magi) were the disciples of Zadust (Zoroaster), who believed that the zodiac was divided into 12 segments of time during eras of good and evil, in alternating order. Apparently this system allotted 1,000 years to each sign of the zodiac. Many people like Newton and Kepler took the 12,000-year period as the literal truth, even though there is no astronomical cycle that goes around the zodiac in 12,000 years.

Dupuis proceeds, "Here is the theological idea, which the author of the Genesis took from the cosmogony of the Persians, ornamenting it after his own fashion. Zoroaster, or the author of the Genesis of the Magi, expresses himself as follows:

> The God of Light created a paradise called Eiren or Iran; and that a great serpent guarded this garden. It is unclear whether it was the Persians or the Hebrew who assigned a period of one thousand years to each sign of the zodiac. The period of the formation of the earth till the creation of man took six zodiac signs, equaling six thousand years. Following the creation of man there were to be another six thousand years of life until the fulfillment of one trip around the zodiac which would culminate in the end of the world (Dupuis, p.224).

To repeat, there is no known cycle of 12,000 years that revolves around the zodiac. This false mathematic is obviously to be recognized as a code for a secret number not to be divulged to the uninitiated. This kind of secret Kabbalah conforms to numerous Near Eastern esoteric confraternities. It is the same substitution code as in the Books of Genesis where the Earth is said to have been formed in six days. In the writings of the disciple Peter, it says (2 Peter 3:8), "One day is with the Lord as a thousand years, and a thousand years as one day"

Peter's rule:

- every day of God = 1,000 human years.
- Six days to create the world and make Adam = 6,000 human years.
- From Adam to Noah to Christ was about 4,000 years.
- So, there are about 2,000 years left before the day of judgment.

Dupuis continues (p. 225), "These expressions of 'thousands' were replaced by 'days' in the Genesis of the Hebrews…the Hebrew Genesis makes use of the same expressions as that of the Tuscans…We shall see therefore throughout the whole of this work, that it is principally the religion of the Magi, from which that of the Christian is derived…We shall not look therefore for anything else in the Genesis of the Hebrews, which we shall not find in that of the Magi."

Dupuis then gives us a most illuminating view of the ancient practice of hiding, veiling, and encoding valuable science and information (p. 226), saying, "Allegory was then the veil with which sacred science enveloped itself, in order to inspire more respect to the Initiates or Neophytes, if we may believe Sanchoniaton on the subject."

He continues by saying that,

> The Hebrew Doctors themselves, as well as the Christian Doctors agree, that the books which we attribute to Moses were written in the allegorical style…Maimonides, the wisest of the Rabbis said, "We must not understand or take in the literal sense what is written in the book on the creation…otherwise our ancient sages would not have so much recommended to hide the real meaning of it, and not to lift the allegorical veil, which covers the truth contained therein…the enigmatical talent was not peculiar to Moses or to the Jewish Doctors, but that they held it in common with all the wise men of antiquity."

Then Dupuis finalizes his statements by saying that Philon the Jew and Origenes the Christian agree, "that everything is wrapped up under the veil of enigma and parable."

Templar contact with the Middle East during the Crusades gave rise to a tradition of secret lore (supposedly transmitted by Solomon) that embodied sacred mathematics and geometry in the marvelous construction of the temple that bears his name. Indeed the appellative Templars stands for the *Brotherhood of the Knights of the Temple of Solomon.*

The Date of the Creation of Adam

James Ussher, the 17th-century Anglican archbishop of Ulster, Northern Ireland, deduced that the first day of Adam began at nightfall preceding

Sunday, October 23, 4004 BC, near the autumnal equinox. Ussher's proposed date of 4004 BC differed little from other Biblically based estimates, such as those of Bede (3952 BC), Scaliger (3949 BC), Johannes Kepler (3992 BC), or Sir Isaac Newton (c. 4000 BC).

The *Catholic Encyclopedia* (online, 2/24/08) reports that there are 200 dates for the creation of Adam from Constantinopolitan at 5509 BC to *Rabbinica* at 3760 BC, which is the time Hebrew calendars use for the creation of Adam before the New Era and modern calendar. Therefore, by adding the modern number of years 2011 AD to 3760 BC = 5771 year of the Hebrew calendar. The dates are originally based upon three chronologies for the number of years from Adam to the flood:

Hebrew................1656 years = Adam..............3760 BC
Samaritan.............1307 years = Adam..............3511 BC
Septuagint...........2242 years = Adam..............4346 BC

In modern times, the systems of Biblical chronology that have been adopted are chiefly those of Ussher and Hales. The former follows the Hebrew and the latter the Septuagint. The system of Archbishop Ussher (died 1656) is called the "short chronology."

	Ussher	Hales
Creation of Adam:	4004 BC	5411 BC
Flood:	2348 BC	3155 BC
Abram leaves Haran:	1921 BC	2078 BC
Exodus:	1491 BC	1648 BC
Destruction of the Temple:	588 BC	586 BC

Again, this whole system is based upon this code:

- 6 days = 6,000 years to create the universe and the Earth.
- (Adam, the first man is created on the sixth day)
- 6 days = 6,000 years from Adam until the end of the world.
- 12 days = 12,000 years = 12 signs of the zodiac.

Alexander and Hebrew Bible Chronology

The world was alive with the expectation of the coming of the messiah, a great king who would restore order and peace to the world. This expectation was especially felt in Palestine, which lies under the zodiac sign of Aries. The cycle of the Milky Way (counterclockwise) was near to entering the sign of Aries, while the precessional cycle coming from the other direction (clockwise) would soon cross over both Jerusalem and the cycle of the Milky Way. The messiah would be born in a place where heaven and Earth had become congruent with time and the current cycles of the cosmos. Cosmological traditions from Africa, Europe, the Near East, India, the Far Orient, and Mexica-Maya-Andean culture all believed that these cycles would bring a complete revolution of the social structure and the complete overthrow of the current ruling class. Indeed, prophets and oracles were beginning to broadcast the news of great changes coming throughout the world beginning at Jerusalem.

Alexander of Macedon was born on July 20, 356 BC, exactly 356 years before the time of the greatly anticipated cosmic event. No one was more absorbed in the swirling prophesies of a messiah than Alexander. Though some called him "the Great," Alexander proved to be a scourge and the destroyer of nations and their cultures. The megalomaniac son of Philip became the "Grim Reaper of the Orient," who cruised from Palestine to Iran and onward to India, destroying manuscripts and libraries while slaughtering priests and philosophers in an effort to annihilate the past in order to clear a road for his own future historical importance and achievements.

The deluded Alexander saw himself as the messiah, and after destroying the culture of the Canaanite Phoenicians, he pressed on to Jerusalem around 332 BC. Here, I would imagine that the rabbi told him that he was about 332 years too early. Not fazed by this, Alexander replied to the rabbi that it was they who were mistaken about the dates—that he knew he was the "Great King," and that they should review and adjust their chronologies around Alexander. The rabbi did this and afterward decided that this kind of interference could happen again in the future. Such a blasphemy could do irreparable harm to the prophetic structure and rituals of the Hebrew religion.

The rabbi, therefore, encoded their chronologies in the universally accepted cosmological-mythological format, using the current zodiac as a single clock face for the hands of many cosmological cycles. The excitement in the world and the personal machinations of Alexander demonstrate the amount and fervor of prophecy and anticipation that was current at this time in the world.

Alexander's arrogance subtracted 356 years from the date for Adam, so that the correct date for Adam should be 356 + 3760 = 4116 BC. The Septuagint date for Adam is 4346 BC. The coincidental about these two dates is that they are close to the date of 4320 BC, when the precessional cycle was in Gemini, the sign of Adam and Eve under the tree of life entangled by a snake.

Anniversary Chronology of the First Adam

In cosmology, the sign of Gemini denotes the creation of the first human being, Adam. Whenever the sun or any of the cosmic cycles enter into the sign of Gemini, the anniversary of the first creation of man was celebrated. This is exactly what birthdays and religious festivals are all about—the remembrance of a past occasion through a coincidence of the current position during the yearly movement of the sun or any of the other astronomical cycles. All religious festivals of Christians, Jews, Mohammedans, and others are based upon this anniversary astronomy.

As the great global flood belongs to the sign of Capricorn and the great fire belongs to Cancer, the creation of man belongs to Gemini. The reenactment of cosmic anniversaries may also be celebrated in the triangle to which a particular sign belongs. And therefore, the cold-natured triangles of Libra and Aquarius (Atlas and Morocco) share in the nature and anniversary of Gemini.

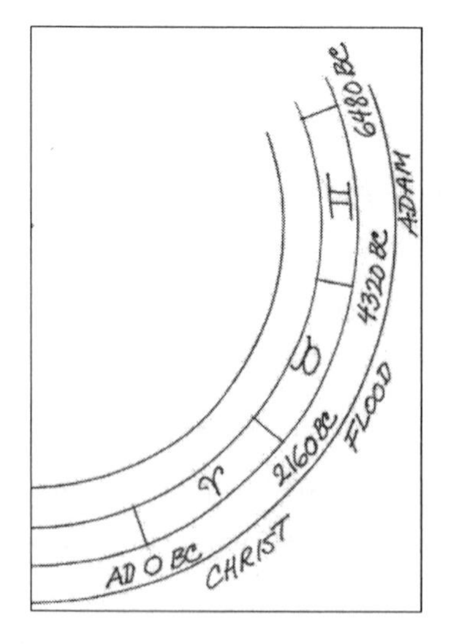

The date recorded in the *Septuagint* for Adam is an anniversary day that brings us directly back to Gemini by backtracking the precession of the vernal equinoxes (2,160 years per 30° a sign). Gemini is two signs backward in precession and therefore exactly 4320 years BC. It is noteworthy that Ptolemy Philadelphus II (285–247 BC) contacted Eleazar, the chief priest in Jerusalem, to arrange for six translators from each of the 12 tribes of Israel to come to Alexandria to translate the Torah (Pentateuch), the first five books of Hebrew Scriptures. They accomplished this in 72 days, and their translations all agreed. It may be noticed that 6, 12, and 72 are all astronomical numbers from the sexagesimal system.

Curious Coincidences among Adam, Atlas, and Newton

Adam is associated with the sign of Gemini, which is the shoulders and arms of the cosmic body. The island of Eden is shown on the Hereford map directly under the sign of Gemini. Also, Gemini is the cosmological house of Hermes/ Mercury, the planet that is spoken of as the wise teacher of astronomy. Adam is described as an astronomer and cosmologer who forecast the destruction of the world by fire in Cancer and by flood in Capricorn. Adam is presented with an apple by Eve. The apple is said to inspire knowledge to all who eat from it.

Atlas lived in Fez-Morocco under the sign of Aquarius which is a member of the triangle of Libra, Aquarius, and Gemini (the sign of Adam). Atlas is portrayed holding the celestial sphere resting upon his shoulders, held by his arms (shoulders and arms = Gemini of the cosmic body).

Adam and Atlas are both astronomers. Atlas is credited with naming the constellations and stars. Adam is credited with naming all of creation. Adam is portrayed in Gemini under a tree guarded by a serpent. Atlas is associated with the golden apples of the tree in the Garden of the Hesperides which is also guarded by a huge snake (named Ladon), just like the serpent protecting the tree of knowledge in the Garden of Eden.

The tree of knowledge is a cosmic symbol for the axis of the Earth. Those who know the cycles of this wobbling axis (which causes the cycle of precession of the equinoxes) are the astronomers who carefully guard their science and its valuable precepts. The serpent on the tree of knowledge is, of course, the ancient symbol for the circle of the Milky Way. Mannikka (p. 162) tells that the snake Vasuki at Angkor Wat lives in the Sea of Milk. The Babylonian astronomers identified the Milky Way as the "Great Serpent," according to cuneiform inscriptions from 1150 BC.

In our modern era, Newton stands out as one of the leading astronomers and cosmologers. It is a strange coincidence that the concept of gravity should concern a falling apple during a moonlit night, which inspired Newton to associate the Earth's pull upon the moon with the Earth's pull upon the apple. Here too the mythic story about Newton associates knowledge with an apple.

There are other inescapable similarities between Adam and Atlas:

- Both are portrayed naked, as befits ancient gods and progenitors of great families and tribes. Adam holds the apple, symbol of the globe and the universe, while Atlas holds the celestial globe of the stars.
- Adam's wife was Eve, while Atlas' wife was Pleione. Both are regarded as the mother of nations and of a great portion of mankind.
- Adam's lineage includes one of the founders of the three great races of mankind, Japhet, while Atlas' father is Iapethus, a close homophone.
- Adam's Japhet comes from Noah, whose private parts his children saw when Noah was drunk with wine. Atlas comes from the descent of Uranus, whose private parts were cut off by Atlas' brother, Cronus/ Saturn. Josephus (1.73) says, "For many of the angels of God now consorted with women, and begat sons who were overbearing and disdainful…in fact the deeds that tradition ascribes to them resemble the audacious exploits told by the Greeks of the giants."
- Japhet, son of Noah, had seven sons (Josephus 1.122) who ruled from the River Don in Asia to Cadiz in Spain—"so numerous are the nations founded by the sons of Japhet." Among these nations were the names that we recognize: Paphlagonians, Phrygians, Aeolians, and Thracians. Cadiz is right across from the homeland of Atlas, who had

seven daughters who were the founders of great nations. In Hebrew tradition, it is only through the female side of the family that one is entitled to claim that they are Hebrew. The island of Cadiz is an ancient home of the Phoenicians and, before them, an earlier home to other ancient Atlantic families.

Hebrew Traditions

Traditions about the Patriarch Abraham come from the Torah, the Bible, and Josephus, who writes in *Jewish Antiquities* that the Babylonian historian Berosus recorded, "In the tenth generation after the Flood, there was among the Chaldeans a man righteous and great, and skillful in the celestial science (1.7.2)." Josephus, without evidence, presumes that Berosus is writing about Abraham. Josephus also says that the Greek writer Hecataeus wrote a book about Abraham. Genesis (12:10) says that Abraham had moved to Canaan, but a famine forced him to seek refuge in Egypt. Josephus then tells that Abraham taught arithmetic and astronomy to the Egyptians, who allowed the nation of Israel to grow to maturity for 400 years after Abraham. The *Book of Mormons* says that Abraham received his knowledge from the writings from before the flood. In this, he resembles Agathodaemon in Egypt, who transcribed the *Books of Thoth*, written before the flood. Abraham derived his astronomical knowledge from direct communication with God, who explained to him the laws of his creation. The remainder of his knowledge was imparted by the Urim and Thummim, which he received from the Lord of Ur in the land of the Chaldeans.

It seems reasonable to suggest that Hebrew tradition derives from the Atlantic and Mediterranean Phoenicians (Canaan and King Hiram, friend of Solomon), and from the Babylonians and Chaldeans, and finally from the Egyptians who supported and fed the Hebrews in their times of famine and trouble. The travels of Abraham and Joseph certainly underscore this assertion. The traditions and usages of conservative Jews express a cosmological foundation. Hebrew life is built around simplicity and austerity without the use of icons.

Real Numbers (Not Symbolic) of the Hebrew Calendar

It may be seen from the following that the Jews never for a moment believed that the cosmos was actually timed in terms of days or thousands of years. Below is an example of real Hebrew chronology taken from Remy Landau, *Hebrew Calendar Science and Myths,* and reproduced in Easton's Bible Dictionary.com, 12/31/07:

- The time of birth of the new moon is called the Molad.
- This period of the Molad was determined to be 29 days, 12 hours, and 793 parts. The exact same value, in sexagesimal notation, is also found in Claudius Ptolemy's *Almagest (4.2).*
- The traditional time of the *molad* period is slower by about 1 day in every 15,304 *years* than the presently accepted time of the mean lunar conjunction. This is called the Molad Drift.

The gradual change over time in the difference between the Hebrew year value and the Gregorian year value usually goes unnoticed, since most who map Hebrew dates onto the equivalent Gregorian dates normally do not use spans that exceed 10,000 years.

We are accustomed to determining the Hebrew year at Rosh Hashanah by adding the constant 3,761. For example, by adding 3,761 to Gregorian year value 1996G we get the Hebrew year value 5757H.

If we assume, for purposes of formal calculations, that the rules of both the Gregorian and the Hebrew calendar remain fixed indefinitely, then the assumption of the constant 3,761 can be seen to be formally incorrect over an indefinitely long time. That value can actually be seen to be *decreasing* over unrealistically large periods of time at the rate of one year in approximately every 84,500 Gregorian years:

- By the year 22,203 (Georgian) the value will be 3760
- By the year 106,716, it will be 3759
- By the year 191,305, it will be 3758
- By the year 613,756, it will be 3753

It is apparent that when Hebrew chronologists speak about their calendar, they are not averse to declaring that there are 613,756 years within the realms of their worldview.

Hopefully it has been demonstrated that Hebrew tradition uses the terms "days" and "thousand-year" periods in a symbolic framework and not in a literal sense. Days and thousand-year periods were never meant to be accurate assessments but only served as allegorical placeholders for real numbers. This manner of disguising and hiding cosmological history and science is common among all ancient people.

CHAPTER 6.2

The Legend of the Five Suns

The Legend of the Five Suns is common to Central and South America. It tells of a sequence of four or five creation and destruction epochs. The legend compares to the Bible in that it speaks about the age of the great flood that destroys humankind. The Legend of the Five Suns compares to the Greek generations of the gods in that both accounts speak of epochal ages of the death of the old gods and the birth of the new gods. Most telling in their correspondence is the fact that both accounts follow the counterclockwise movement of the cycle of the Milky Way as well as the elementary sequence of moist-hot-dry-cold through the epochal ages. This is a rather stunning result in comparing cosmologies from around the world. It certainly confirms a global cosmic understanding.

Creation and destruction cycles are extremely long epochal ages. They are a long step above the paltry cycle of the precession of the equinoxes. Carl Johan Calleman, in *The Maya Calendar*, also affirms that he has *not* come across any Maya documents that relate the cycle of precession with the creation and dissolution of the great cosmic ages of mankind referred to in the Legend of the Five Suns. Linda Schele, in *Maya Cosmos*, affirms that the Milky Way generates the epic world flood, as is clearly shown in Maya art (p.106, *fig.2:35* Dresden Codex, p. 74).

Every culture begins its story with a cosmology about the creation and destruction of the world. The creation, and later, the destruction invokes one of the four cosmic elements of water, fire, drought, and cold. The "cosmological worldview" of people around the globe is not very different from one another. Hebrew and Middle Eastern traditions lead off with the separation of the darkness and light as well as the waters from the land and the heavens. Then came Adam and Eve, followed by the destruction of the world during the great flood of Noah. The Greeks have their tales about Atlantis and Atlas of Morocco, whose daughters were called the progenitors of many nations of the Mediterranean world. Later, Atlantis and Morocco were overwhelmed by tsunami and earthquakes. The Libyans recall how their territories of fruitful swamps and verdant pastures were completely scorched by the fires of the sun's chariot, driven by the youthful and reckless Phaeton, who transformed one of the most blessed lands into a desert. The Mexica-Maya-Andean cultures on the other side of the world are already several creation-destruction episodes ahead of everyone else. They are into their fifth sun, having experienced four catastrophic annihilations of the previous ages of the world.

These cosmologies remind us that the world can be a terrible, dangerous place and subject to powerful astronomical cycles of climate and nature. We have studied the beauty of the cosmic mother-goddesses who feeds us and cares for us. But we have also studied the dichotomy of the universe and the awful actions of the cosmic monster. Human progress is often thwarted by wars, pestilence, overpopulation and expansion, drought, famine, ignorance, and greed. The cosmologies are telling us a common story of the advancement of civilizations, their high points, and their destruction by mighty telluric changes. Many of the common destructions of cities were caused by the planets of our solar system. But the great epochal episodes of creation and destruction were caused by the cycle of the Milky Way. These overwhelming and catastrophic natural disasters destroyed entire nations. Only a few intelligent survivors are cast back into a primitive state of existence from which they must struggle forward once again. Obviously, the purpose of the cosmos is not the advancement of humanity, but rather the preservation of humankind by checking the growth and development of civilizations.

Many of the world's cosmologies feature enlightened persons stepping forward to revive the ancient wisdom of the planet, such as Agathodaemon translating the stones from before the flood, or a falcon or phoenix bringing a sacred papyrus tied with a scarlet ribbon to the priests, or strangers coming by boat to our shores bringing science and wisdom. All of these tales are the recollections of people and places that had recently undergone powerful natural disasters. The point is that tribes and nations go through the same cycles as in nature: birth, maturity, degeneration, and death—hopefully followed by a renaissance and regeneration.

Mexica-Maya-Andean Creation

The people of Mexico, Yucatan, and the Andes share a similar creation myth. The connection of these stories to astronomy is amazing. But more amazing is their sophisticated philosophy and extraordinary knowledge of the universe. Karl Taube, in his *Aztec and Maya Myths* (p. 31), tells us that the Aztec believed that:

> Creation is the result of complementary opposition and conflict. Much like the dialogue between two individuals, the interaction and exchange between opposites constitute a creative act. The concept of interdependent opposition is embodied in the great creator god, *Ometeotl,* God of Duality, who resides in the uppermost thirteenth heaven of Omeyocan, the Place of Duality. The Duality possesses both the male and female creative principles. Ometeotl was also referred to as the couple *Tonacatecuhtli* and *Tonacacihuatl,* Lord and Lady of Our Sustenance. Although Ometeotl constitutes the ultimate source of all, his and her progeny of lesser but still powerful deities perform the actual deeds of creation…Two children of Ometeotl, *Quetzalcoatl* and *Tezcatlipoca,* play a very special role in Aztec creation mythology. Sometimes allies and sometimes adversaries, these two gods create the heavens and the earth.

Taube confirms that this Aztec notion of the "creative duality of opposite forces" is also a principle of Maya creation. He tells us (p. 54) that earth and mountains rose from the primordial waters by the very speech of the gods, "Huracan and Gucumatz who began to speak [as well as argue] to one another, discussing the creation, the first dawn and the making of the people."

Isaiah (55:10), in the Hebrew tradition at the other side of the world, professes the creative power of the Word of God:

> For as the rain cometh down, and the snow from heaven, and returneth not thither, but watereth the earth, and maketh it bring forth and bud, that it may give seed to the sower, and bread to the eater:
>
> So shall my word be that goeth forth out of my mouth: it shall not return unto me void, but it shall accomplish that which I please, and it shall prosper in the thing whereto I sent it.

In addition, creation through speech is recorded in the Gospel of John in the Christian tradition:

> In the beginning was the Word [*logos*], and the Word was with God, and the Word was God. The same was in the beginning with God. All things were made by him, and without him was not anything made that was made…And the Word was made flesh, and dwelt among us" (John I:1–14).

This coupling of logos and creation has always seemed to be one of the achievements of Hellenistic thought, but here it shows itself in the Mexica-Maya-Andean creation tradition. Hunbatz Men, in *Secrets of Mayan Science/Religion* (p. 136), speaks about Maya word inversions, double and reverse meanings, saying that "Than" = speech, while the inverted "Nath" = pliers in the sense that "a person who speaks can lock us into his or her grip. It can also mean that when we speak we can control the person that we speak to, as if we are gripping them with pliers." These Mexica-Maya ideas about "the creative power of speech" are examples of extremely sophisticated cosmic philosophy. Their astronomy has shown us the heights to which they have ascended. Their creation stories now show us the universality of cosmic thinking and language around the globe. To equate the power of speech with creation certainly ranks as the pinnacle of human thought.

These traditions recall the story of Adam "naming" the animals. But Adam does not *create*, but rather assumes power and dominion over creation by attaching names to everything. This seems to harken back to a "gripping pliers" type of speech that Hunbatz Men has mentioned above.

The Legend of the Five Suns

The heavens have been employed as a recording device for myth, history, and the duration of all astronomical cycles. The astronomer also recognizes the asterisms, or constellations, whose individual star groupings are imaginary images that have been accepted by long usage. The astronomer perceives the conglomerate band of hundreds of billions of stars that form the Milky Way, which also contains the so called "dark constellations" shadowy forms within the Milky Way's clouds of stars.

Karl Taube, in his *Aztec and Maya Myths* (p. 34), tells us that we live in the age of the Fifth Sun, the Age of Maize of the Corn God. Taube says that there are at least 10 versions of this myth. He relates a version from the earliest and important sources, *Historia de los mexicanos por su pinturas* and *Leyenda de los sols:*

In the highest of the 13 heavens, the creator couple gave birth to four sons. These brothers are the four elements—water, fire, wind, earth—which are the four elemental natures moist-hot-dry-cold (This sequence moist-hot-dry-cold is correct for the counterclockwise cycle of the spinning of the Milky Way Galaxy). These gods were the rulers of the Four Suns, the four ages of the past.

Miller and Taube, in *The Gods and Symbols of Ancient Mexico and the Maya* (pp. 68–71) relate the Legend of the Five Suns that appears in the Quiche Mayan *Popol Vuh*. First, the gods made people out of mud, but they were soft and weak and were soon destroyed. The gods fashioned the second generation out of wood for the men, and rushes for women. These creatures could speak and multiply but lacked understanding. So the gods sent down a great flood and a rain of pitch to destroy them. Also, daemons, animals, and even their household utensils attacked these wood and rush people. Those who escaped this destruction became the monkeys that we see today. Then the gods made humans from the nine drinks made out of corn. These humans were a bit too wise for the liking of the gods. Therefore, the gods demanded that, "They were blinded as the face of a mirror is breathed upon. Their eyes were weakened. Now it was only when they looked nearby that things were clear" (Schele, p. 112). After this creation, there will be destruction when animals, some gods, and men will turn into stone. Because the theme of the legend is a cyclical destruction based on the four elements—which are recognized worldwide—it should be possible to compare this tradition with other cultures of the globe

Below is a graph that presents a correspondence between Mexica-Maya-Andean, Greek, Egyptian, and Biblical traditions based on the cycle of the Milky Way:

Sagittarius	Capricorn	Aquarius	Pisces	Aries
Ocelotl	Ehecatl	Quiahuitl	Nahui Atl	Hunahpu
Jaguars	Wind	Fiery Rain	Water	Maize
Giants devoured	Destroyed by	Rain, Lightning	Flood	the Current Age
By jaguars	the Wind	of the god Tlaloc	people turned	people of the corn
	Monkeys	butterflies, dogs, turkeys	into fish	Huitzilopochtli
Helios	Cyclopes	Atlas & Saturn	Jupiter	Helios-Invictus
Ra-Atum	Agathodaemon	Cronus-Geb	Isis & Osiris	Horus-Harpocrates
	Noah			The Messiah, Christ

Sagittarius (Hot) Giants, Jaguar, Helios.

In Sagittarius the Mexica-Maya-Andean tradition of Ocelotl-jaguar, sun god, corresponds perfectly with the Greek Helios and the Egyptian Ra-Atum. Miller and Taube state (p. 104), "The Maya particularly identified the Sun with the jaguar. The daytime sun, often represented as patron of the number 'four,' can be represented with jaguar features; but the nighttime Sun, the Jaguar God of the Underworld, patron of the number 'seven,' is clearly a jaguar in his full body depictions...occasionally appears with a star sign on his back (perhaps to tell us that he is also a constellation)." The jaguar is also a symbol of royalty as is the sun.

Capricorn: (Dry) Wind, Agathodaemon, Monkey.

Though Capricorn is the scene of the global flood of Noah, generally it belongs to the nature of drought and wind. This tunes in well with the Mexica-Maya-Andean tradition of Ehecatl, the wind god. This triangle of Capricorn-Virgo-Taurus features an exaltation of Hermes-Mercury and the Moon who are both noted for their wit and intelligence. Therefore this matches well with the Greek Cyclopes and the Egyptian Agathodaemon. The ape was one of the major symbols of Thoth-Agathodaemon, god of Egyptian scribes and writing. In Mesoamerican traditions, monkeys are likewise associated with many aspects of Mercury such as talismans of good luck as well as merchants and those who are gifted in the arts, song, dance, writing, stone carving, and calculating. Miller and Taube say that (p. 118) Hun Batz and Hun Chuen are turned into monkeys. They are the *alter-twins* and stepbrothers to the divine twins. "These monkey twins occur widely in Classic Maya art as the patron gods of art, writing, and calculating...the Monkey scribes are often depicted as gifted and industrious."

Aquarius: (Cold) Fiery rain and Lightning, Cronus-Saturn.

The fiery-rain and lightning of Tlaloc does *not conform* to the Greek Atlas and Saturn, or the Egyptian Cronus-Geb. This is the constellation of the "water-bearer" who is carrying a jug of water. Cronus-Saturn is associated with chronology, time-keeping, and also depicted as the "grim reaper" and the finality of death. In Mexico-Maya-Andean tradition, the people of this age are turned into butterflies, dogs, and turkeys. Dogs were regarded as guides to the souls through the underworld or as guardians of the underworld in Greek-Egyptian traditions. In Egyptian cosmology, Anubis is the jackal-headed god who weighs the heart of the souls against the weightless feather of Maat, the truth. Mercury and Saturn are the lords of this triangle, which includes Libra and Gemini. Miller and Taube report (p. 80) that dogs were buried with their masters and frequently appear in underworld scenes on classic Mayan pots as Xolotl, the dog-headed guide of the underworld.

Pisces: (Water) Nahui Atl, the Age of Water, Jupiter, Isis and Osiris.

The Mexica-Maya-Andean tradition of Nahui Atl, water, accords well with people turned into fish in the epoch of Pisces. The Greek traditions of Zeus-Jupiter and the Egyptian Isis and Osiris are all about moisture and water. Throughout the globe, "fish men" are said to appear like Oannes in Babylon-Chaldea, who instructed the natives in all manner of science. This sign is a member of the water triangle of Pisces-Cancer-Scorpio. Pisces alone is the exaltation of Venus, patroness of the divine feminine and moisture.

Aries: (Hot) Huitzilopochtli, Hun Hunahpu, Horus-Harpocrates, the Messiah, and Christ.

The Mexica-Maya-Andean tradition of Hun Hunahpu and Huitzilopochtli sympathize well with Aries which is the house of the warrior Aries-Mars, but also the exaltation of the sun. This theme matches the Roman Helios-Invictus, the Egyptian Horus-Harpocrates (the avenger of his father), and the Jewish-Christian Christ. The "people of the maize" also works well with the epoch of Aries.

The Aztec also concurred that there were four previous worlds or "suns" before our own. Each age had a different name, a different deity, and a different race of humans. Each sun was linked with water, fire, wind, or earth. Each of these four elements relates not only to the nature and composition of its world, but also to its destruction (Taube, p. 34). The famous Aztec calendar stone in Mexico City has the current sun god in its center surrounded by the four worlds and the four elementary epochs of the sun.

Orion and the Cosmic Turtle

Cultures around the world have a special regard for the constellation Orion, the Pleiades, Taurus, and Gemini. The Maya Long Count is recorded to have begun in 3114 BC. If we backtrack 3,114 years in the precessional cycle from zero degrees, Aries, we arrive at 13.25 degrees of the zodiac sign of Taurus, where Orion is located. The Egyptians equate this constellation with Osiris, and the Assyrians equate it with Nimrod. Orion is located on the celestial equator, close to the Milky Way.

In Maya cosmology, the three prominent stars of the belt of Orion are associated with the hearth of creation and the birth of the Maize God out of the cracked shell of the Cosmic Turtle. The three stars of Orion are called the "hearthstones" and the "turtle stars," and below them is a hazy nebula called "the smoke from the hearth" (A.P. Mercier, pp. 259–78).

The *Paris Codex Zodiac* also equates the "turtle stars" with the zodiac constellation of Gemini. Some of the Maya may have joined Gemini and Orion together because of their traditions regarding the divine twins, *los Heroes Gemelos* (Gemini), who are involved with the birth of the Maize God. The Maize God breaks forth from the *caparazon of the tortuga.* He is attended by the second appearance of the divine twins, who also went into the underworld and defeated the gods in a ritual ballgame. It is possible that the Aztec associate the rectangular layout of the stars of Gemini with a cosmic ballfield.

The three hearthstones, or turtle stars, are named Tepu, Gugumatz, and Huyubkaan. The star Huyubkaan forms a triangle with the feet of Orion, and this triangle, or pyramid, encloses the sacred precinct and house of the high god Hunab K'u. His house is one of the most powerful locations in the sky and contains the place of the "new fire." Here also is the "city of light," necessary for eternal life.

Alloa Patricia Mercier, in her *Los Secretos de los Chamanes Mayas* (p. 273), also describes the triangular house of Hunab K'u below Orion's belt. This triangular house is called the smoky fire of creation in the Great Turtle. The smoky fire is actually the great nebula M42 in modern science. This star cloud emits brilliant light of a strange ultraviolet nature, which some scientists have suggested has a relation to the amino acids that structure life forms here on Earth. Orion's belt and region of the Cosmic Turtle are 180 degrees in opposition to the *Grieta Oscura*, the "black hole," which is the central matrix of our galaxy.

The White Road—the Avatars of the Milky Way

The cycle of the rotation of our Milky Way Galaxy influences culture, science, and religion upon the Earth. This rotation is very slow moving from zodiac house to house in 18 million years. As we have said above, anniversary rituals of these great galactic episodes of gods and natural events can be celebrated every year as the sun enters into each of the 12 signs of the zodiac. In addition, greater and longer celebrations are in order when the cycle of the precession of the vernal equinoxes enters into each of the 12 signs of the zodiac for periods of 2160 years per sign (2160 x 12 = 25,920). In a sense, precession opens a brief doorway to the energy or avatars of past and future galactic ages.

As we see in the story of Adam, the Hebrew cosmologers choose to honor a galactic anniversary within the context of the precessional cycle. Hebrew cosmologers used the number of years from precessional Gemini to their own contemporary age in order to track the position of a far-distant galactic era. Since the zodiac is the common clock face of all the cosmic cycles, each zodiac house is a commodious "bag of information" containing natural events, demigods, avatars, myth, and history.

Karl Taube makes a very interesting remark that supports "the bag of information" that each zodiac sign contains:

> Although none of the colonial *Chilam Balam* manuscripts predate the eighteenth century, they often contain references to ancient myth and history probably copied from earlier colonial texts and still older screen-fold books. A great many of the texts describe auguries concerned with repeating cycles of time. The repetitive nature of these cycles frequently makes for telescoping or overlapping of time, so that a single passage can contain events pertaining to colonial, pre-Hispanic and even mythical eras" (p. 24).

The telescoping or overlapping of time that Taube refers to is exactly what we have spoken about: "the nature of the common clock face of the zodiac," which records the events of many different cycles upon one sign of the zodiac. The zodiac becomes a heavenly *quipu*, a memory device of the cosmos written in the stars.

Blood Sacrifice

Sacrifice signifies the end of one cosmic era and the beginning of a new age. The blood of the dead god literally nourishes the new savior. Karl Taube quotes the *Popol Vuh*, which says that people are made to provide nourishment for the gods in the form of prayer and sacrifice. "Humans have an inherent responsibility—literally, a blood debt to the gods who make existence possible. The repeating series of world creations and destructions is a continual reminder of the consequences of neglecting this obligation" (p. 54, 75)."

The gods have sacrificed themselves and expect sacrifice in return. There is an imperative of cosmic physics at work here. The myths tell us that every cycle in the Maya sky is an important fulfillment. "Myths of world creations and destructions are frequently couched in terms of calendrical events," says Taube (p. 75). Every "fulfillment" of destruction brings about the birth of a new cycle of creation. Taube writes, "Relationship between calendrical events and myth is not simple metaphoric: the calendrical cycles were used to predict potential periods when the world might be destroyed. These calendrical period endings were seen as powerful and frightening times of living myth, when the gods and other forces of creation and chaos would again do battle in the world of mortals."

Page one of the Fejervary-Mayer Codex (a 260-day calendar) depicts the warrior god of fire and time standing in the center of a four-quartered, Maltese-like cross. The god is being nourished by four streams of blood coming from the dismembered limbs and head of the former god, Tezcatlipoca (Taube, p. 14). It is therefore to be understood that the former god's blood sustains the new god.

Taube writes (p. 50) that,

The myth of the five suns presents sacrifice as an essential means for maintaining human life and cosmic balance. Through the penitential offering of their own blood, the gods create the present race of mankind. An even greater sacrifice occurs at Teotihuacán, where the gods slay themselves so that the sun can follow its course. In their own acts of bloodletting and sacrifice, humans are simply following a tradition set down by the gods at the time of creation.

The Physics of Creation, Destruction, and Restoration of the Worlds

Both of the gods Tezcatlipoca and Quetzalcoatl are the dynamic agents who destroyed the previous four suns. But they are also credited with the recreation of the heavens and the earth, not as adversaries but as allies, according to Taube (p. 36). Aided by four other deities, the four sons of the creator couple fashion four roads leading to the center of the Earth. The Earth is divided into four quadrants, and the eight gods rise up to the heavens. Tezcatlipoca and Quetzalcoatl transform themselves into enormous trees to support the sky. One tree is marked by shining mirrors, the other by the plumes of the emerald quetzal bird.

In another myth, they make the heavens and the earth out of the great earth monster Tlaltecuhtli, a hermaphroditic dual-sexed monster. This creature is sometimes identified with the great caiman, whose spiny crocodilian back forms the mountain ranges of the world. Tlaltecuhtli is seen striding upon the sea. His/her elbows, knees, and other joints have gnashing mouths that hunger for flesh to eat. Tezcatlipoca and Quetzalcoatl transform into serpents and tear the monster in halves, which become earth and heaven (Taube, p.36).

The flood caiman earth-monster and cosmic-monster. Courtesy of Karl Taube

To repopulate the Earth after the flood, Quetzalcoatl must go to Mictlan, the underworld, to retrieve the human bones of the last creation from Lord Mictlantecuhtli. After much to-do, Quetzalcoatl carries the broken bones to Tamoanchan, a miraculous place of origin. The old goddess, Woman Serpent, grinds the bones into flour meal, which she places into a ceramic vessel. The gods gather around to shed drops of their blood upon the ground-up bones. This produces the new race of people (Taube, p. 38).

The creation of the Fifth Age, the Fifth Sun, took place in the ancient city of Teotihuacan, considered to be the place where time began. "The place where time began" may simply mean the location where science and the measurement of time originated. Two gods contested the honor to become the leader of this new age; one was humble while the other was arrogant. Two hills were made for these gods, the Pyramids of the Sun and the Moon, 25 miles northeast of Mexico City. One of the gods becomes the sun, while the other becomes the moon. But the sun will not move, so the gods all agree to be sacrificed by Quetzalcoatl at Teotihuacán. As the gods gave up their hearts in sacrifice, so too humans must give up their own hearts and blood to ensure that the Fifth Sun continues to move in its path.

History, science, and religion are combined in cosmic myth to represent the cosmic trinity of Humans, Earth, and God. This worldview espouses a morality based upon balance, harmony, and equality created by the cosmic forces. These stories reflect a sophisticated and integrated philosophy of moral order emanating from the natural harmony of cosmic physics.

Part 7

Mexica-Maya-Andean Culture and Astronomy

The ancient culture and astronomy of the American continents is so very exciting and informative because it is still extant and in place, vibrant and thriving in the face of the progress of the modern world. Praise to the many researchers and students who have helped to conserve so much delicate information from unknown worlds that have existed in the past.

CHAPTER 7.1

Mystery of the Maya Long Count Cycle and the year 2012 AD

There is much to-do and excitement about the upcoming year of 2012 AD. Some people have made calculations that this date represents the fulfillment of the latest Maya Long Count cycle on the day of the winter solstice, December 21st. Some prophesy that the world will go through a spiritual awakening. Others predict catastrophe and disaster. The best handle to get at the truth of these matters is to examine the entire Maya chronological systems in order to understand the real significance of the Long Count cycle. The last chapter on the Legend of the Five Suns tells us that the great Mexica-Maya-Andean cycles of creation and destruction are linked to the ponderous cycles of the Milky Way, which fulfill themselves during millions of years—a realm far beyond the 5,200 years of the Long Count period. However, the Long Count is famous on its own account.

The Long Count cycle is so accurate that the National Aeronautics and Space Administration says that it only varies in time by .00000007 from that of an atomic clock, each operating over a period of 180,000 years (A.P. Mercier, p. 287). This accuracy of Mayan astronomy is the reason that researchers have taken the termination of the Long Count cycle with such seriousness.

Hadingham, in *Early Man and the Cosmos* (p. 219), confirms that Mayan cosmology and mathematics were phenomenally precise. One of the remaining rare hieroglyphic books "contains a scheme for the correction of Venus observations which insures an accuracy of approximately *two hours within five hundred years.*" Hadingham tells us that the numbers and pictures in the bark books were studied in 1880 by Ernst Forstemann, the chief librarian of the Royal Public Library at Dresden and caretaker of the *Maya Codex Dresden*. It was he who announced the discovery of the astronomical significance of the Dresden Codex. Initially Forstemann discovered that eight pages of the Dresden Codex are filled with a table that is clearly devoted to the timing of lunar eclipses. One column of numbers consists mostly of the figure 177 repeated over and over again. Every now and then, the number 148 intrudes among the monotonous recital of 177. The number 148 equals the days in five lunar months. Once a lunar eclipse happens, then the next one will occur on one of three possible dates in the future: 177 days later, 325 days later (177 + 148), or 354 days later (177 + 177). The noted archaeoastronomer Anthony Aveni remarked upon this discovery in the terms that "the reduction of a complex cosmic cycle to a pair of numbers was a feat equivalent to those of Newton or Einstein."

In the chapter, "Man Is the Measure of All Things," it becomes apparent that cosmology consists of a trinity of heaven (God), humans, and earth (nature). The Maya also recognized this trinity and fashioned their systems around a human element, namely the cycle of the average period of human gestation (nine months, or 260 days). Hadingham comments (p. 210) on the Temple of the Inscriptions at Palenque, saying that, "The entire design on the sarcophagus lid asserts the importance and divine status of the individual within the framework of nature, intimating that the Maya placed man literally at the center of all other natural forces."

Miller and Taube, in *The Gods and Symbols of Ancient Mexico and the Maya*, say that the Tzolkin cycle (also called the Sacred Round) of 260 days was important to,

> midwives to calculate birthdays, working from the first missed menstrual period until the day of birth, approximating the 9-month human gestation period. In many parts of Mexico, humans and gods took their names from their date of birth in this calendar…the 260-day almanac was the fundamental guide to the future, and every day and

> number offered clues for interpretation. Gifts and shortcomings were bestowed by one's date of birth (p. 48).

The cosmologers of Mexico and the Maya were certainly astrologers who believed in astronomic cause. It is one of the tenets of astrology that the day of creation, the day of impregnation of the human seed, is an especially significant guide to the character of that person. It is a secret look behind the curtain of life. Therefore it may also be accurate to name the Tzolkin cycle "the astrologer's cycle" because of the dual importance of insemination and birth into the world.

Everything in Maya cosmology had to be related to, and centered on, the human gestation cycle of the Tzolkin Sacred Round of 260 days. In true Maya synchronism: 260 ÷ 9 months = 28.888888 days x 12 months = 346.666666. This number closely approaches the modern value of the Eclipse Year of 346.62 days. Milone and Kelley tell us an *eclipse year* is the length of time it takes for the sun to move from one of its intersections with the path of the moon, or node, until it returns to the same intersection, or node. It measures 346.62 days in length. Hence, an eclipse half-year totals 173.31 days, and three eclipse half-years add up to 519.93 days. In Mesoamerican terms, this value would be rounded to 520 days, or the equivalent of two rounds of the 260-day sacred almanac.

Synchronizing this eclipse cycle in the Dresden Codex to the all-important Sacred Round of 260 days required almost 33 years, totaling 405 lunar months (11,958 days in the table were near to 11,960 days of 405 lunar months and 46 Sacred Rounds (46 x 260 = 11,960). This term of 405 moons allows us to arrive at an average for the length of one lunar month that falls only seven minutes short of the accepted modern value. This is because 11,960 days ÷ 405 moons = 29.5308 days (29.53059 is the modern synodic value). Irwin says (pp. 109-20) that Olmec astronomy was inherited by the Maya, whose year was more accurate than the Julian and Georgian calendars of Europe:

Modern calculation........................365.2422 days
Maya calculation............................365.2420 days

The Midwife's Cycle

One of the confusing elements of Maya astronomy is the many possible names for the all-important 260-day calendar cycle:

- Midwife's cycle
- Agricultural cycle for ancient mountain maize
- Sacred Round
- Tzolkin cycle
- Tonalpohualli cycle (Miller and Taube, p. 49)
- Astrologer's and Diviner's 260-day almanac cycle

The variety of different names confuses the importance of this most pivotal cycle of Maya astronomy. The main significance of the 260-day cycle is that it synchronizes the ancient agricultural cycle and the human cycle with the time period of nine moons. The 260-day cycle is a human, agricultural, and moon cycle. Also, three times 260 days equals the synodic period of Mars, 780 days. As mentioned above, 260 days is also a medium to arrive at the eclipse cycle of the moon. Maya astronomy was truly cosmologic because it was not about one cycle but all cycles; it was not only about numbers but about geometry and the harmony of numbers; it was not only about sun, moon, and planets but about humans, the divine, and the natural world.

Therefore, Maya cosmology is all about relationships of heavenly bodies with each other, with the cycles of the cosmos, and with humans. The incorporation of the moon into the cycles of the sun, Earth, Venus, Mars, Jupiter, and Saturn was the ultimate synthesis of their cosmology. Hadingham admits (p. 224) the importance of the moon as a partner in the Maya cycles when he says that, "A long series of observations of lunar phases, averaged over the years, as well as of actual eclipses themselves, must lie behind the whole system." Hadingham further says that the Maya system is fundamentally different from our own thinking and that of the Babylonians and Greeks which concern themselves with orbital motions. Hadingham had already observed (p.203), "The Maya seem to have been obsessed with the search for harmonious, resonating whole number cycles—perhaps with the quest of one supreme whole number—which would divinely organize and unify both the heaven and human affairs."

The Dresden Codex was carefully analyzed by Forstemann, concerning the cycles of the appearance and disappearance of the planet Venus as a morning and evening star. Venus as a morning star was depicted as a fierce warrior spearing a victim; she was feared as much as the onset of a solar or lunar eclipse. The softer side of Venus is her appearance as an evening star in her character as *Chasca,* "tangled or disheveled hair" because she casts dewdrops upon the Earth when she shakes her hair (K&M, p. 464).

One Venus year can vary between 587 to 581 days, producing an average of 584 days. The main concern of the Maya astronomers was to keep the Venus cycles in perfect step with several other calendar counts. Hadingham says that, "They achieved this result by devising a phenomenally accurate correction scheme, so that the tables would function perfectly for century after century."

Hadingham says that the most interesting feature of the Venus pages of the Dresden Codex is a pair of dates associated with the long-term correction scheme. One of these dates concerned the mythological birth of Venus 1,366,560 days before the start of the table. Hadingham remarks, "This number can be divided exactly by seven separate calendrical or planetary cycles. Indeed, its properties are so remarkable that it has been called 'the super-number of the Dresden Codex.'" This discovery was originally made by Floyd Lounsbury. Forstemann's and Lounsbury's examination of the Dresden Codex penetrates deep into Maya synchronicity—a journey that must convince everyone that the Maya worldview was a clear attempt to relate everything in the universe to everything else in the universe.

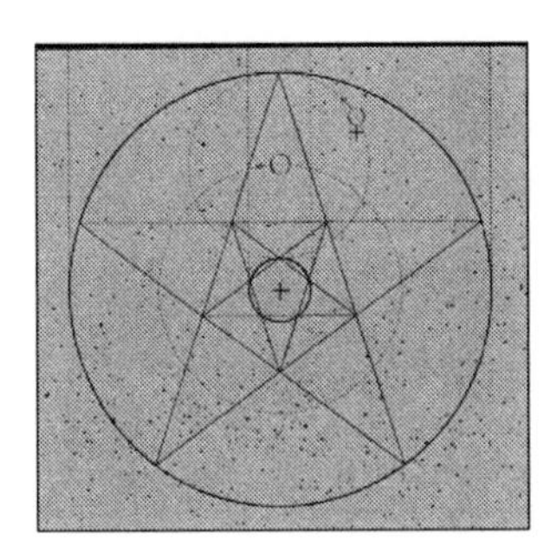

Image by John Martineau

The Basic Venus-Earth Numbers

All the myriads of Maya numbers are born from the simplest of all sources, a basic relation of 5 + 8 = 13 between the planet Venus and our Earth. From a geo-centric viewpoint the planet Venus describes a five-pointed pentagram-star in the sky over a period of eight Earth years, while she is circling the Sun

13 times during her 13 Venusian years. The numbers 5, 8, and 13 are also Fibonacci numbers in the sequence: 1, 1, 2, 3, 5, 8, 13, 21, 34 in which the product of the last two numbers create the next number. These numbers are related to the creation formula of pi (.618) which unfolds all things. In plane geometry the numbers 5-8-13 help to design the famous mollusk spiral:

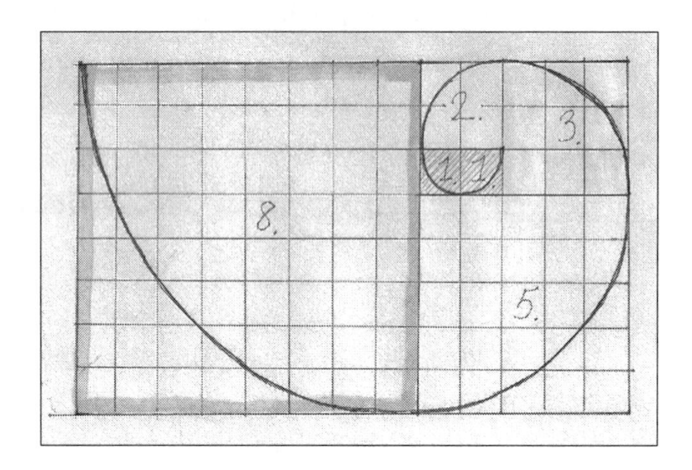

C. W. Johnson in *The Aztec Calendar, Math and Design* says that Mexica-Maya make extensive use of the mediation/duplatio method of computation of doubling numbers, as well as tripling them:

5 + 8 = 13 (5 x 8 = 40 Jupiter & Saturn conjunctions in 800 yrs.)

13 + 13 = 26 (260 day human gestation cycle. 13 days x 20 periods)
(260 days x 3 = 780 day synodic period of Mars)
(260 years ÷ 20 conjunctions of Jupiter and Saturn = 13)
(26,000 year return of the Pleiades cycle, or Precession)

26 + 26 = 52 (the 52 year Calendar Round (52 x 365 = 18,980days = 260 x 73). The festival of the New Fire. It was symbolized by a bundle of 52 sticks tied together.

52 + 52 = 104 (Double Calendar Round includes the Venus Round 8 x 13 = 104), (5 x 8 x 13 = 520)

The above interrelation of the numbers and the cycles is exquisite and accurate. Because of this interwoven feature, the system is easy to remember, as the numbers unfold out of themselves like a blooming flower. The numbers five, eight, and thirteen create a veritable synchronic and mnemonic universe. These numbers and geometry were revealed by looking at man, nature, and the heavens. The cosmos has been revealed through its parts.

The Maya Long Count Cycle

Forstemann's ground-breaking research into the nature of ancient Maya calendrics made it possible for Joseph Goodman and others to determine the base date of August 2 (or August 13), 3114 BC for the present Long Count cycle (Taube, p. 27). Historically, the most important era base was a date *13.0.0.0.0* namely, *4 Ahu 8 Cumka*, which was both the zero date of a new era and the completion of 13 Baktuns (13 x 400 = 5,200 years). The average precessional period, according to the Maya, is 26,000 years, which they called the *cycle of the Pleiades*. Cutting up this cycle by the five-pointed Venus star resulted in five periods of 5,200 years each (26,000 ÷ 5 = 5,200).

In order to better understand the Long Count, it should be asked what happens after 5,200 years and what other cycles conform to this period. Below are the coincidences of all the cycles that happen every 5,200 years of the Long Count cycle:

- 100 cycles of 52 years, the Calendar Round
- 260 conjunctions of Jupiter and Saturn
- 20 cycles of 260 years
- 13 baktuns of 400 years
- 1/5 of the precessional cycle, the Maya cycle of the Pleiades

The abovementioned synchronisms prove that the Long Count is an absolutely beautiful and remarkable chronological cycle. This, however, does not, by any stretch of the imagination, make the Maya Long Count cycle of 5,200 years a creation or destruction cycle.

The story of Adam and Atlas, the Greek generations of the gods, and the Legend of the Five Suns concern the great cycles of creation and destruction. The lengths of these great epochal periods in the cycle of the Milky Way are hundreds of thousands and millions of years in duration. The Long Count cycle is a mere 1/5 of the cycle of precession (also called Pleiades: 5 x 5200 = 26,000 years).

26,000-Year Cycle of the Pleiades

As was said above, every 52 years the Tzolkin cycle (Sacred Round) of 260 days synchronizes with the Haab cycle (ordinary or vague year) of 365 days. This 52-year period is known as the "Calendar Round." Five-hundred of these 52-year cycles are called the Pleiades cycle (52 x 500 = 26,000 years), which is another name for the cycle of the precession of the vernal equinoxes. It is amazing that the "Return of the Phoenix" from Arabia to Heliopolis in Egypt was said to happen every 500 years, using the same number as the Maya (500 x 52 = 26,000). The phoenix, or *Bennu* bird, is said to have been based upon an ancient larger heron of the Persian Gulf. Like the Maya, the Egyptians regarded Venus as one of the keys to the synchronization of the cosmic cycles. Therefore, the Egyptians called the planet Venus "the star of the ship of Bennu-Osiris."

Two times the 52-year cycle was called the "great cycle" by the Aztec. Every 104 years the Haab (365-day cycle), the Tzolkin (260-day cycle), and the Venus round synchronize (during 104 years ÷ 8 = 13 cycles of Venus pentagrams were completed). Miller and Taube say that, "Such numerical coincidences of interlocking cycles appealed to Mesoamerican calendar keepers and facilitated calculations." After what we have learned above, this must be regarded as the understatement of all understatements regarding Maya astronomy.

Other 2012 Data and Conclusions

According to the 2012 AD advocates, the winter solstice of this year lines up with the black hole at the center of our galaxy. Leading astronomers have remarked that this coincidental alignment has been in operation since 1850

AD and will continue to be in force up to 2200 AD. Actually, the proposed date of December 21, 2012, does not link up with any of the known and important cosmic cycles:

- The 5,200-year Long Count minus the start date of 3114 BC actually equals the date 2086 AD and not 2012 AD.
- On December 21, 2012, there are no solar or lunar eclipses. The other eclipses of 2012 do not fall anywhere near the geography of Mesoamerica.
- In 2012 there are no conjunctions of Saturn and Jupiter. The conjunctions of these two planets occur in 2000, 2020, 2040, 2060, and 2080 AD.
- In 2012 there is a transit of Venus across the face of the sun during the summer but not during the important month of December. Bob Berman, in his *Venus Touches the Sun* (2004 *Farmer's Almanac*, p. 79), tells us that a transit of Venus occurs if Venus arrives at an inferior conjunction (between the Earth and the sun) at precisely one of the two spots along its tilted orbit that perfectly intersect the Earth-sun plane. Venus' orbit is such that its transits have two distinctions: 1) they occur only in June and December, and 2) they occur in a double cycle, or in a pair. There are eight years minus two days between the two transits in each pair, and the pairs alternate between 121.5 and 105.5 years apart. The last pair of Venus transits occurred in December 1874 and December 1882 (121.5 + Dec. 1882 = June 2004). On June 8, 2004, the first half of the double cycle occurred. Eight years from then, on June 6, 2012, a second transit will complete that cycle.

Finally, it must be said that there is much disagreement as to when the last Long Count began. Milone and Kelley write (p. 359), "Unfortunately, the era base had ceased to be used before the Spanish arrived; so the Long Count position is not known, and we do not know if any shift in the Calendar Round occurred. Determining the equivalence between our calendar and the classic Maya dates is the *correction* problem." Over 30 corrections have been proposed in the past century, differing by over 1200 years.

The Nazca Lines

The numbers 25,920 and 26,000 years express the cycle of the precession of the vernal equinoxes, which is referred to by many other names, such as: the Great Year, the Platonic Great Year, the Great Return, the 52 Returns of the Phoenix, and the Pleiades cycle of the Maya. In order to study a cycle of this length, you must know how it functions within even greater cycles like that of the rotation of the Milky Way.

Astronomers tell us that ancient solstical and equinoctial temple alignments are not changed by precession. But temple alignments to stars do change with precession. Therefore, after a full cycle of 25,920 years, the alignments to the stars should "return" to their former locations. Calling precession "the Pleiades cycle" seems to suggest that the Pleiades returned to their former place of alignment when the last cycle of precession began. Here is where the Nazca lines may possibly come into the picture. After a full rotation of the Return of the Pleiades (precession), the correspondence of the star alignments in the heavens could be checked against their Nazca orientations to determine their constancy (return) or the measurable amount of movement and shift since the last precessional cycle.

Success Destroyed the Maya Empire

One of the great conundrums of Maya astronomy is the tremendous accuracy that they achieved. Their astronomy continually sacrificed short term perfection to achieve long term results for enormous cycles of time. What kind of a culture would do this to so concern themselves with segments of time that really would only interest God?

While the Maya empire has vanished, the Maya continue to live on within their ancient and vibrant culture. The Empire was too successful and thereby too demanding upon the resources of people and the environment. They became too successful, too good at what they did, resulting in overexpansion and overdevelopment. In the words of Shakespeare, "One fire drives out one fire, one nail one nail. Rights by rights do falter, strengths by strengths do fail."

The point is that the Maya understood astronomy to such an extent that it helped them to master their environment. Hadingham tells us (p. 241) that in the 1960s the University of Pennsylvania conducted a detailed survey of the area surrounding Tikal. They were amazed to discover a "downtown core" of 2.5 square miles of temples and pyramids surrounded by some 75 square miles of outlying suburbs, accommodating about 72,000 people. The density of the settlement around Tikal was probably eight times greater than conventional Maya methods can support today. In the late 1960s the first evidence of irrigation canals and terraced fields came to light on the western and northern fringes of the Mayan lowlands. Thousands of square miles of artificially modified terrain could be recognized from the air. The climax came in 1979, when a U.S. Space Agency aircraft was chartered to fly over wide areas of Belize and Guatemala. The aircraft carried a radar scanning device for monitoring the surface of Venus. In the resulting radar imagery, it was possible to trace a lattice-like pattern of lines running across swamps and the edges of lagoons and rivers. Ground surveys showed these to be canals supporting a population of 1.25 million people.

If we may believe the testimony of Hunbatz Man, the Maya encouraged astrological birth control by advising their citizens to breed only on auspicious and fruitful days and to abstain during malevolent and unlucky times. This manipulation may have accelerated the number of above average healthy individuals which in turn produced more of their kind. In most societies there is a balance between the healthy and the unhealthy. People became too healthy, sociable, and successful and spread beyond the normal and natural bounds of human growth. This is not to say that astrology was, of itself, successful, but it did serve as a disciplined system—and indeed most disciplined systems do succeed. This theory certainly may sound too fantastical to some if it were not for the following fact. At the other side of the globe, aerial photos were also taken above Angkor Wat, an extremely advanced astronomical and cosmological temple site like Tikal.

The Greater Angkor Project of the University of Sydney in cooperation with Cambodia and France conducted an extensive aerial survey of the countryside surrounding this astronomical temple site. The ground-sensing radar revealed an amazing number of 94 new temple sites within a developed area of an incredible 3,000 square kilometers. The radar showed that the main closely inhabited suburban area extended to 1,000 square kilometers around Angkor Wat. Again the researchers were astounded to see that the surrounding neighborhood was dedicated to cities, villages, and agriculture to serve a population from ½ to 1 million inhabitants. The main theory based upon these observations concludes that an extensive water-management system caused environmental damage. This system ultimately failed, leading to food shortages and famine (newscientist.com, 8/8/10). Success is the fruit of detailed management. Failure is the idea that you can manage everything in detail forever. Success in the form of overpopulation and overextension of resources and political power destroyed the Roman Empire, as it also destroyed the Maya and the Khmer of Angkor Wat.

CHAPTER 7.2

Mexica-Maya-Andean Culture, Tikal and Teotihuacán

Both the Inca of Peru and the Aztec of Mexico fit into the same pattern. They both created great empires around themselves. They were both conquered by the Spanish supported by rebellious native tribes. They both had prophecy concerning the return of an ancient benefactor and hero. It is important to remember that the Aztec and the Inca freely admitted that the extraordinary megalithic works in their countries were the work of a great culture that came before them.

The historians Duran and Shagun (De Roo, pp. 567–76) tell that Quetzalcoatl (Topiltzin, Kukulcan, and many other names) foretold that he would return after 512 years from the place where the sun rises in the form of white bearded men like himself. The American natives call these men "the children of Quetzalcoatl." A few days after this pronouncement, the colossal pyramid at Cholula was destroyed by a giant earthquake, a fact that imprinted the memory of Quetzalcoatl's prophecy forever in the minds of the Mexicans. A few years before the arrival of the Spanish, a great light broke forth in the east full of fire, sparks, and stars. The great Lake of Tezcuco became violently agitated and overflowed its banks, sweeping away many buildings. There were countless predictions of a forthcoming calamity from the astrologers, including that the king's son would unite with the foreigners.

Meteors also reappeared in the sky and many other unusual portents. Prophets and old men around the country were closely questioned respecting their knowledge of the ancient traditions; old paintings and records were taken from every archive. The Peruvian Inca and his kingdom were likewise assaulted by comets and signs from the sky, and the moon was girdled with rings of fire of many colors. One of the royal palaces was struck by a thunderbolt and burned to the ground, while an eagle, the king of birds, was ripped apart by several hawks and fell to the ground at the feet of the Inca in the great square of Cuzco. In Mexico City it was decided that the children of Quetzalcoatl returning in fulfillment of the ancient prophecies should be received with kindness and friendship.

In 1900 Peter De Roo presented a history compiled from many ancient and recent historians regarding the Americas prior to Columbus. These reports detailed the unbelievable variety of native groups from white to black, and every tint of color in between, who inhabited ancient America. De Roo marvels at the different racial types, their unique physiognomy, and especially their diverse languages. De Roo cites (pp. 305–7) Humbolt and Bancroft, who state that, "The various tribes and nations differ so materially from one another as to render it extremely improbable that they are derived from one original stock." De Roo also cites Rafinesque, who says that "American anthropology teaches that there were men of all sizes, features and complexions in this hemisphere before AD 1492, notwithstanding the false assertions of many writers, who take one nation for the whole American group." De Roo mentions numerous tribes as white as the Spanish and many as black as Africans. Rafinesque actually wrote a book on this subject, *Account of the Ancient Black Nations of America.* In 2005 Charles C. Mann resurrected this same theme and also detailed the development and cultivating of numerous foods without which the modern world could not feed itself.

The works of De Roo and Mann clearly establish that the Americas are very ancient and have originated their own particular science, religion, and culture. Yet these facts are noted as "interesting" but the conclusion that they present has not been acted upon or accepted as an academic theme or theory.

Maya Origins

The great achievements of Mayan astronomy have been traced to their predecessors, the Olmecs, who lived in the region of the present state of

Veracruz. At Tres Zapotes archaeologists found a flawless block of basalt 6 feet high and 18 feet in circumference weighing over 10 tons, which had been quarried 10 miles away and brought across a 30-foot-deep gorge of an arroyo. This block represented a finely carved head with broad nose and thick lips. Numerous other heads were found some as tall as 8.5 feet and 22 feet in circumference. These stone heads of the Olmecs at La Venta on the east coast of Tabasco depict faces with features common to Negroid, Egyptian, Semitic, Phoenician, Asian, and other races; but it could also be said that the heads exhibit unique features that we do not recognize but only associate with those people that we know. Peter Tompkins, in his *Mysteries of the Mexican Pyramids* (pp. 351–353), discusses many similarities between the Maya and the Phoenicians:

> Hieroglyphic writing, the custom of deforming the heads of newborn children, infant sacrifice, the use of incense, phallus worship, the depiction of deities floating horizontally over the heads of mortals involved in conversation, twisted rope borders on sarcophagi, and seals, pyramidal temples that rose in terraces to a truncated top, where they were used as astronomical observatories...clay figures depicting dwarfs...the rain god Tlaloc...by the figure of a white man with a handlebar mustache and long beard, holding a thunderbolt of lightning—just as did his Phoenician counterpart *(see Charnay's vases).*

Tomkins goes on to say that when the ancient Phoenician stronghold of Tyre fell to Nebuchadnezzar in the sixth century BC, Carthage became the greatest trading city in the world. Tomkins reports on the 1975 discovery of stones near Cape Cod inscribed with southern Iberian alphabet attributed to the Phoenician Hanno in 475 BC. Also caches of Carthaginian coins were discovered on Corvo, the northwestern island of the Azores. Finally, Tompkins seems to agree with Professor Cyrus Gordon, as well as Charles Michael Boland's *They All Discovered America,* in which Phoenicians, Carthaginians, Greeks, Romans, Irish, Welsh, Basque, and Scandinavians are credited with travels to America.

Our Maya guide said that there are 6,000 temples and pyramids in Yucatan alone, most of them unexplored and unrestored. Some of the great pyramids and temples are of such antiquity that the Maya of olden times had them restored. In many instances, exact reproductions of pyramids have been engineered directly over the old pyramids, as is the case in Chichen Itza and the Templo Mayor in Mexico City.

At Lamanai, "the submerged crocodile," in Belize, archaeologists have found that this large ceremonial center has been continuously occupied at least since 1500 BC. The pyramid at El Mirador in Guatemala, though still not fully excavated, may turn out to exceed the mountainous height (66 meters) of Cholula in Mexico. The El Mirador complex boasts the Danta Complex, which is 300 meters on each side of its base. Its height is a phenomenal 70 meters tall. Another pyramid at this complex is El Tigre at 55 meters in height. And nearby this amazing center are two other overgrown centers called Calakmul and Nakbe.

The real Indiana Jones–type adventurer, Frederick Albert Mitchell-Hedges (1882–1959), discovered one of the crystal skulls at Lubaantun, "the city of Fallen Stones," built with stones that were slightly rounded to fit in with the other stones (Morton, p. 6–9). Mitchell-Hedges, a member of the Maya Committee of the British Museum, believed "that the cradle of civilization was not the Middle East, as was commonly supposed, but the legendary lost continent of Atlantis…and that its remnants were to be found in Central America." The crystal skull was said to be over 100,000 years old and was used by the Maya priests to accurately predict eclipses.

The crystal skulls were not made with steel tools. There are special properties of quartz crystal, possibly to store information or communicate through time and space, like the tiny silicone crystal chips at the heart of modern computers. "Scrying" is known as crystal gazing. Other scrying materials were polished black obsidian ("the smoking mirror"), brass plates, and even bowls of water as used by Nostradamus. The skulls are said to have shown images of how the Earth's land masses looked in former times and many other major changes and natural disasters. One of the supposed messages of the skull is that modern scientists have grossly misunderstood the use of light, sound, and matter.

Tikal—Renovation, Renovation, and Renovation

All Mesoamerican people added to, enlarged, and renovated their temples and monuments. Burials of their noble ancestors were conducted within the temples. This presence sanctified these sites where buildings often were continually built upon former and more ancient structures. Mary Ellen Miller, in her *Maya Art and Architecture* (p. 51), records that when archaeologists tunneled deeper into the Copan Acropolis, they discovered a nine-level pyramid and many buildings upon buildings. "Archaeologists have nicknamed the early buildings that overlie one another like onion skins deep underground..." This building upon building is a common feature throughout all sites in Mexico and Central America. Miller continues (p. 65) to say that when archaeologists pierced the north staircase of the Castillo at Chichen Itza that they exposed a complete smaller version of the same pyramid underneath. Again at the Temple of the Warriors at the same site, archaeologists were amazed to find that a nearly identical version was hidden inside this temple as well.

Harrison, in his *The Lords of Tikal* says that Tikal is flanked by two large wetlands of seasonal swamps that have been crossed by channels to better distribute water. Many of these swamps yielded ground mists, fog, and thick dew at early morning sunrise. This action helped agriculture by nourishing the rain forest. The multitudes of channels are indicative of a once-intensive agricultural system that is not dependent on seasonal rains and can therefore outproduce ordinary farming methods. The tropical forest provided great wealth in mahogany, tropical cedar, and termite-resistant sapodilla wood. There were also the *amapolla*, used to make an intoxicating drink, and condiments for cooking like cilantro and pimiento. The rain forest is also a source for an incredible array of medicines, cures, and an abundance of wildlife, such as white-tailed deer, brocket, peccary, rodents, turkey, and quetzals—for their prized feathers.

Harrison (p. 29) reports that "Tikal" in Yucatec Maya divides the word into "ti," meaning "place of," and "k'al," meaning "spirits" or "place of spirits" or "place of spirit voices." On our own visit to Tikal, we noticed a pronounced "lightness and exuberance" upon entering the site and for the duration of the entire visit. Other tourists also remarked upon identical feelings of freedom from stress and worries. The emblem glyph of Tikal is a "tied bundle." Time was regarded as a bundle carried by the gods. Harrison says that time was a sacred and magical concept, and days, months, and years were viewed as deities carrying a bundle or burden of time. There were good and bad deities and therefore good and bad days, so that the calendar became an instrument of astrology for every member of society. Kings and priests ruled and directed agriculture, wars, and society. When they were successful, they were seen to be the "Masters of Time."

Even after all the efforts of the national government and the University of Pennsylvania, Harrison says that less than 10% of those structures known by mapping have been excavated. The massive pyramid in the area known as the "Lost World" was partially explored and dated from 600 BC to 350 BC. William R. Coe says that (*Tikal*, p. 21) over 3,000 separate constructions have been found over the six square miles of the central site of Tikal. Burials and ritually cached offerings have been found by the hundreds, as have chultuns, subterranean chambers of enigmatic function carved in the bedrock. He demurs, "Perhaps as many as 10,000 earlier platforms and buildings lie sealed beneath the surface features mapped during 1957–1960."

Our Guide at Tikal, Antonio, revealed that the temples of the main complex had been added to in major renovations at least seven times and that the plaza courtyards had three major surfaces superimposed upon one another. Most amazing of all was the fact that an ancient stone map-model in high relief was found interned in one of the temples of the Great Plaza that showed that the final version of Tikal had been planned from the very beginning in the far reaches of antiquity. We can only marvel at the discipline of the Mesoamericans to adhere to such a conception through thousands of years. The site definitely has calming emanations of earth-energy. The existence of such a grid would ensure that the site plan would be followed throughout the ages.

Antonio, our guide, was born at Tikal Maya village, which was eventually moved down the road when the park was initiated. He had studied all the works of the archaeologists pertaining to Tikal. But, more importantly, he had studied under the Maya priests of his community and was able to convey certain matters not generally found in books. He said that the Maya recognized seven directions: north, south, east, west , up, down, and center. He also announced something that I did not understand at that time, namely that the 360-day cycle was related to the east and west axis, while the 260-day cycle was a product of the north and south axis. East-west is of course the path of the sun and the cycle of 360-365 days. North-south is the direction of the Milky Way, which transfers human life through a gestation cycle of 260 days to our planet. Antonio hoped that the 2012 event would be the beginning of a worldwide "spiritual awakening."

There are about 14 major *aguada,* or reservoirs, around the site of Tikal. Coe says that there is a solid mantel of porous limestone underlying Tikal, and practically all of the Peten retains water very poorly. There are no underground rivers or wells such as the *cenotes* in Yucatan. Antonio went to great lengths to explain the engineering of the platforms, ground levels, and the angle and inclination of pyramid steps, which were all disposed to direct water from the channels filling the aguada. Considering the huge populations gathered around these complexes, one might consider that the Maya were favored with dependable rainy seasons. Yet, Maya architecture shows that the Maya were able to adapt to a variety of circumstance. Miller (*Maya Art*, p. 24, 36) contrasts the annual rainfall of 28 inches in Northern Yucatan with the 120 inches of annual rainfall in the rain forests of Chiapas, yet both areas boasted great Maya cities. Miller tells us that at Palenque, Maya engineers had canalized the Otulum River, bringing running water into the palace as well as supplying water for three toilets in the Tower court.

Miller (*Maya Art*, pp. 28–35) says that the great cities of the Peten, like El Mirador and Tikal, grew up around swampy areas that were more favorable for agriculture than lakes and rivers where rains quickly drain from the poor surrounding land. We personally saw road cuttings in the area that revealed only a four-to-eight-inch layer of poor topsoil covering the ever-present karst limestone rock. Miller reveals that the elevated roads span swampy areas to link complexes built on solid outcroppings of rock. Miller also says that outside of the unique Peten region that the Maya castles and temples were sighted strategically to command lookout views of key points along rivers, confluences, and lowland plains.

Antonio revealed that the Maya had practiced crop rotation on their extensive terraces. Archaeologist discovered that the Maya surrounded their complexes with a medicinal arboretum, which became the drugstore for their community. These were the trees that seeded themselves to eventually cover over and hide the sites after they were abandoned. Studying skeleton remains demonstrated that rulers were typically around six feet tall and lived to between 60 and 100 years of age. The middle-class merchants, scribes, and artisans were about 5'6" in height and lived to between 45 and 60 years of age. Farmers and laborers were often between less than five feet tall and 5'6", and their lifespan was 28 to 45 years long.

These standards were directly influenced by the quality of diet. Farmers usually have access to food, so this is a difficult statistic to accept. However, close to the abandonment of these sites the rulers introduced more and more games and 20-year festivals in place of the more distant 52-year celebrations to assuage the general populace as drought, disease, and overpopulation continued to assault Maya civilization. We were amazed at the prevalence of many ball courts within the same complex. If, indeed, the Olmec (which means rubber) inspired the Maya, the presence of rubber-ball courts certainly proves a strong connection with these earlier people.

Mexico City

The 2003 article "Museum of the Great Temple" from the INAH—Instituto Nacional de Anthropologia e Historia—says (pp.13–17) that the Great Temple of Tenochtitlan was enlarged seven times, and on four occasions only the main façade was extended. A double aqueduct conducted a large stream of water to the fountains and reservoirs at Tenochtitlan. In its final glory, it measured 80x80 meters at its base and 40 meters in height before it was destroyed by the Spaniards and its building blocks used to construct the new cathedral and city. The monumental size of the square, 500 meters x 500 meters, and the exquisite design of the city located in a high mountain volcanic zone protected from the winds all testifies to the antiquity of this premier site.

The pyramids near Mexico City are located at Teotihuacan, said to have been built by the gods long ago. It was also called "the place where the sun was born," "the place where the heavens meet the earth," and "the place of the men who knew the road of the gods."

Morton says (p. 115,135) that Toltecs, the Teotihuacanos, and the Maya preceded the Aztec, who were strangers to the land of Mexico and came from the place called "Aztlan" and also a region called "the seven caves." The native historian Jose Salomez Sanchez writes that the Aztec betrayed the native races, regarding themselves as the "chosen people." They also rewrote history after destroying the historical documents of the past.

Morton continues (p. 131) to say that the Aztec adopted and became obsessed with the science of the "ancient skywatchers" and based their culture around the observation of the skies. Their buildings were all oriented to the four cardinal directions of the compass and, "Furthermore, most of their deities were placed among the sky forces. Their daily lives and all their rituals and ceremonies were guided by the movement of the heavenly bodies." Even the practice of human sacrifice had astrological significance, as they believed that the sun was a mortal being that had to be fed the blood of humans.

The language of the Aztec features extremely long, multisyllabic names. This is an indication of a fresh and newly forming tongue, while older languages have curt and abbreviated names for people and things.

Teotihuacán

Anthony Aveni (p. 229) writes that Doris Heyden (1975) of Mexico's Instituto Nacional de Antropologia e Historia believes that the placement of the great Mexican Sun Pyramid was determined by the location of the multichambered flower-shaped cave discovered beneath it. This cave is the place "where time began," and "the birthplace of the gods." One 16th-century historian wrote that a god went into the cave and came out as the moon. Teotihuacán is a mandala representing the ancient cosmovision of sky, earth, mountain, cave, and time in a scientific and religious context.

The main orientation of Teotihuacan is about 15½° east of north based upon an ancient pecked-cross symbol on stone. Aveni says that this orientation may have been directed toward the Pleiades star group and is no longer functional because of precession. Of course, this alignment would once again function after a full cycle of precession after 25,920 years. Ancient cosmologers thought in terms of millions of years during which numerous cycles of precession had been fulfilled. The pecked-cross engraving and alignment is shared by buildings of Toltec design at Tula, and the Temple of the Warriors at Chichen Itza. It is noteworthy that the Toltec Atlantean Warriors bear a strong stylistic resemblance to the statues at Tiwanaku, Bolivia. The east-of-north orientation is shared with many ceremonial centers in Central Mexico and Mesoamerica. Even a 17° alignment has been found at the Temple of the Plumed Serpent at Xochicalco and also in raised fields in the tropical lowlands of Veracruz to Belize (pp. 234–5).

Teotihuacan is called a place of origin, where the gods were born and where time began. But the complex is centered on the "Avenue of the Dead." One must also marvel at the Mexica-Maya preoccupation with ceremonial walls of skulls at Chichen Itza, the Templo Mayor in Mexico City, and that their gods carry skulls on their belts. If it is correct that the ancient prime meridian on the Atlantic separates Capricorn from Aquarius in a scheme where the Earth is laid out to correspond to the regions of the heavens, then Mexico and Central America correspond to the zodiac region of Scorpio, which is the entrance gate of all souls to the underworld. Phallic symbols, circumcision, and penis-blood-letting (connected with Scorpio) are extraordinarily developed ritual usages in these regions. Is it possible that a universal global system of cosmology was developed in ancient times that linked regions of the globe with the celestial sphere? This would have meant that all ancient people recognized Teotihuacan as a powerful place, the portal to the underworld and communication with the past. Scorpio/Sagittarius in modern terms is the exact location of the black hole matrix of the Milky Way Galaxy. The ancient people certainly knew more about the galaxy than we did. All of this sounds pretty bizarre to our uninformed minds, but what if it is all true?

Yucatan Maya

Yucatan presents an extraordinary landscape of crumbling limestone undermined by great underground rivers that erode and cause enormous deep sinkholes to appear in the countryside. Those who have not swum in the sweet waters of the sacred Cenote of *Ik Kil* cannot have complete knowledge of the land and culture of the Yucatan Maya. Ik Kil is a gigantic sinkhole caved in under a pig searching for water in ancient times. Access is by a long, serpentine stepped tunnel cut out of the limestone with two *miradors* at different levels looking down upon the pond that lies about 300 feet below the beautiful garden above. They say the water is 150 feet deep, communicating with an underground river that keeps the water extremely fresh and potable. The surface of the pond is about 80 yards across. While swimming, it is amazing to look up to the gigantic hole in the roof of this cavern, whose tall sides are clothed in creeping vines, as some water spills downward irradiated by the bright sunshine from above. A large, flat area below accommodates entry and exit from the pool. Stairs lead up to elevated diving platforms. Breezes enter through the tunnel and recirculate above, keeping the atmosphere immaculately fresh. The pool is full of swimmers, divers, and jumpers being admired by the spectators from the miradors above. The intense sunshine is filtered by the cool, wet limestone sides covered with jungle vegetation. The effect of such a scene is ethereal and engraved upon the mind.

In sharp contrast to this paradisiacal beauty is the hard, crumbled limestone surface above, which is only covered by inches of dried soil. Hurricanes periodically level the larger trees (which thrive growing out of the cracks of the limestone), leaving the country looking like it received a short crew cut from the barber. Much of Ireland suffers the same predicament, where only a skin of soil covers the limestone. In Ireland, however, the Gulf Stream–driven Atlantic storms give life to an otherwise uninhabitable geography. Likewise, in Yucatan, the summer rainy season helps to replenish the underground circulatory system of rivers refreshing the parched country above.

Quetzalcoatl-Kukulcan

The history, science, and religion of Mesoamerica is pervaded by Quetzalcoatl in Mexico, who is called Kukulcan by the Maya in Yucatan. This god is identified as the lord of sun, rain, and all things in nature and the cosmos. Kukulcan is mostly portrayed in sculpture as a human head born out of the mouth of a serpent whose scales are feathers and who sometimes has wings and bird talons—hence his name, "the feathered serpent." The symbolism is obviously that of a snake whose wisdom of natural science has been elevated to the skies. Again the Egyptian icon at most temple entrances is that of a solar sun disc, two royal serpents, and the wings of an eagle. These elements combined together might suggest "the entrance to the Temple of Cosmological Wisdom of the cycles of the sun." Andean art substitutes the condor whose magnificent wingspan allows him to adapt to the thin air of the extreme high elevations.

Dual serpents usually denote the equinoxes. Such a representation appears on the Killamery Stone Cross in Ireland. On the reverse side of this particular cross is a spiral symbol that may denote the Milky Way galaxy, rather than a simple solar image. The Pyramid of the Magician at Chichen Itza is a cosmic temple that expresses the measures of the universe like the Temple of Solomon and Angkor Wat. Aveni writes (p. 300) that the pyramid is radial, with the temple surmounting it being accessible by stairways on all four sides. Looked at from above, it resembles the quadripartite diagrams of the universe the ancient Maya painted in their codices that show four directional gods, planets, trees, and animals. The monument's proportions are laden with numbers and directions that bespeak the ancient Maya organization of cyclical time. Landa said that it has four stairways looking to the four directions of the world with 91 steps each (4 x 91 = 364 plus the temple). The Castillo also has nine platforms—the same number as the calendrical cycle represented by the nine lords of the night or underworld. The stairways that bisect them result in 18 platforms on each side (18 x 4 =72), which is the number of months in the

Maya year (18 x 20 = 360). Finally there are recessed panels that adorn each pyramid face. There are 52 of these, the same number of years in the Calendar Round when the same day and month in the 365-day calendar realigns with the 260-day calendar.

Irwin, in her *Fair Gods and Stone Faces* (Ch. 4), relates that Quetzalcoatl is said to have come from the east, where the sun rises. He was a fair-skinned and bearded god dressed in a flowing robe. He appeared and settled in several places in Mexico, bringing information and knowledge. He is the traditional master builder of American civilization. Some believe that Quetzalcoatl is a combination of several personages—one who came very early in the far-distant past and others who followed him. Confusingly, Toltec high priests assumed this name with their office.

The Maya and Aztec had written records of ages past, including the knowledge, exploits, and military conquests of Quetzalcoatl. When these documents were burned in the holocaust of the Spanish Franciscan Inquisitors, the native priests cried out in terrified anguish, and many committed suicide. Columbus visited Nicaragua and reported that their books were "large sheets of cotton very elaborately and cleverly worked, and delicately painted in colors." The destruction of these manuscripts was soon regretted, and Spanish chroniclers searched oral sources. Franciscan Bernardino de Sahagun consulted the oldest and most learned natives and set up schools translating traditions into the Roman alphabet. One of his creations praises all the arts, crafts, and skills that Quetzalcoatl taught to the Toltecs at Tula and the abundance of corn and squashes that he grew there. It is also told how he punctured his legs (or private parts) with thorns in penance until the blood came forth.

Juan de Torquemada, a late 16th-century chronicler, says that the people of Quetzalcoatl were dressed in long robes of black linen, as the natives use to this day in their dances. They came by way of Panuco (near modern Tampico in the north) to Tula and finally settled in Cholula, where his people remained and multiplied and sent colonists to Upper and Lower Mixteca and the Zapotecan country. The remains of their edifices are still to be seen at Mictlan. They were people of great knowledge and clever in all arts, except masonry and the use of the hammer. Quetzalcoatl, Toltec, and Tula are part of one story. Tula is located about 50 miles north of Mexico City. Excavations exposed the gigantic pillars called "Atlantes," whose heads are as tall as a man. Before the coming of the Aztecs, the Chichimecs had succeeded the Toltec, who were called "the master builders."

Torquemada says that Quetzalcoatl wore a long, yellow, straw-colored beard. Elsewhere it says that Quetzalcoatl was a large white man, broad-browed, with huge eyes, long black hair, and a great rounded beard. Some said he appeared in a white robe decorated with crosses. Not everyone concurs that Quetzalcoatl came from the east as the native interpreter of Cortez proclaimed. Many said that the god simply just appeared. He became a catchall of multiple attributes: sun god as well as god of the wind and air.

The great pyramids of Mexico City are located at Teotihuacan, a name associated with the pre-Toltec builders of this site—people who are said to have known "the road to the gods." The Teotihuancanos were also responsible for Cholula (60 miles southeast of Mexico City) and Azcopotzalco. The great pyramid at Cholula covers 45 acres, an area larger than that covered by the Great Pyramid at Giza in Egypt. It is constructed of sun-dried bricks and covers an even more ancient ceremonial precinct composed of a maze of temples, where they have come across frescoes similar to those found at Teotihuacán. Irwin writes (p. 59) that legends of the Tower of Babel at Babylon are similar to the legends of Cholula, which say:

> After the deluge which destroyed the primeval world, seven giants survived. One of them Xelhua, then built the great pyramid of Cholula in order to reach heaven. But the gods destroyed the pyramid with fire and confounded the language of the builders.

This idea of "reaching heaven" is similar to "the road to the gods" spoken about Teotihuacán. Here the great Pyramid of the Sun rises in four levels and was surmounted by a temple that contained a colossal statue of the sun god burnished in gold and silver, which the Spanish Bishop Zummaraga destroyed. Most importantly, the Temple of Quetzalcoatl at Teotihuacan features his symbol of the feathered serpent alternating with the symbol of the rain god Tlaloc, and these symbols are joined by a lower relief bearing an undulating design suggestive of waves. Underneath the waves are images of seashells. The site of Teotihuacan is enigmatic and still hides its ancient origins. Archaeologists do agree that the site was extensively altered, redecorated, and rebuilt in 150 BC, possibly because of a change in religion (Irwin, p. 53).

Purposeful Mutilation and Cranial Deformation

Constance Irwin (p. 251) discusses Gladwin's theory. He begins in the Near East with the Armenoids, whose noses first appeared on the frescoes depicting the ancient Hittites, later becoming the hallmark of all peoples of the Eastern Mediterranean. In the Levant, these Armenoids intentionally flattened the heads of their children. The same practice is in Samoa, Tonga, the Marquesas, Fiji, and throughout Polynesia.

According to Drew in *The Lost Chronicles of the Maya Kings*, history shows us many instances of elite classes who built monuments and temples, lived in luxury, consumed the best produce, and either enslaved—or by some other means held captive—a significant labor force. These elite ruling classes often demonstrated their position above the common herd of humanity through physical signs, sometimes contorting the human body in specific forms.

Irwin writes (p. 103) that, according to S.G. Morley, depressed foreheads were considered a mark of beauty among the ancient Maya, and this deformation was achieved by binding the heads of the babies between a pair of flat boards, one at the back of the head and the other at the forehead. These boards were left in place for several days, and after they were removed, the head remained flattened for life. Maya representations of the human head in profile show that this practice must have been almost universal among the upper classes, the priests and nobles. It is also known that Maya mothers strove to make their children cross-eyed by attaching a ball of wax to a forelock and leaving it to dangle between the eyebrows. The beak-nosed Maya god, Itzamna, was shown to be cross-eyed. Certain adult Maya also wore artificial nose pieces to make the bridge of the nose seem higher.

In Peru sites were discovered where the cranium was deliberately deformed to an extraordinary elongated shape by forcible compression; this was produced by binding the heads of infants between a pair of wooden boards. Some skulls of infants were found with the boards still attached. There are some on display in the Museum of Cuzco.

Mayan and Peruvian aristocrats followed the example of the Egyptian types of beauty in preferring dolichocephalic (eggheads) to flattened platycephalic (flatheads), or round heads. In addition, an aristocratic mouth and chin was preferred to the Neanderthal jaw. In the British Army these type of aristocrats were called "chinless wonders," most of whom advanced to the officer's grade. The authors of these articles find that groups espousing these special elite forms of beauty were aiming for perpetual "dominance" over other groups. Furthermore, they say that sociability, kindness, and social responsibility are now known to have evolved associated with that area of the normal human brain within the high forehead of modern humans. The purposeful flattening of the forebrain (*platycephalic* skull) by elitists is indicative of the loss or atrophy of normal humanitarian feelings and traits. On the other hand, Native Americans had a tradition that used "cradle boards" to flatten the *back* of the skull to promote more humanity in their children and therefore prevent authoritarianism and elitism, which has occurred many times in human history.

CHAPTER 7.3

Mexica-Maya Cosmos

Mexico, Yucatan, and the Andes Range lie in the geography of Scorpio and Sagittarius. According to the Greek generations of the gods the geography of Scorpio belonged to the era of Uranus and Ge, while Sagittarius belonged to the time of Helios and the Titians.

The Portal of the Sun at Tiwanaku shows a kneeling cosmologer surrounded by condor men who represent the astronomical priests associated with the condor, the king of the birds of the air. Mexica-Maya-Andean astronomy represents a most sophisticated tradition of ancient science that has been recorded in history and that is a living tradition still practiced today. Included in this category are the customs of the Kogi of Columbia. Many European scholars from the time of the Renaissance to the Elizabethan Age have regarded America as Atlantis, most notably Francis Bacon, who wrote *New Atlantis* modeled upon the idealized Atlantis in the *Timaeus* of Plato. In modern times, the Indiana Jones prototype and a member of the Maya Committee of the British Museum, Frederick Mitchell-Hedges, believed that the cradle of civilization was not in the Middle East but rather upon the continent of Atlantis, whose remnants were found in Mesoamerica.

Of course, one of the great fascinations of the Americas was the extent and accuracy of their astronomics from the simple but highly accurate Medicine Wheels of North America to the world-class complexes of Teotihuacán, Chichen Itza, and Tikal in Middle America and finally to the wonders of Peru and Bolivia, to which nothing can compare. Karl Taube writes (p. 75) that,

> Ancient Mesoamerican calendrics, astrology and mythology were thus integrated into a single compelling system of belief… The profound influence on Mesoamerican life of the movements of the sun, stars, planets and other celestial bodies was also reflected in the mythology… the stars and planets may have served as a basic structural model for the development of Mesoamerican mythology.

An important clarification to the above statement is that myth is the historical record of the past. Cosmologers discovered the relationship between history and astronomy, encapsulated in the paradigm, "on earth as it is in heaven."

Taube introduces (p. 14) the subject of Aztec-Maya calendrics, saying that these systems were not used simply to delineate periods of time:

> They also distinguished intervals that were especially charged with sacred and often dangerous powers. The peoples of ancient Mesoamerica keenly observed the sky and used the calendar to predict solar and lunar eclipses, the cycles of the planet Venus, the apparent movements of the constellations and other celestial events. To them, these occurrences were not the mechanical movements of innate celestial objects but constituted the activities of gods, the actual recapitalization of mythical events from the time of creation.

The Mexica-Maya worldview related ancient mythology and history to the constellations that make up the yearly path of the sun. This rich tapestry represents a vibrant picture of the past, current, and future events of the world drama. Their worldview is likened unto a sacred lemon tree, where new blossoms coexist with green ripening fruit and yellow fruit in its complete maturity. This is so because larger cycles are still moving onward, middle cycles are completing, and new cycles are beginning. Therefore every moment of time contains the threefold richness of the past, the present, and the future.

In *Maya Cosmos* (p. 112), Linda Schele has composed an exquisite summary of Maya cosmology called "Creation and the Sky":

When we put together the Creation images and texts of the Classic period with the myth of the Popol Vuh, the miracle of the entire story touched us to our deepest core. The great cosmic symbols of the ancient Maya are a map of the sky, but the sky itself is a great pageant that replays Creation in the pattern of its yearly movements. Sunset on August 13 darkens the sky to reveal Itzam-Yeh (Seven Macaw) falling from the tree after he has been shot by the firstborn twin, One-Ahwa (Hunahpu). Then the Crocodile Tree transforms into a canoe. This canoe runs east to west, propelled by the Jaguar Paddler and the Stingray Paddler, or by Itzamna, the original shaman. As the canoe sinks under the water, it brings the Maize God to the place of Creation, the space between Gemini and Orion. The Paddler Gods and other Itz'at center the sky by setting the three stones of Creation [Orion's belt]. This is also the hearth where the first fire is drilled. They draw the picture of the turtle and the peccaries on the earth and the sky simultaneously at First-Three-Stone-Place at Lying-down-Sky. There also, Hun-Nal-Ye, the Maize God rises reborn from the cracked turtle shell. The copulating peccaries of Gemini…lie nearby. Perhaps the Maya also once shared the Aztec definition of Gemini as a star ballcourt—the one where the Maize God stayed after he was reborn so that humanity could worship him. As the Maize God is reborn from the Turtle-Peccary of Orion, his umbilicus stretches out to become the ecliptic on which his sons, Venus and the Sun, and his wife the Moon, will travel through the new Creation. When the day dawns, the first acts of Creation come to fruition. On February 5, sunset finds First-Three-Stone-Place still at the center of the sky. It sinks toward the west, taking the handful of seeds (the Pleiades) to be planted in the earth. This is also an image of four hundred boys (stars) falling to their death. After midnight, the Black-Transformer appears and from this great sky-wide portal the Wakah-Chan rises, along the entire eastern horizon until it is arching from north to south across the heavens. First Father has raised the sky in the form of the Milky Way, a great tree with its buttress roots in the south. This Wakah-Chan arches north to touch the heart of heaven, the black void that was the celestial north

> in ancient times. When he raised the sky, First Father created a house in the north made of eight partitions. On earth these unfold as the *kan tzuk, kan xuk*, "four partitions, four corners." When all was finished, First Father started the constellations moving in the circular motion "that sustains the very vault of heaven until the end of time"—until the next Creation. The gods wrote all of these actions in the sky so that every human, commoner and king alike, could read them and affirm the truth of the myth.

When Schele's wonderful description is reduced to plain English, it translates as a straightforward astronomical ephemeris of the rotation of the sky. But even the uninitiated may appreciate the vibrancy of the cosmic images associated with ancient myth, religion, and cosmology.

Mexica-Maya Number Systems

The great Pyramids of the Sun, Moon, and Quetzalcoatl at Teotihuacán celebrated the great trinity of sun, moon, and child. Quetzalcoatl was the newborn incarnation of the spirit. This site is far older than the Aztecs who celebrated its antiquity with annual pilgrimages. When you name a locale "the place where time began," you are in fact saying, "the place where people first began to measure time and astronomical cycles." In a word, Aztec and Maya became astronomers and cosmologers and Masters of Time. This was the structure of the worldview by which their world was defined and through which the rulers created order for their society. Astronomy was used in every aspect of life, art, and the planning and layout of sites and buildings. Important astronomical manuscripts from the Mixtecs, Nuttall/Zouche, and Maya have survived the burning of books by the Inquisition of the Holy Roman Church. Some of these are the Borgia, Vienna, Dresden, Paris, Madrid, and Grolier codices.

Most ancient people guarded their science and trade secrets so well that, among both Egyptians and Maya, there is no evidence of development. Irwin quotes Diringer, saying (p. 109), "At the time of their first appearance, the Maya script and astronomical and mathematical knowledge are fully developed, and this presupposes a previous evolution of long development—of which nothing is known..."

It would seem that the Maya used a system based upon sticks, which equaled a hand of five digits. In olden times, shepherds counted groups of five sheep by reaching out a hand to count by fives. Mayan mathematics, like that of other American aborigines, was vigesimal (by twenties, the sum of fingers plus toes). The Maya indicated place value vertically rather than the Western fashion of horizontal place value. Ones were shown by dots or pebbles, while fives were indicated by lines or sticks. The first level in vertical placement indicated values from 1–20. On the second-highest level appeared lines and dots whose value was 20 times the first level. The third level represented values that were 400 times the first level. The ultimate level of lines and dots meant 8,000 times the first level.

The Mesoamericans used the zero in very olden times as a conclusion after 19 and as a new beginning before 21. There is some evidence that the Babylonians at one time in the past used the notation of zero, which later reappeared in India. Zero allows one to use large complicated numbers with some ease. Aboriginals in Australia can count up to four, but their number for five is "many." C.W. Ceram remarks that even the Greeks regarded the number 10,000 as "a large, uncountable aggregation." He also says that, "It was not until the nineteenth century that the concept of a million becomes common in the West." While a Mesopotamian cuneiform text records the number 195,955,200,000,000, such a sizeable amount did not enter the realm of calculation until the days of Descartes and Leibniz. The modern age is still a time that does not easily conceptualize large numbers well.

Large Maya Numbers

One of the Maya secrets may be the 819-day "never-ending" cycle composed of the holy numbers 7 x 9 x 13 = 819. The 819-day count mediates computations between the 360- and the 364-day count cycles. Miller and Taube (p. 52) say that it is related to the four cardinal directions and always counted backward from the Initial Series. C. W. Johnson, in *The Aztec Calendar, Math and*

Design, says that strange numbers appear in the historical record, such as 756, 819, 151, 840, and 1,366,560, which reveal unsuspected interrelationships.

Milone and Kelley report that many of the monument dates are badly eroded. Variant forms of glyphs for extremely large periods of time are known from a number of inscriptions. No one has devised names for the glyphs of the longer periods known only from the Yaxchilan inscription. The longest period in this inscription refers to 10,240,000,000,000 *tuns* (years of 360 days). The date is that of a ballgame played by the Maya ruler of Yaxchilan.

Mesoamerican and Maya Calendrics

Ancient Mexica-Maya calendars may be traced back to the Olmec. But there is no definitive start date because of the antiquity of the many astronomical cultures of the Americas, such as the Kogi of Columbia and Tiwanaku on the border of Peru-Bolivia.

Western European culture is based upon a four-part (quartered) division of the year into seasons of spring, summer, autumn, and winter, demarcated by the equinoxes and solstices. Mexica-Maya-Andean culture marked the equinoxes and solstices, but they also divided the year into three (triangular) agricultural-ceremonial seasons. The threefold partition of the seasons was also employed by the Egyptians in their seasons of Inundation (June–September, four months), Emergence (October–February, five months), and Harvest (March–May, three months). It is most curious that this pattern follows the 5-4-3 form of the Pythagorean triangle. Again nature is found to be in accord with geometry and mathematics.

The Mayan system may be seen in their 360-day cycle of 18 x 20 days, which can also be divided into three seasons of 120 days each (120 x 3 = 360 days). The number 18 is, of course, reminiscent of the Vedic system of 666 (6 + 6 + 6 = 18). The Mayan system is a curious composite of the sexagesimal and the vigesimal, which could also be called the "quadradigital" (4 x 5). Therefore, the Mexica-Maya-Andean system may be seen as the oldest and most inclusive of all mathematical systems, because it can accommodate and synchronize quartered and triangular counting systems. Thereby many possible geometric forms are compatible with this amazing system.

Review of the Calendar Round

The 360-day period plus five "nameless and unlucky" days at the end of the year composed the 365-day calendar. The famous Calendar Round occurred every 52 years when both the 260- and the 365-day cycles coincided on the identical day (73 x 260 =18,980 days = 52 x 365).

Miller and Taube say (p. 54), "Such numerical coincidences of interlocking cycles appealed to Mesoamerican calendar keepers and facilitated calculations... Because of the extreme malevolence associated with Venus... special attention was given to the risings of the morning and evening star immediately following conjunction, as well as to points of maximum brightness, maximum elongation, and to stationary points."

Mexico and the Maya lands are under the sign of Scorpio when the celestial sphere is cojoined with the geographic globe. In astrology, Venus and Mars are daytime rulers of the triangle of Scorpio-Pisces-Cancer. Therefore, the movements of Venus and Mars were extremely important in this particular geography. On the cosmic human body, Scorpio is related to the private parts of the anatomy. This region of the globe is extraordinary in the preponderance of phallic symbols, circumcision from ancient times, and blood offering from incision into the secret parts. Large quantities of the phallic images were removed, hidden, and destroyed during the prudish reign of Maximilian.

William Coe, in his *Maya Methods of Dating at Tikal*, says that the Calendar Round is a permutation, or meshing, of three basic cycles:

The Sacred Round:

1) 13 numbered days.

2) A second cycle of 20 named days. Maya notation of "zero" came after 19, thus (18, 19, 0, 1, 2, 3...), "Zero was conceived of as completion in one sense and as beginning in another."
   13 x 20 =260

3) The solar year, or *Vague Year* of 365 days.

The Sacred Round was used in reckoning ceremonial matters. Coe says, "260 and 365 have 5 as their common 'divisor'; thus 5 x 52 x 73 = 18,980 days. The number 18,980 is also rationally divisible by their holy number 13 = 1460." It is really not such a coincidence that 1460 (days) is the same number as the Egyptian Sothic cycle of 1460 (years) because 13 has been shown to be a holy matrix number.

The Maya Long Count (sometimes called the Initial Series) stems from extreme antiquity and is known from a few very early monuments in the Olmec and Izapan styles. Again we must reiterate that Maya cosmology was extremely accurate because it was rectified and synchronized through the use of numerous independent astronomical cycles:

- *Kin* = 1 day
- *Uinal* = 20 days (1 x 20)
- *Tun* = 360 days (18 x 20) also (6 + 6 + 6 x 20)
- *Katun* = 7,200 days (360 x 20)
- *Baktun* = 144,000 days (7,200 x 20)
- *Baktun 9* x 144,000 days = 3,600 years
- *Calendar Round* = *Baktun 13* x 144,000 days =1,872,000 days =5,200 Years (1/5 of the Precessional cycle of 26,000 years).
- *Pictun* = 8,000 years (360 day years) [400 x 20]
- *Calabtun* = 160,000 years (360 day years) [8,000 x 20]
- *Kinchiltun* = 3,200,000 years (360 day years) [160,000 x 20]

It is certainly curious that the *Baktun* cycle of 144,000 days compares to the Middle Eastern astronomical cycle of 144,000 years or people to be saved at the Last Judgment. The Book of Revelation says that 144,000 will be saved; 144,000 is a prime sexagesimal number, which, when divided by the sexagesimal fractal 216 = 666.666. Maya astronomy appears to include a combination of sexagesimal and vigesimal. There is also a high preponderance of the use of the number 144,000 in the Maya world. William R. Coe says that, "Most of the recorded dates on the monuments at Tikal and other Maya sites are associated with Baktun 9, which is 9 x 144,000 =1,296,000 days."

CHAPTER 7.4

Astronomy of the Andes

In 2009 in Miraflores, Peru, I discovered an amazing book about the ancient astronomical culture of the Andes. The 2008, fifth edition of *Genesis de La Cultura Andina* (continually updated since 1983) is the culmination of a life's work of Carlos Milla Villena, member of the College of Architects, Society of Astronomy, Archaeology, Culture, Urban Development, and countless other societies. His book documents the unique range of ancient cosmology on this side of the planet. It convinces us that this astronomy is the most ancient—and yet still existing—science in the world.

The Andes of Columbia, Ecuador, Peru, Bolivia, and Chile contain one of the richest assemblages of megalithic sites on our planet. But what good does it do if these stones do not tell their story and explain their meaning. Professor Milla Villena guides the reader through symbols, mathematics, geodesy, astronomy, and celestial observatories of ancient people who lived in the Andes long before the time of the Inca. The Inca were like the Aztec: powerful administrators and organizers who restored many ancient sites but had nothing to do with their original intention and layout.

Carlos Milla Villena explains (p. 35) that Andean cosmology is focused toward the South Pole and more precisely upon the four stars of the Southern Cross, the *Cruz del Sur.* In Andean astrophysics, our galaxy, which contains our solar system, which in turn is home to our Earth is all being swept along toward the Great Attractor in the universe located in the direction of the Cruz del Sur. Ancient festivals were celebrated during the appearance of this constellation around the night of the 2nd of May. Peru is home to an amazing number of light-and-shadow plays to mark astronomical phenomena.

Milla Villena demonstrates that the cup holes in giant rock formations were filled with water to accurately mirror and observe the precise time of the overhead culminations of sun, moon, constellations, and stars. The capillary nature of water combined with the shape of the bowl compensates for the refraction and reflection of celestial light. These cup holes are found all over the world but are often wrongly identified as grinding mortars because degenerate peoples later used them as such. Moreover, Milla Villena shows countless examples of portable ceramic sighting vessels as well as miniature images of astronomers using these bowls. These figures suggest that astronomers working in unison in such broad planes as Nazca could have marked out constellations accurately and in perfect proportion to other constellations employing the Earth as a gigantic celestial chart. The water bowls pick up the starlight in the same relationship as a human sees the stars in the sky. Therefore the geoglyphs are in exact proportion to the stars in the sky.

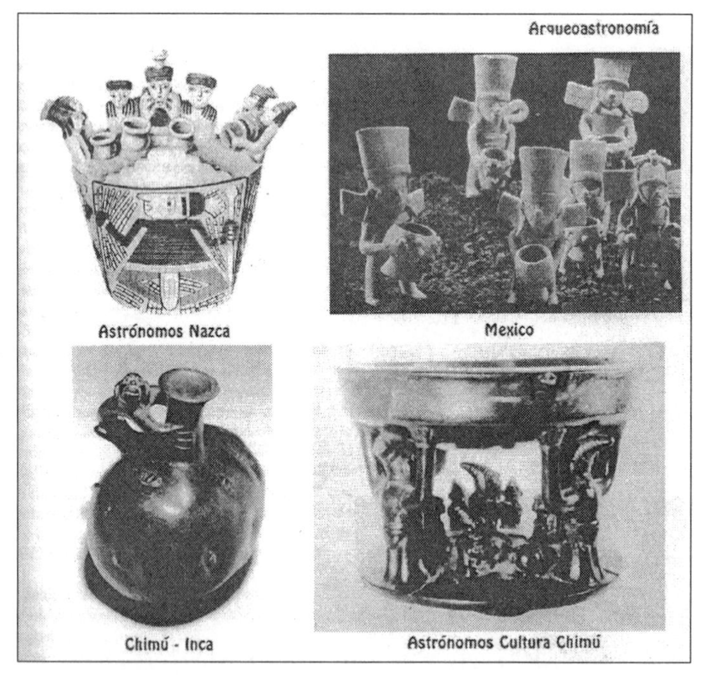

Astronomers using bowls to determine exact star correlations on the Earth. Courtesy Carlos Milla Villena

Milla Villena (p. 82) proposes that Andean astronomy came from Salinas del Chao, an ancient complex centered around a geoglyph of the Southern Cross. Students of Western culture are accustomed to the golden-mean relationship of phi (.618 ϕ) in art and architecture. However, Andean culture is based upon the diagonal of a square, which represents the major axis of the height of the Southern Cross, while any side of the square represents the arm of the Southern Cross. Andean culture celebrates the quadrature of the circle and the concept of pi (3.14 π), which they call "Katari." The Andean square stepped cross, the "Chakana," is divided into 13 squares, the holy number of all Mexica-Maya-Andean culture, as well as the rest of the world.

Milla Villena then goes on to show that the Muyucmarca area of the famous astronomical site Sacsayhuaman (above Cuzco) was an astronomical mirror and sighting pond. Such structures are to be found worldwide, many of them in the form of ornamental fountains, such as the one in the plaza in front of the Pyramid of the Moon at Teotihuacán outside Mexico City.

Carlos Milla Villena discusses various Luni-Solar calendar sites beginning with Chankillo in Casma, Peru, which is laid out very similarly to Avebury in England. In the Aymara language, such calendar sites are called *Purana Wasi,* "the house of the full moon." The Purana Wasi of Chankillo watches the rise of 13 full moons each year from their elevated observatory against 13 distant, truncated pyramids that act as foresights to determine the position of the moon. The moons, therefore, accurately depict the Earth's perihelion during winter near the solstice and the proximity of the spring and fall equinoxes as well as the closeness to the summer solstice, which marks the aphelion position of the Earth.

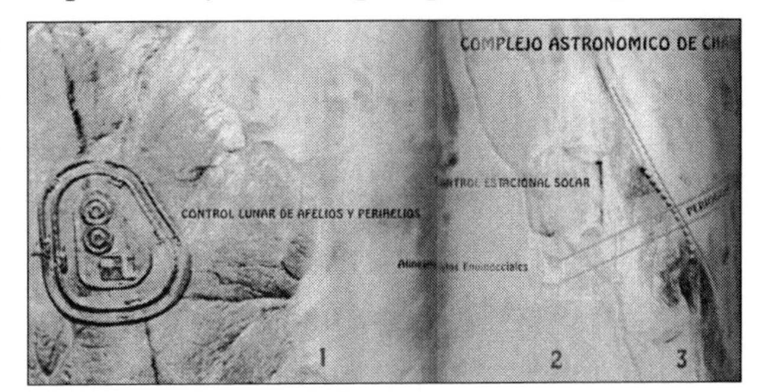

<u>*Cycles of the Moon*</u>

The movement of the moon is subject to numerous perturbations that make the exact location of the moon difficult to pinpoint. The moon completes a full rotation from the same stars (in the background) back to those same stars in 27.321 days. This is called a sidereal period—from star to same star). But during a month, the Earth has moved along considerably in its own orbit around the sun, so that the Moon has to go star-to-star plus catch up to the movement of the Earth. This is called the synodic period, a conjunction with the Earth till the next conjunction with the Earth (new moon to new moon). This period is about 29.530 days.

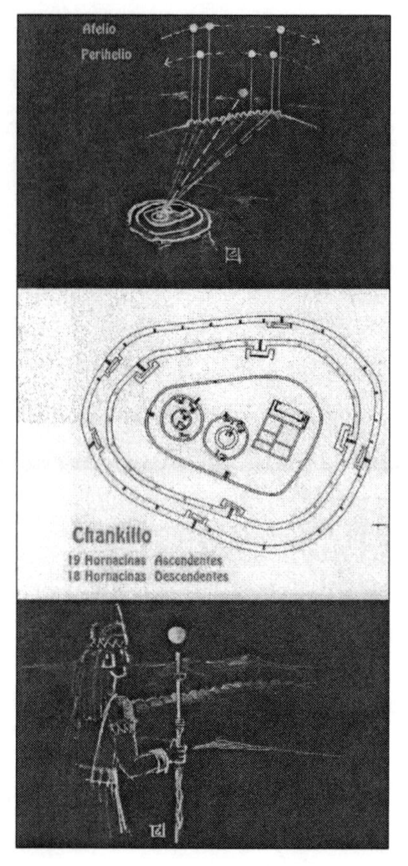

The Lunar observatory, *Purana Wasi,* of Chanquillo, Peru. Courtesy Carlos Milla Villena, *Genesis de la Cultura Andina*

The Moon's orbit around the Earth is elliptical. And this ellipse slides along in one complete rotation in 8.85 years. The reason for this sliding is that the foci of the ellipse cannot stay in place because the Earth's rapid motion around the Sun. Therefore all the phases of the moon appear up to 26% larger or smaller at different times. This is, of course, especially noticeable during the full moon. These two points of the ellipse are called the *apsides,* where one is perigee and the other is apogee (further away from the globe). *The Moon and How to Observe It by* Peter Grego gives some good particulars about these matters.

<u>*The 19-Year Metonic Cycle of the Moon*</u>

Over a period of 18.618 years (or almost 19 even years) the ascending node of the moon shifts 19 spaces relative to the horizon at its most southern standstill on the horizon. After moving over these 19 spaces, the moon moves back over the 19 spaces to its most northern standstill on the horizon and finally moves back over the 19 spaces to its most southern standstill. The completion of these three cycles put the moon in an eclipse position close to where it occurred the last time. The exact calculation of the time presents some difficulties with the following solutions:

3 cycles x 19 years = 57 years
19 years + 18 years + 19 years = 56 years
3 cycles x 18.618 years = 55.854 years

The problem has always been the difference between the cardinal numbers (1,2,3…) and the ordinal numbers (first, second, third…). If an ancient astronomer constructs 19 pillars on the horizon (called backsights) to observe the most northern to the most southern settings of the moon, this eclipse cycle will be completed in about 54 years. If we mark 19 places on the horizon, it takes 54 years to complete the forward, backward, and forward motion over the 19 markers:

0 1 2 3 4 5 6 7 8 9 10 11 12 13 14 15 16 17 18
36 35 34 33 32 31 30 29 28 27 26 25 24 23 22 21 20 19 (18)
(36) 37 38 39 40 41 42 43 44 45 46 47 48 49 50 51 52 53 54

Therefore, three cycles of 19 markers equal about 54 years (not 3 x 19 = 57).

And to confirm this abovementioned theory, the actual and precise time of the triple Assyrian Saros period used in the prediction of eclipses is 54 years and 33 days. And once again the magical numbers make their appearance: 54, 108, and 216. It would therefore appear that the triple Saros cycle is as close as any astronomer has ever come to synthesizing the solar and lunar cycles, as is verified by the eclipses at 54 years and 33 days.

Professor Milla Villena then reveals that there is a Purana Wasi, a house of the full moon, at Manchu Picchu along the north-south aligned wall of alternating windows and vacancies that observe the

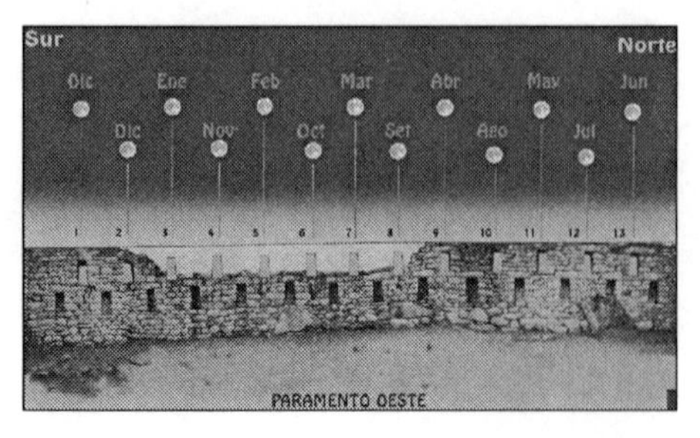

ascending and descending nodes of the moon along with the 13 full moons of the year. Milla Villena also proceeds to the Purana Wasi at the Island of the Moon on Lake Titicaca. Following this, Professor Milla Villena proceeds to the Purana Wasi at Quenko Grande above Cosco, another phenomenal site that appears to include a carved oracle chamber beneath a solid hill of rock whose crown has also been carved over the millennia.

David Furlong, in his article, "Egyptian Temple Orientation" (keh42.dial.pipex.com 6/5/10), tells that the Hatshepsut temple at Deir El Bahari is orientated to the midwinter rising sun. He affirms that the correctness of these solar alignments holds up for a very long period of time. He also says that the north and south standstills of the moon (and other lunar alignments) are likewise good for long periods of time. He cites the Ptah temple at Karnak (aligned to the major southern standstill of the moon), Stonehenge, and Caithness (aligned to the 19-year Metonic cycle) as examples of lunar alignments that are still accurate. Furlong also mentions that halfway through the 19-year cycle that lunar oscillation is at its smallest and that these are called the minor standstills of the moon.

The above photos in this article are reproduced here by the kind permission of Carlos Milla Villena, *Genesis de la Cultura Andina.* The site Quenko, above Cozco is the most extraordinarily interesting site in the world.

Eclipses of the Sun and Moon

In the ancient world, the king and queen of every land were regarded as the incarnate sun and moon here upon Earth. The divine right to rule as kings and queens derives directly from the cosmic order of all things. Sometimes, however, heaven did not favor the rulers with good harvests and victories in war. Therefore when an eclipse of the sun or moon occurred without forewarning, it was taken as a mandate from heaven for a change in the ruling family.

Kelley and Milone record that modern archaeoastronomers use eclipse dates to confirm incidents of history (p. 240). Furthermore Kelley and Milone write that, "All of the scholars we have discussed recognize major relationships between religion and social order. To the extent that a perceived concept of the heavens serves as the pattern for social relationships, any change in the way that heaven is ordered may be regarded as a mandate for change in social relationships (p. 478)."

Therefore, it was primarily important for the astronomers to be able to predict eclipses far in advance to show the people that the king and his scientists were indeed Masters of Time and the Universe. The ability to arrive at a perfect prediction demonstrated the power to control, and therefore the rulers did not have to step down from their positions.

Prediction of eclipses is a difficult matter, because the Earth's orbit around the sun, and the moon's orbit around the Earth have no known resonance. A lunar year of 12 synodic months is 354 days, which is 11 days short of the 365-day year. The factors that contribute to the irregularity of the moon's movements are the inclination of its orbit (between 5.14°–5.9°) to the plane of the ecliptic of the sun's position. The moon's orbit is also precessing, or revolving, relative to the stars and therefore crosses the plane of the ecliptic in only two places, called the nodes of the moon. Ancient astronomers from Mexica-Maya-Andean culture to the Atlantic islands, to Greece, Egypt, Iran, and Vedic culture devised formulas for adequate eclipse prediction:

> Metonic Cycle: a *calendar cycle* named after Meton of Athens (432 BC). Based on 19 tropical years equaling 235 synodic months, or 6,940 days. Used by the Chaldean, Babylonians, Greeks, and Jews. Catholics and Jews use it to fix the date of Passover and Easter. All the 19 years have 12 months, except the years 3, 6, 8, 11, 14, 17, and 19 (mythicalireland.com/astronomy/moon.html 5/6/2003). If there is a

full moon on your birthday this year, there will be another one on your birthday in 19 years time (Martineau. *Coincidence,* p. 33).

Saros Cycle: an *eclipse cycle* of 18 years and 11.333 days, or 223 synodic months of 6,585 days. This cycle equals 242 draconian (from one eclipse to another with respect to the same lunar node) = 239 anomalistic months, from one perihelion to another perihelion (eclipse. gsfc.nasa.gov./SEsaros.html 6/5/10). Similar eclipses will occur after 18 years (Martineau. *Coincidence,* p. 33).

The geometry of the Earth, sun, and moon will be nearly identical after one Saros. However, the orbit of the Moon precesses during that 18.618-year cycle so that the moon will be in a different place relative to the stars. The triple Saros of 54 years and 33 days will actually allow an eclipse to fall at the same time of day.

Further above it was noted that the diameter of the moon is 2,160 miles (in accord with the 216 fractal of 6 x 6 x 6). The abovementioned triple Saros is 54 years (54 + 54 = 108 + 108 = 216). In very old times, *Saros* meant "3,600 years" (3600 ÷54 = 66.666).

In *A Little Book of Coincidence* (p. 33), Martineau tells us that the eclipse year is composed of 18.618 x 18.618 (made up of 6 + 6 + 6 = 18; and phi ϕ .618) = 346.62 days which is the scientifically correct Eclipse Year. He also explains that 12 full moons = 18.618 x 19 days which is close to the Lunar or Islamic year (353.74 is close to 354.36 days). The solar year is 18.618 x 19.618 = 365.24.

The conclusion to all this must be that the moon exhibits many perturbations in its movements, but the formal structure of the moon shows that it is a congruent part of the synchronic system of the cosmos made up of the number 6 and .618, the golden mean proportion.

Los Camasca Amauta Runa

Carlos Milla Villena tells us that in Peru, there was a succession of governors of the Los Camasca Amauta Runa, apparently a ruling body of scientists, master architects, and astronomers. These elite scientists, sometimes designated as the Capaccuna, "the great ones," were always 108 members in number.

Felipe Guaman Poma de Ayala and Roland Hamilton, in *The First New Chronicle and Good Government* (2009), tell us that this council also interpreted the stars, comets, eclipses, storms, winds, animals, and birds. They saw signs and foretold what would come to pass—the death of the great kings of Castile and the kings of other nations around the world, as well as uprisings, hunger, thirst, pestilence, war, good years, and bad years. They were said to be descendants of Viracocha.

According to the blogspot (2009) of Victor Mazzihuaycucho, the Amauta were the oldest group of ordered philosophers who carried logs and Quellca quipos containing vital information composed in mnemonic songs. The Amauta were chosen by the Inca and formed a council that proposed rules and laws for good government. They were learned astronomers who believed that the sky was a great river [of information]. They studied and anticipated climate cycles for planting, recommended population control, and were the managers of the quipu. The 108 (x 2 = 216, the sexagesimal matrix) were the skywatchers and official historians of the realm.

The Golden Child

The main idol in the Coricancha, the very much still intact Inca Temple of the Sun in Cusco, was a solid-gold image of a naked baby clothed in sumptuous raiment. Cosmology is about a relationship between God, nature, and humankind. The Blessed Virgin Mary is an embodiment of the Earth, substance, and matter. She accepts the invitation to become filled with the Holy Spirit of God. Here is the cosmic union of matter and spirit producing the golden child of dual nature, a creature both of spirit and matter –just like all of us. The golden child's mission is brief, and he must be sacrificed so that the spirit may return untainted back to heaven—as it was given, it was also quickly retrieved.

This cosmic covenant is rarely enacted only by the highest cycles of the universe as a flash of light, life, death, and resurrection conceived through the spirit of God. It must be apparent that the golden child would not have human descendants in this world. His life and being is the covenant of the continuing relationship of God and the universe with humankind and the earth. The effort to adduce a human family of Christ is a contravention of the entire mystery of His appearance. God has constantly shown us that He loves all of his human family of all races and types. To presume that God would exalt one particular family above others is against the cosmic order and balance.

The daily ritual at Coricancha revolved around an image of the sun. Juan de Betanzos, a conquistador who married an Inca princess, said that this idol was of solid gold and shaped like a naked year-old baby. It was dressed in a tunic of the finest brocade and wore a royal fringe, a gold paten on its head, and golden sandals. His description sounded suspiciously like that of a Catholic Christ child. Pedro Pizarro, who actually saw one such idol, described it as, "a small covered statue which they said was the sun" (Hemming and Ranney, p. 79).

Tiwanaku

One of the most famous sites in the world located by Lake Titicaca is that of Tiwanaku, said to have been founded before the great world flood. The city is called "the center of the world," just as so many other places that were the centers of the great world ages, like Tenochtitlan. Tiwanaku is also called one of the places where the sun, moon, and stars were created, that is, studied and observed. The site is aligned to the equinox.

A surviving Huari textile gives some indication of the nature of the calendrics involved at the site (K&M, p. 462). The textile shows 36 columns of 10 color-coded circles (10 x 36 = 360) and patterns of 5 x 72 = 360, and 8 x 45 = 360 (These are Venus/Earth numbers: 5, 8, and 13. Kelley and Milone (p. 464) cite the Andean Book of Cobo (1653 AD), which says that the ancient Peruvians believed that there was a patron in heaven for each of the animals and birds that provided for their preservation and increase. They identified a star in the sky for every species of animal and for this reason worshipped many stars and made sacrifices to them. They had names for all the stars of the first magnitude. To other stars, like the various signs of the zodiac, they gave various duties to care for, guard, and sustain—some in relation to flocks, others for the lions, others for the serpents, others for planets, and so on for all things. Some groups said that in each of these gods, or stars, there existed the ideals and models of those living beings whose welfare was their responsibility; and so they said that such and such a star had the shape of a llama, because it was its duty to protect and conserve llamas. This philosophy of connecting life here upon Earth with ideal generative prototypes in heaven certainly precedes the notion of the "ideal forms" of Plato. This Peruvian idea from Cuzco also makes better sense in the astronomical format than in the story of Plato about *abstract shadows* of real forms. The ancient Peruvians thought that these patron stars originally came from the Pleiades.

Jupiter (called Illa Tecce, Wiracocha) was the guardian of Peru, its granaries, treasures, and stores. Mercury (Catu illa) is lord of merchants, travelers, and messengers. Mars (Aucayoc) is "he with enemies." Saturn (Haucha) is "fierce," responsible for carnage, pestilence, famine, lightning, and thunder. He has a staff and bows and arrows to punish and thrash mankind for its misdeeds (K&M, p. 464).

The Incas believed that they lived in the Fifth Age of the world epochs, or suns. Urton writes that the modern Quechuas substantiated the records of the ancient astronomical beliefs of the Andean culture (K&M, p. 466). Also the Quechuas remind us of the importance of the Dark Cloud or nebula figures in the Milky Way, also called the "River of the Sky" or the "nocturnal rainbow."

Graham Hancock in *Fingerprints of the Gods* (Ch.8-11) writes that Tiwanaku "appeared suddenly in the course of a single night" according to the Inca chronicler Pedro Cieza de Leon. This of course is mythological idiom for "there is no one who remembers the date of the foundation of this ancient place."

Professor Arthur Posnansky, the German-Bolivian scholar from the University of La Paz wrote the book *Tiahiuanacu: the Cradle of American Man.* Posanansky theorized that during the course of 41,000 years the obliquity of the earth's orbit varies between 22.1 degrees and 24.5 degrees. The current obliquity is 23 degrees 27 minutes. He demonstrated that at the time of the building of the Kalasasaya temple that the obliquity was at 23 degrees 8 minutes, and 48 seconds, corresponding to a date of 15,000 BC according to the International Conference of Ephemerids. Posnansky was one of the early pioneers to attempt "astronomic-archaeological investigation" and his findings were supported by several experts from the Observatory at Potsdam and the Vatican.

During his excavations of the site Posnansky also discovered evidence of human remains mixed with domestic items, pots, and animals in a sort of mud soup. This evidence was found in other excavations around this locality suggesting a very violent earthquake followed by a gigantic tsunami which washed over Tiwanaku and the adjoining site of Puma Punku. Evidence around the lakeshore of Titicaca also demonstrates that the entire lake was tilted by some great natural disaster at some time. The efforts to reconstruct the site certainly make it more accessible to tourists, but the real value is the disarray and violent destruction of the site as testimony to the natural cycles of destruction on earth which continually throw advanced civilizations back into a primitive state. There are fortunately still pockets of disturbance to be seen, and hopefully these will be excavated in the future with all features left in position and in place as a dramatic record of what actually occurred here. Tiwanaku has also been vandalized and pillaged for its beautiful stones for many centuries.

Old photo of Tiwanaku in 1903. Courtesy of Bing images: blog, Abramelin. Jan.8, 2010

Monster stones tossed around at Puma Punku. Author photo

Ecuador and Other South American Sites

The Spanish Conquest describes two astronomical temples in Quito, one for the sun and one for the moon. Two tall columns on the sides of the door of the Temple of the Sun were used as gnomes to mark the solstices. There were 12 smaller gnomes around the temple plaza, the shadows of which marked the beginnings of the solar months. Velasco says that the temple was "very well known for its adjacent astronomical observatories to which their kings were very devoted." Water channels were apparently used as mirrors for stellar observation. There were also lines that correspond with the major southern lunar standstill, pointing to Catequilla Mountain, which means "he who follows the moon."

In Bororo in Brazil as well as in Bolivia, the heliacal rising of the Pleiades and Orion's belt is marked. In Sherente, Brazil, there are villages located in eight-group pattern and called after the sun and the moon. Among the Kogi, Moche, and Quechua, the central star in Orion's belt is called the Jaguar and the Lord of Fire (K&M, p. 468). Also, an old path and a new path of the stars are associated with the Pleiades.

Cantogrande, the earliest known astronomical site in South America nearby Lima, shows deliberate corrections of earlier lines, demonstrating the recognition of the precession of star alignments prior to the very early date of 2000 BC (K&M, p. 439).

PART 8

THE ANTIQUITY OF THE AMERICAS

The exquisite sophistication of ancient astronomy and architecture of the Americas and the uniqueness of their culture plus the wealth of absolutely diverse language groups supports the idea that the inhabitants of this side of the globe were always there since the beginning of time. Communications between the two hemispheres were effectively cut off on the Atlantic side by the Phoenicians who occupied Old Marmora in Fez-Morocco by the Straits of Gibraltar, and the island of Cadiz on the north side of the Straits of Gibraltar. Contact between America and Asia came by way of the northern currents down the California coast, which have produced Japanese Jomon remains and sea anchors from Chinese vessels.

CHAPTER 8.1

The New World Is the Old World, and the Old World Is the New World

It is unreasonable to suggest that the American continents were always hidden from contact with the rest of the world, when extraordinary detailed maps of Antarctica provide evidence of high technology in the far-distant past. One can only surmise that the Phoenicians cut off everyone else from trade with the Americas and that, later, the monarchs and patriarchs of Europe followed this Phoenician secrecy by keeping their maps and trade routes to themselves. The knowledge of the American continents was never lost but always concealed. Since the time of the Phoenicians, it has never been the position of governments and states to reveal the extent of their knowledge or their trade secrets.

The discovery of America by Columbus created a nightmare for the Roman Catholic view of world history. Roman Catholicism had adopted Hebrew tradition of the sons of Noah being granted Africa, Europe, and Asia, but there was no mention of a son who had been given America. Jewish chronology also gave too recent a time for the creation of man and the evolution of civilization and culture. It is furthermore apparent that a significant part of world history had been played out upon the American continents, which boasted very ancient and extensive sites and magnificent temple complexes. The large, well-maintained cities of the Americas, with their huge populations, surpassed the habitations of Europe. The conquistadores were utterly amazed by the cities that they saw in the so called new world.

The Evidence of the Map

It is not possible that sailors, scientists, cartographers, kings, and Popes of the Roman Church were unaware of an entire hemisphere and two major continents on the other side of the world—complete with unique peoples, their diverse language groups, and their own unique sciences. It is really nonsense to believe that the American continents were ever "unknown" except to those outside the scientific, commercial, and hierarchical communities within society.

The Great Pyramid at Giza demonstrates that it is a scale model of the Earth in the proportion of 43,200 Great Pyramids equal to one Earth. The equatorial circumference of the Earth is 21,600 nautical miles, which is 60 nautical miles for every degree of longitude. Why, then, did people like Eratosthenes feel that they had to demonstrate the size of the Earth?

Eratosthenes (276–195 BC) was born in Libya. He was an extremely talented athlete, poet, and inventor. He became a citizen of Alexandria and was appointed the third chief librarian of the Library of Alexandria. He coined the word "geography"; reintroduced systems of longitude and latitude; was a close friend of Archimedes; invented the armillary sphere; calculated the tilt of the Earth, its distance from the sun, and its circumference; introduced the "leap day" in the calendar; and even had time to discover the algorithm of prime numbers (the Sieve of Eratosthenes). He also knew of the importance of the Giza pyramids and encouraged scientists to adopt them as the line of the prime meridian instead of the ancient Atlantic prime meridian.

Eratosthenes calculated the journey from Alexandria south to Syene (located on the Tropic of Cancer) to be a distance of 5,000 stadia. Syene had a deep well, and on the summer solstice the sun shone directly down to the bottom of the well. Eratosthenes was actually slightly north-west of Syene when he calculated that the great obelisk at Alexandria cast a shadow that had an angle of 7°12', which equals 7.2° (because 12' ÷ 60' = 0.2), on the day of the summer solstice.

There are some basic problems with this story. First of all, in order to get an accurate measure of the polar circumference of the Earth, Alexandria needs to be exactly north of Syene, which it is not. Syene is almost three full degrees east of Alexandria. Second, the well at Syene by the Tropic of Cancer is too much of "a coincidental given" in the problem, that is, it is just too extraordinarily convenient. It requires advanced skill to determine the exact location of the Tropic of Cancer, Tropic of Capricorn, and the equator. Syene is a couple of minutes north of the Tropic of Cancer.

Eratosthenes does not really even need the well at Syene. He only needs the *exact northerly* measurement of distance from Syene to Alexandria. On the day of the summer solstice, he can exactly calculate the degree of the shadow cast on the ground from the top of the obelisk at Alexandria.

Eratosthenes needs only to calculate that 360° of the Earth's polar circumference divided by 7.2° of the shadow equals 50. Then he can multiply 50 times the distance measured between Alexandria and Syene to arrive at the total polar circumference. His calculation was that 500 miles x 50 = 25,000 miles in total circumference.

The calculations of Eratosthenes (276–195 BC) and Posidonius (135–51 BC) were very accurate approximations of the polar circumference of the Earth near to the accepted modern figure of 24,816.8 geographical miles. There is something very curious and coincidental about these numbers and figures that were encountered in previous chapters, namely the universal astronomical figure of 72 that continually appears. Eratosthenes was a librarian, a reader of books. It seems remarkably contrived that Eratosthenes' figure for the angle differentiating the latitude of Syene and Alexandria should happen to be 7.2°.

The Nilometer located at Syene from *La Description De l'Egypte*. 1838

These figures are just too textbook, or papyrus-like, as if this information came off of a shelf in the Library of Alexandria as a paradigm from the ancient builders of the pyramids. It is worthy to remark that the town of Syene has always been a center of scientific research and record keeping. Syene is located just across from the island of Elephantine, the location of the famous

Nilometer, where the heights of the Nile flood were recorded every year to gauge and predict the potential harvest for all of Egypt.

The engravings from the Napoleonic expedition show the Nilometer to be a very large structure built out of squared stone, finely calibrated by internal staircases that served as measuring devices. This is all to say that Syene was not just a random town with a convenient deep well located on the tropic. This well was assuredly the time-keeping mechanism of this important and historical scientific center.

The Atlantic prime meridian shown on the greater majority of ancient maps and their copies seems to lay a few degrees west of La Palma of the Canary Islands. One of the features of this prime meridian is that its complete meridian circle encompasses all of Asia, including Japan and China. Therefore this prime meridian encloses the entire known world from Europe and Africa to Asia, equaling an entire hemisphere (half of the globe). What happened to the other half of the globe?

Posidonius had already questioned these distances and remarked that the supposed ocean between western Spain and eastern China was nearly equal (a hemisphere) to that of the known world from Spain eastward across the landmass to China. Some of the maps of Marinos of Tyre actually stretched Europe and Asia to an impossible 15 hours (225°), leaving the rest of the globe to be nine hours (135° + 225°= 360°). The actual and original figures of the circumference of the globe were altered, interpolated, and misquoted by later geographers. Posidonius' first estimate of the globe was around 24,000 miles. He used the difference in altitude of the star Canopus as seen in Rhodes and at Alexandria (7.5° over 5000 stadia). Hapgood has shown those maps that depict the coastline and ports of the American continents. And once again his findings have been aggressively disputed, while the map that Columbus used has mysteriously disappeared, even thought it was known to exist during the last 60 years.

Peter De Roo devotes his *History of America before Columbus* (1900) to the knowledge of, and contact with, the American continents before 1492 AD. This book is composed of 613 pages including documents from the Vatican

Library. Many of these classical authors, some even before the time of Plato, speak of the great American islands and landmasses. Something had to lie in the Western Ocean to balance the mighty landmasses of Europe, Africa, and Asia. European mapmakers knew well that they were only presenting a hemisphere of the globe to the people.

Evidence of American cocaine and tobacco in the toxicology of Egyptian mummies, scientifically accurate portions of ancient maps, icons of American corn and turkeys portrayed in Europe, commonly shared cosmological myths and ideas, and abundant European and African artifacts are all evidence that the channels of communication were open throughout the world.

Peter De Roo writes (p. 48) that most Europeans took Plato's account of Atlantis to be America. Opmer and others believed that Adam and Noah were among the inhabitants of America. De Roo continues (p. 117) to say that the fragments of Sanchoniathon and other Phoenicians show a familiarity with the history and cosmogony of the American , whom they also called "Atlantides" and identified with the sciences of Uranus. De Roo (pp.120–147) cites a litany of classical authors who have mentioned land, islands, and continents across the Atlantic Ocean. Among them: Hanno the navigator, Theopompus (380 BC), Aristocles, Euripides, Herodotus, Solon, Plato, Aristotle, Diodorus Siculus, Strabo, Pindar, Plutarch, Cicero, Theophrastus, and Pliny. De Roo relates that the following Europeans believed that America was indeed Atlantis: Ortelius, Mercator, Gomara, Jose de Acosta, Las Casas, William de Postel, Wyfliet, Bacon, Cluver, George Horn, the Swiss Bircherodus, and the mapmakers Nicolas and William Sanson. De Roo notices that the further back in time one goes, the more detailed the facts are about America. Pythias of Marseilles (f.325 BC), who described the moon's gravitational pull upon the tides, traveled to the British Isles, visiting Stonehenge, and to the far North, the lands covered with ice and the Land of the Midnight Sun. While the most ancient documents of Theopompus clearly state that American continents were comparable to all of Asia, Europe, and Libya (Africa). He also mentions that there were many populous cities in America having more than a million inhabitants.

False Theories

European conquerors claimed that the American continents were largely virgin territory and sparsely inhabited by primitive and insignificant native groups. However, the Spaniards, looking for the first time at the Aztec capital city of Tenochtitlan, had been overcome by awe at the sophisticated order, beauty, and splendor that lay before them, of this lake-island city approached by great causeways and set in a fertile and well-tended countryside. Nothing in their education had prepared them for the fact that a culture outside any they knew could achieve something of such a spectacular nature. In their brutal actions against Tenochtitlan one can sense their hatred for another people who had achieved so much.

Paul Binding discusses these issues (Ch. 15), where he discloses that the great geographer Abraham Ortelius and his contemporary age "had enormous difficulties in reconciling their Christian and classical background with the discovery of the Americas…Whole peoples had been found to exist in countries unknown to and unsuspected by these ancients; civilizations had arisen making no use whatever of tenets that they (Europeans), and generations of their disciples, had considered indispensable truths." In truth, many European scientists and intellectuals during the Age of Discovery wrestled with the problem of integrating the Americas into their worldview. Many of the questions were handled in Bartolome de Las Casas' *Short Account of the Destruction of the Indies.*

Ortelius also recognizes the difficulty with origins when he writes that the ancients divided the world into Africa, Europe, and Asia—"from whence the holy writ bears record that mankind had their first original, and first was seated." One of the great untruths about America was the Hebrew account of Shem, Ham, and Japheth occupying Asia, Africa, and Europe, which did not account for any people in the Americas. It was then hastily proposed that the natives came from Asia across a northern land and ice bridge. This is quite a large serving of speculation to be digested at one time, because none of this is historical truth.

In truth, many of the European intellectuals, such as the great mapmakers Abraham Ortelius and Mercator, believed that the classical ancients knew about the Americas. Ortelius' map of the Americas, based on Mercator's "lost map," actually portrays shipping on the Pacific Ocean. Ortelius writes,

> I have often wondered how it could so long have been hidden from our world. Some there are which suppose that this continent was described by Plato under the name of Atlantis...Plutarch...makes mention thereof under the name of a main continent. Some think that Seneca... presaged the discover hereof in these prophetical verses (second act of *Medea*), "Then shall huge lands appear, Typhis shall then detect New Worlds; nor Thule [Iceland] then shall bound the paths of men.

Paul Binding concludes (Ch. 15) by saying that it seems reasonable that, long before Columbus, Europeans and Asians had crossed over to America and that the ancients like Plato and Seneca knew about the Americas. Binding also asks the question of why God Himself had withheld the Americas so long from Christian Europeans.

In spite of the musings and suspicions of the scholars, Hebrew and Catholic scholars immediately realized that their cosmology of the creation of Adam and Eve was dangerously threatened by the entry of these far-distant, highly civilized, and astronomically astute cultures into a confined worldview of simple progress from the Garden of Eden to Mid-Eastern, North African, Mediterranean, and European culture. Happily a solution was quickly fabricated. The 16th-century Catholic Jesuit scholar Acosta proposed an ice-land bridge from Asia to account for the human populations of the so-called "New World." The Roman Church needed a prompt explanation for the Americas—a richly woven tapestry of humanity and science that was not discussed in the Bible. Acosta afforded an explanation that kept the Garden of Eden in the East and allowed a population of the New World from Old World stock.

The son of a Sephardic *converso*, Fray Jose de Acosta entered into the Society of Jesus, where he faithfully served in the evangelization of Peru and founded colleges in Lima and Cuzco. In 1590 his *Historia Natural y Moral de las Indias* was published featuring the theory of an ice-land bridge connecting both worlds. Acosta's theory appeared 140 years before Danish Captain Vitus Bering proved the connection between the Pacific and Arctic Oceans in 1733–1743. Acosta's theory was magically developed without any empirical evidence but on the firm conviction of strict Biblical evidence. Acosta adamantly proposed that the inhabitants of the Americas were descendants of Adam and Eve. Unbelievably, the question as to whether the Indians were human or not was debated for over 100 years until 1537 AD, when the papal bull of Pope Paul III declared that the American natives were rational beings possessed with a soul. This bull called for their immediate evangelization. Rather than resolve all issues, ecclesiastical lawyers then hotly debated if the natives could be used as slaves for the benefit of their own conversion to further the expansion and goals of the Roman Church.

European Definition of America

Succeeding waves of Europeans conquered the American continents. Europeans spoiled Native American land, fishing, grazing, and migration rights. Usually conquerors accepted tribute and fidelity in exchange for respect of religion and culture of the conquered people. There is no evidence that this common humanitarian practice was ever offered by the invaders. Europeans disparaged and destroyed native documents and artifacts of culture, science, and religion. In terms of all the conquests throughout all of world history, there has never been such an unprovoked and wholesale rape, pillage, destruction, infection, and genocide of native peoples as that which occurred upon these two continents.

Books like Plato's *Republic* and Bacon's *New Atlantis* fostered the idea that America could be regarded as an experiment for creating a new republic (Plato) or a new utopia (Bacon). The ultimate disdain of the Europeans came in the form of their rude definition of the people they encountered as Indians, aboriginals, and indigenous native peoples. This disrespectful and demeaning practice served to override the noble and true ancient names of the inhabitants and their land:

> Anasazi, Aymara, Aztec, Chavin, Chile, Diquis, Honduras, Hopi, Inca, Itza, Itzachilatlan, Kekchi, Kogi, Maya, Mexicas, Mixe, Mixtec, Mopan, Nahua, Olmec, Popoluca, Quechua, Tajin, Teotihuacán's, Tiwanaku, Totonac, Xoltales, and Zapotal. This mystical Western continent should once again be referred to as the Garden of Tamuanchan, where gods and humans originated.

The worst of all was the identification of America as "the New World," suggesting a virgin, blank, and pure landscape bereft of history, just waiting and ready to be developed. "The New World" serves as a pejorative term for the land of the inhabitants who could only have had infantile perceptions to be corrected by the wise executors from the "Old World." This custodial attitude permitted any manner of dealing with the environment and its peoples, no matter how unjust, quixotic, or illegal. "The New World" terminology justified the atrocities, burning, and destruction of native possessions and the imposition of European culture.

How could this place be "the New World" when its geography and environment present some of the oldest strata in the world? Here, too, are the greatest and most magnificent examples of long-term wind, water, and glacial erosion existing on the planet. The Earth does not contain too many places like Yosemite, the Grand Canyon, the Painted Desert, Monument Valley, and Yellowstone.

Phoenician Trade Secrets

Phoenician policy and culture dictate absolute secrecy and discretion in business. Their livelihood was directly connected to their knowledge of commerce and the procurement of desirable and rare goods. It was they who single-handedly misrepresented global measurement and hid the American continents from the world. They fostered a program of propaganda among navigators that the oceans beyond the Pillars of Hercules were unnavigable, congested with foul debris, and full of sea monsters, and water spouts. They promoted ideas that the Earth was flat, producing a horizon from which a ship would fall off into space. Constance Irwin, in her *Fair Gods and Stone Faces* (p. 116), writes:

> Beneath the towering Rock of Gibraltar, ships were patrolling the gate to the Outer Ocean with the intention that none but their own should pass beyond. In 613 BC the sentinels of the sea were still—after six hundred years—the Phoenicians.

De Roo (p. 145) cites Aristotle's "Treatise on Heaven" (2.xiv), where he writes that the Carthaginians discovered land beyond the Atlantic but the Carthaginian Senate forbade colonization of these territories perchance the colonists might in the future become too powerful and interfere with the trade and possessions of Carthage upon those shores.

Tompkins, in his *Mysteries of the Mexican Pyramids*, says that, "So impressive is the evidence accumulated by scholars to the effect that the Phoenicians reached the shores of both North and South America. It is hard to understand why it continues to be shunned."

The Phoenicians were in possession of the famous island of Gades by the Straits of Gibraltar and operated over 100 colonies along the shores of Fez and Morocco, among them their famous commercial center of Emporium. Later Morocco was colonized by the great ocean navigators the "Atlantians." Accurate sea charts must also have been available to several of the sea cultures on the Atlantic, such as the Veneti of Vannes in Brittany, who possessed the strongest and best-built deep-ocean-going vessels on the Atlantic. It is likely that the Fir-Morocchi of Ireland and Scandinavia were ancient Atlantians or Phoenicians from Fez and Morocco.

Charles Hapgood, in the Preface to his *Maps of the Ancient Sea Kings*, says that the Minoans of Crete and the Phoenicians were in possession of ancient sea maps inherited from prior times. These Minoan and Phoenician maps were later collected and studied in Alexandria and Constantinople. Hapgood says that during the Fourth Crusade (1204 AD) that the Venetian fleet captured Constantinople. Hapgood assumes that the Venetians discovered a treasure trove of ancient maps because, shortly after this campaign, maps of the Americas, the Arctic, and Antarctic seas *free of ice* began to appear in circulation. These extraordinary maps were so refined that they were designed for longitudinal markings of a caliber that did not appear in the world until the late 18th century of our current era.

Jewish Mapmakers

It is no coincidence that most remarkable cartographers of historical times were associated with schools located along the Atlantic prime meridian. The famous works and globe of Martin Behaim (Bohemia) are associated with the Azores through his marriage to the daughter of the governor of those islands. There are some curious stories and assertions that Behaim (1459–1507) should be credited with the discovery of the Americas and that the Straights of Magellan were depicted on a Martin Behaim globe in the treasury of King John II of Portugal, to whom Behaim served as chief cartographer.

It was the Jewish schools of cartography, especially on the Canary Island of La Palma, that most likely inherited the maps of the Atlantians, the Fir Morocchi, and the Phoenicians. Thankfully, they safeguarded these ancient treasures and resources, which became the basis of modern maps. La Palma lies within a few degrees of the ancient Atlantic prime meridian. The La Palma school produced the Dulcert superportolano of the Mediterranean, a document based upon the most scientific of projection techniques. The remarkable Abraham Cresques (c.1381 AD) and his son operated out of this school. Considering the early dates of these mapmakers located far out in the Atlantic—more than 100 years prior to Columbus—the question may be posed: what were they doing out there? Mapmaking centers are commonly located right in the middle of commercial trading centers. Was trans-Atlantic travel and commerce such a rarity, as we have been taught to believe?

Norman Roth, in his *Medieval Jewish Civilization*, mentions the cartographers and makers of nautical charts of the Schools of the Canary Islands, the Azores, and Majorca, as well as the schools of Barcelona. Most prominent in Majorca was the Jew Angelino Dulcerti, around 1339 AD, followed by Abraham Cresques around 1381 AD and his son, Judah, who later took the Hispanic name Jaime Ribera to avoid the persecutions of the Jews in Spain. Juan I, son of Pedro IV of Aragon, sent Charles VI of France a wonderful world map by Cresques, who may have lived in Barcelona for a time. Judah-Jaime Ribera put together the amazing *Catalan Atlas.* He and Master Moyses put together the maps used in the discovery of Brazil. Gabriel Vallsecha, another Jewish *converso*, made the world map of 1439 used by Amerigo Vespuchi. As early as 1065–1136 AD, Abraham Bar Hayya of Barcelona made a drawing of the world showing the poles and the equator. Judah Ibn Zara made a world map in Alexandria in 1497, while Abraham Farrisol of Avignon (1451–1525 AD) was the earliest Jewish writer to mention the "unknown" New World (p. 138). Some scholars acknowledge that Christopher Colon was of Hebrew ancestry and worked closely with the Jews, who required passage as they were being expelled from Spain in the year of 1492. A large contingent of the Jews moved to the Netherlands, where they helped found the United East India Company. Other Jews relocated to the Morocco and the Cape Verde Islands, where they took up the slave trade to the Caribbean and the Americas.

Hapgood says that some of these maps were composed prior to the last great ice age, because they show the North and South Poles completely devoid of ice. These maps prompted Toredo to advise Columbus that he could go to the East by sailing west—perhaps through the Northwest Passage. One of the assignments of the Royal supported English pirates like Drake and Cabot was to look for this much-prized quick route to the Far East. Later, President Thomas Jefferson dispatched Lewis and Clark to test if the Northwest Passage might offer some connection between an unexplored western stream and the Mississippi. Today, with the melting of the ice caps at the pole, the Northwest Passage has once again become a reality.

The Uniqueness of America

The astonishing capabilities of the Maya in mathematics and astronomy, the Mexican pyramids, and the Mexican genius for urban planning and engineering are only a few of the scientific and technological achievements that have impressed the world.

Charles C. Mann's *1491, New Revelations of the Americas before Columbus*, presents a groundbreaking study that radically alters our understanding of the

Americas before the arrival of the Europeans in 1492. The jacket flap proposes that "Mann reveals how a new generation of researchers equipped with novel scientific techniques came to previously unheard of conclusions."

In 1491 there were probably more people living in the Americas than in Europe. Some estimates say that on the central Mexican plateau alone there were 25.2 million people. In general estimates theorize that about 95% of the native populations were wiped out of existence through imported epidemics and disease carried by European swine and cattle. Hence, most of America's civilizations were destroyed. Europeans then classified the distraught natives as primitive, simple hunter-gatherers—a state of being that everyone is reduced to after a great natural disaster or pandemic.

Certain cities—such as Tenochtitlan, the Aztec capital—were far greater in population than any contemporary European city. Furthermore, Tenochtitlan, unlike any capital in Europe at that time, had running water, beautiful botanical gardens, and immaculately clean streets. The earliest cities in the western hemisphere were thriving centers of culture and science before the Egyptians restored the great pyramids at Giza.

Pre-Columbian Indians in Mexico developed corn by a breeding process so sophisticated that the journal *Science* recently described it as "man's first, and perhaps the greatest, feat of genetic engineering."

Amazonian Indians learned how to farm the rain forest without destroying it, a process that scientists are studying today in the hope of regaining this lost knowledge.

Native Americans transformed their land so completely that Europeans arrived in a hemisphere totally "landscaped" and environmentally managed and utilized by human beings.

Mann also tells us (p. 192) that the ancient Mesoamerican farmers have developed peppers, squashes, beans, and tomatoes—an astounding three-fifths of the crops now in cultivation, which serve to feed the world's great populations today.

Carlos Milla Villena says (p. 373) that Titu Yupanqui Pachacuti of Peru wrote 3,000 years after the flood that both Brazil and the Andes were overrun by great armies and ferocious peoples who destroyed the records of Andean culture. Five-hundred years later, the seventh Pachacuti forbade the use of letters because they were too insecure and unreliable. After this, Andean culture used the special knotted cords called *quipu* for the purpose of record keeping. Aveni confirms (p. 309) that Urton has shown that quipu recorded historical and cultural tradition in addition to their practical accounting of materials. The South American quipu, a long cord from which knotted strings hang, was regarded as an interesting variation to a method of record keeping. It now appears that these record cords were textile expressions where the fabric type (cotton or wool), the various colors, the spin and ply direction of the string, the slant against the cord, and the direction of the knot (recto or verso) all contributed to the meaning. Charles C. Mann writes (p. 375) that the "seven-bit binary array" of each knot plus the other factors produced 1,536 information units, which surpassed the abilities of the Sumerian cuneiform signs and was double that of the Egyptian and Maya hieroglyphic symbols. The sequence of knots on strings formed a binary code reminiscent of today's computer languages. It was by means of this unique form of communication that the Inca controlled the largest and most diverse empire in human history.

In Chapter 9 of *Amazonia*, Charles Mann reports on the five-month voyage from the Ecuadorian Andes down to the Amazon River by Francisco de Orellana and his forces in 1541 AD. The diaries of the chaplain Gaspar de Carvajal depict a prosperous and crowded land. He writes of villages one after another over a stretch of 180 miles along the river. Following this, he describes a gigantic settlement at the mouth of the Tapajos River of homes and gardens that lined the river banks for over 100 miles and proceeded a distance of up to two leagues inland. Charles Mann remarks that these reports and modern investigations certainly debunk the propaganda that the Americas were a virgin million-year-old wilderness. He further says, "Physical scientists were especially unwilling to accept Carvajal's depiction of the Amazon. To ecologists, the great tropical forest in South America was and is the planet's greatest wilderness, primeval and ancient, an Eden-like zone touched by humankind lightly if at all. Constrained by its punishing climate, poor soil and lack of protein, these scientists argue, large-scale societies have never existed—*can* never exist—in the river basin." Corliss reports (*S.F.* #180) that the unfortunate deforestation of the Amazon basin is continually exposing ancient earthworks, terraces, and stone fences and foundations. Their earthen infrastructure has not all been eroded away. There are road networks, municipal plazas, canals, and grand thoroughfares kilometers long, showing that sophisticated cultures once throve there. Recently giant geometrical figures have been discovered cut deep into the soil. These are shaped like circles, diamonds, hexagons, and interlocking rectangles and are up to 350 meters in diameter and outlined by trenches one-to-seven meters deep. Many are approached by broad earthen avenues 50 meters wide and up to a kilometer long. So far, 150 of the giant glyphs have been found, and it is supposed that many are still hidden below the jungle canopy. These seem to be in a category with the famous Nazca lines of Peru, but so far, the Amazonian lines do not depict any creatures.

Mann tells (p. 107) of the great cities and ceremonial centers of the Caddo on the Texas-Arkansas border and the Coosa in western Georgia, whose monuments were destroyed and their populations reduced by 96%.

He asserts (p. 179) that, "California alone was the home of as many as 86 tongues, which linguists have classified into between 5 and 15 families... Across the Americas, Indians spoke some 1,200 separate languages that have been classified into as many as 180 linguistic families. By contrast, all of Europe has just 4 language families." Recently it has been reported that almost 3,000 native languages have been lost in the Americas in historical times.

The multifaced stones from Puma Punka set up at Tiwanaku. Author photo

Evidence from Puma Punku in Bolivia shows large-scale stone manufacturing techniques of 70 orthogonal faces per unit, an accomplishment that modern machines are not capable of reproducing in quantity.

The first Europeans who investigated American cultures were amazed at the sophisticated range of architecture and art. To them this variety of excellent artistry seemed to substantiate the story of Atlantis. Brasseur de Bourbourg rediscovered and published key documents that would lead to important decipherments of Maya art and writing. He also insisted that, "Maya civilization was the intellectual wreckage of the sunken continent Atlantis" (Miller, *Maya Art*, p. 14). However, as many European scholars praised the diversity of the Americas, there were others who felt the need to denigrate native achievement. Miller reveals that such notable achievements by brown-skinned savages were repugnant to some archaeologists of that period. Even today some Judeo-Christian groups sponsor that idea of American "exceptionalism." Many of the racist ideas emphatically discount the possibility of the cyclical rise and fall of different societies from around the globe.

Irwin writes (p. 14), "Generations of Americans have been drilled to believe that for eons the Western Hemisphere, isolated by two great oceans, lay totally unheard of—till ...Christopher Columbus stepped ashore..." Irwin continues (p. 32) to say that American Indians lack important facial features of the Asiatic Mongoloid, whom the Jesuit Acosta uses to populate the Americas via his land bridge idea. Most American Indians do not have the slant of the eyes and the "Mongoloid fold." The hawk-like nose of the Plains Indians scarcely mirrors the flat nose of the Asiatic Mongoloid. Anyone who has ever visited the Peabody Museum at Harvard University in Cambridge will appreciate the classic individuality of the portraits of Indian leaders, which are truly representative of a distinct and unique theater of humanity. Nine out of ten Native Americans—and almost all South Americans—have type *O* blood. This blood type is common to the Irish, Basque, and many African and European people who live along the Atlantic coast. Most other Europeans are evenly split between types *O* and *A* (Mann, p. 111).

It is permissible to think that there has always been contact with the Americas since the most ancient times. This is, of course, the theory of "cultural diffusion" evidenced by artifacts from foreign visitors from China, Japan, Egypt, Phoenicia, Libya, the Basque, Ireland, and Morocco. There is no reason why this should not be true. But it does not negate the fact that America originated and sprang out of itself. Anyone who has ever visited or studied the antiquities of America must recognize a unique individuality in their art and architecture. The pueblos of the Anasazi, Tenochtitlan, Chichen Itz, Tikal, Tiwanaku, Ollantaytambo, Cuzco are absolutely unique in character.

Contact across the Atlantic

For many Irish, Vikings, Basques, Japanese-Jomon, and Chinese, the Americas' discovery was not "unexpected" at all. The Vikings had sent colonies out there. The Irish had done the same and left dolmens and Ogam letters carved in stone. The Basque had their secret fishing places for their famous salt cod cash crop off the coasts of Newfoundland. Barry Fell, in his *America BC*, recounts numerous places where Roman, Moroccan, and Phoenician carvings and artifacts were discovered. Thousands of Chinese anchors have been located off the coast of California, and Asian ships were actually recorded in Spanish ship logs during their voyages along the California coasts. Indeed, the Native cultures of Meso and South America tell of contact with white and non-native visitors—as the Olmec heads, with their multiracial caricatures, amply authenticate. In addition, maps in possession of the Turkish Admiralty at the Topkapi Palace in Istanbul showed the eastern American coastlands in fine detail and perfect position, a fact which Hapgood has demonstrated to the world.

Constance Irwin, in her *Fair Gods and Stone Faces*, says that ocean travel is a matter of following the known great ocean "roadways" or currents and meticulously staying far away from the coastlands, which are full of offshore rocks and dangerous cross-currents. In the Atlantic Ocean, taking the Canary Currents, the North Equatorial Stream brings one directly into the Yucatan Channel. The return trip is slightly to the north, where the Antilles Stream flows into the Gulf Stream, returning to Europe and Africa. On the other side of the world on the Pacific Ocean, the North Equatorial current brings one from Mexico directly to China and Japan. The return trip is a comfortable current that flows back around to Vancouver and down the coast of California.

The Egyptian priests also told Solon that the waters of the Atlantic were disturbed for a long time after the disappearance of Atlantis into the ocean.

Crichton, a noted navigator in his own right, tells us, in his *Golden Thread of Time* (p. 230), that the Sargasso Sea off the American coast is to be avoided at all costs by sail-driven ships. It is a terrible place to die a slow lingering death, with no winds, thick seaweed, and flotsam and jetsam; and at 2,000 miles across, anyone caught in this section of the sea has no chance of escape or survival. Finally, the small populations of Europe and the Mediterranean, reduced by plagues and disease, did not really need new territories for expansion.

Science Frontiers (#182, March 2009) reports that, "Maize (American Corn) is popping up everywhere in the Ancient World. Our files contain 20+ articles on Pre-Columbian signs of maize on all continents save Antarctica." Since maize is a New World plant, it is anomalous to find it in Europe, Asia, and Africa before Columbus set sail. Images of maize are found in India (11th cent.), in Henan, China (1st cent.), and at the temple of Hatshepsut at Deir el-Bahri (1,470 BC).

The discovery of Andean cocaine and American nicotine in Egyptian mummies is a landmark instance of proof of communication with the Americas. Long before the voyages of Columbus, American sweet maize corn, turkeys, and aloe were depicted in European sculpture and art. American wild turkeys were painted in the Schleswig Cathedral in about 1280 AD by an artist from Lubeck, a city of the Hanseatic League, which was active in deep-ocean voyages. Instances of spoken Celtic language, Celtic megalithic chambers, and Ogam carvings appear in Native North America, especially in New England. Roman jars were found in the Bay of Jars in Brazil, and current South American place names appear on maps long before any surveys of discovery were attempted or sent to those regions. The voyages of Thor Heyerdahl testify that long ocean voyages across the Atlantic and Pacific were possible in balsa rafts. Yet the point of these adventures somehow failed to grasp the imagination and attention of the academic community.

Because of a Roman plan to attack King Juba of Mauritania, he and his entire court and treasure barely escaped the Romans by sailing first to the Cape Verde Islands and from there to the mouth of the Mississippi and up the Ohio River, where they established a safe refuge (Frank Joseph, *The Lost Treasure of King Juba*).

Corliss reports (*Science Frontiers* #177) that in the 1470s, American natives, a man and a woman, reached Galway Bay, Ireland. They were interviewed by Columbus himself. The same paper reports that at the Temple of Warriors at Chichen Itza, wall paintings depicted a sea battle with yellow-haired men in boats that resembled Viking craft with shields on the side and animal-headed prows.

Constance Irwin, in her *Fair Gods and Stone Faces* (Ch.2), tells of the many Norsemen who traveled to America, such as Van Ulm, Herjulfsson, Karlsefni, and others. She continues with the legend of the seven Portuguese bishops who fled with their people in seven ships in the eighth century to escape the invasion of the Moors. Irwin also records the discovery of several hundred Roman coins from 350 AD dug up on the shore of Venezuela.

David Hatcher Childress has written *Pirates and the Lost Templar Fleet,* which chronicles the escape from King Phillipe, from La Rochelle in France to the safety of the St. Clair holding in Scotland. These Templars became the Scottish Rite Freemasons, whose ships flew the infamous flag of the skull and bones. From Scotland they supposedly sailed for Canada in the year 1298 AD, taking up their residence there. These Templar marauders were at loggerheads with the Italian and French kings, who were continuously allied with the Pope. They subsequently harassed their enemies in the New World, choosing to steal the gold-laden cargoes heading back to Europe from the Caribbean.

Asian Contact with the West Coast of the Americas

Peter Tompkins, in his *Mysteries of the Mexican Pyramids* (p. 353), says that the earlier report of Chinese travel to America, known as the *Classic of Mountains and Seas*, is the record of a series of journeys around the globe compiled in 2250 BC by the Minister Yu at the request of the Emperor Shan. The Chinese travels describe the land from western Canada to Mazatlan across the Great Eastern Sea, which is now called the Pacific. This ancient work, though much truncated, miraculously survived the repeated burnings of the Chinese libraries.

Chinese and Japanese ships visited the American Pacific coast long before Europeans. Indian traditions tell of many "houses" seen on Pacific waters. Chinese history, too, tells a charming account of voyages to the *Land of Fusang*. Even old Spanish documents describe oriental ships off the Mexican coast in 1576. Japanese explorers and traders evidently left steel blades in Alaska and their distinctive pottery in Ecuador. Recent underwater explorations off the California coast have yielded stone artifacts that seem to be anchors and line weights. One line weight found at 2,000 fathoms is covered with enough manganese to suggest great antiquity. The style, type, and stone of these anchor stones point to Chinese origins for all these artifacts. Apparently, vessels from the Orient had taken the Japanese current to the west coasts of America thousands of years ago (Pierson, Larry J., and Moriarty, James R,; "Stone Anchors: Asiatic Shipwrecks off the California Coast," *Anthropological Journal of Canada*, 18:17, 1980).

The discovery of a skeleton of a 10,000–20,000-year-old man at Kennewick, Washington, on the Columbia River was quickly spirited away under court injunction, hopefully never to see the light of day again. Local Native Americans want to protect their rights and ancient claims to American lands. However, brief examination of Kennewick Man revealed that the cranium and skeletal structure absolutely resembles that of the ancient Jomon, sometimes called Aino, people of ancient Japan. Numerous identical types of Jomon people have been unearthed in caves in Nevada and as far away as Wisconsin.

The Pacific Northwest produces rain forests containing ancient specimen trees of magnificent proportions. There are pockets of sheltered microclimates where the native inhabitants built their wooden homes and heraldic family totem poles, which conquering Europeans immediately snapped up. These warmer and sunnier habitations were essential for the survival of the aboriginal culture, which sustained itself by harpooning and whale hunting for the essential blubber fat that enabled the population to survive the winters of constant rain and sporadic cold. Two of their mythological figures are the Wild-man and the Wild-woman. One could appreciate that if you were ostracized from your community—and if you could survive—that you would tend to grow larger to combat the cold as all northern animals do. Rapid hair growth would immediately set in if you had the will to survive. There is a legend that a native woman was abducted by the Sequatchie. Many years later the woman was recovered from the wild, and she told the people not to shoot or fire upon the Wild-men—because they might be her children.

On a 2009 visit to Puno at Lake Titicaca, our guide informed us that the ancient Amaru peoples of that region possess the Mongoloid dot at the base of their spine. This kind of evidence is impossible to deny and certainly opens up a fascinating area of research.

Native Populations Declare That They Were Not the First People

In 1963, with the publication of *Fair Gods and Stone Faces*, Constance Irwin made the important point that the races that the Europeans came into contact with—like the Aztec and the Inca—were themselves the recent conquerors of more ancient races. The Aztec and Inca were astute nation-builders who purposefully destroyed the evidence of previous rulers in order to exalt their own importance. Yet history records that, by their own admissions, they knew that they were not the "first people".

Irwin writes (pp. 11-12) that for a "long time have we been informed by the writings of our ancestors," said Montezuma, "that neither myself nor any of those who inhabit this land are natives of it, but rather strangers who have come to it from foreign parts." It is most curious that Montezuma later says, "Especially in that you [Cortez] say he [the king of Spain] has long had knowledge of us."

She continues (p.37.), "Quetzalcoatl was only by adoption a god of the Aztecs. He belonged to the Toltecs...a fair and ruddy complexioned man, with a long beard. In Cholula (the largest pyramid in the world) these people remained and multiplied, and sent colonists to Upper and Lower Mizteca and the Zapotecan country; and these it is said raised the grand edifices whose remains are still seen at Mictlan. These followers of Quetzalcoatl were men of great knowledge and cunning artists in all kinds of fine work; not so good at masonry and the use of the hammer, as in casting and in the engraving and setting of precious stones, and in all kinds of artistic sculpture, and in agriculture."

"The Mixtecs claimed descent from the Toltecs...before the puzzling Mixtecs moved in, a little known people called Zapotecs dwelt at Mount Alban...Zapotecs are believed to have worshiped here more than a thousand years...built an astronomical observatory and possessed hieroglyphic writing... the Zapotecs were not the founders of Mount Alban...the general cultural pattern of early Mount Alban bears a marked resemblance to that of the Olmecs...the people who succeeded the race of giants...who flourished during the era when Quetzalcoatl appeared." (Irwin, p.67)

More importantly, says Irwin, the oldest skulls found in America are dolichocephalic (long-headed, as measured from front to back). These early skulls are quite different from the later Amerinds. These skulls fit under the category of Australoid, from which modern white man and African races were at one time said to have descended. Of course, people at all times have traveled all over the globe. And Hooton's observation is most true: "When different races of man come into contact with each other they sometimes fight, but they always breed."

The main point is that the Americas are full of cave and mine findings of skeletons and implements dated from 25,000 to 100,000 years ago, prior to the last great ice age. Irwin mentions (Ch. 3) such sites as Sandia Mountains cave in New Mexico; La Jolla, California; Tule Springs, Nevada; and Denton County, Texas.

Pleistocene Man at San Diego, the Calaveras Skull, and dozens of other archeological anomalies have been dismissed as the hoaxes and misidentifications of nonprofessionals. The latest hint of truly ancient man in America came after heavy rains in 1976 cut through 21 meters of deposits at Yuha Pinto Wash, just north of the Mexican border in California. The artifacts, still firmly in place, and associated bones are undeniably human. The overlying sediments are dated at more than 50,000 years old. (*Science Frontiers #14, Winter 1981*).

Native Americans admit that there was a race of "ancient ones." Some of these were red-haired giants whose remains including moccasins were still found in Lovelock Cave near Lake Lahontan, in Nevada in 1912 and later investigated in 1924 by M.R. Harrington of the Museum of the American Indian. Some Indians claim to be offspring of these giants. (Cassinelli, *Gathering Traces of the Great Basin Indians*, p. 88)

Outside Fort Morgan, Colorado, workmen digging pits for a landfill uncovered a prehistoric campsite 40 feet under the sandy bed of an ancient stream. The diggers found bones, worked flints, and burnt stones arranged in a ring. Excavations were stopped when the importance of the site became obvious. Estimates of the campsite's age were as old as 30,000 years, a figure that would have been heresy a decade or two ago. (Anonymous. "Ancient Camp Unearthed at Colo. Landfill," *Baltimore Sun*, December 14, 1980. AP dispatch.)

Corliss (*Science Frontiers* #178, July–Aug. 2008) writes that there is a site called Paisley at 5 Mile Point Caves in Oregon, "Human coprolites (lumps of fossilized human excrement), dated about 14,000 years old...Bits of fossil seaweed from a stone knife, Monte Verde, Chile...carbon dated at 14,000 years ago...the New World's oldest known city (Caral) was thriving while some of the stones for Egypt's pyramids were still being quarried. In this story of ancient New World mega-ruins, we now have Sachin Bajo, Peru, a newly discovered circular ceremonial plaza, 46 feet in diameter, dated at 2500 BC."

Igor Witkowski's *Axis of the World* presents some controversial diffusion theories than we cannot endorse. Yet his work does contain very good photographs of Puma Punku with excellent commentary upon that site and Tiahuanaco. Here are also some of his recitations of extremely ancient American sites:

> *Pedra Furada* (1963, 1988) an inhospitable mountain region in the outskirts of the Mato Grosso Jungle composed of recesses in exposed rock faces or overhangs, human tools and artifacts 50,000 years old.

Minnesota Minnie (1932) skeleton discovered in road cutting 4 meters under and 20,000–25,000 years old.

Lewisville Man (1956) in Texas 37,000 years old.

Tepexan Man and the *Tlatilco Skulls* in Mexico 10,000–12,000 years old.

Monte Verde in southern Chile in a cool climatic zone exposed to Antarctic winds and sea currents. This city's roofs sheltered not only the buildings but also the streets and sidewalks. Wooden tools and potatoes were found. Dates of 31000 BC make it the oldest permanent settlement and agricultural community not only in the in the Americas but in the entire world.

Other place names of interest include *Topper, Saltville, Cactus Hill,* and *Meadowcroft.*

San Juan Museum, Argentina, 7000 BC human mummy from the Los Morillos graveyard in the foothills of the Andes. The oldest Egyptian mummy is estimated to be around 3000 BC. On the other coast in Chile mummies of the same age as those of San Juan have been found in large numbers near *Chinchorro.* In light of Monte Verde, Chile seems to possess the oldest remains of organized, sedentary societies in the world.

The *Chauchilla Cemeteries* is an ancient site 50 kilometers south of Nazca in Peru that has been outrageously plundered. Because the Spanish totally eradicated Peruvian society, their agriculture deteriorated because no one was left who knew how to clean and maintain the ancient aqueducts and irrigation channels to the terraces where water flow was designed to keep crops from freezing at these high elevations.

On *St. Helen Island by southern Ecuador* inhabitants were cultivating maize and other crops in 6500 BC.

The *Valdivia* culture in *Ecuador* from 4000 BC produced pottery that is almost identical to the Jomon culture of Japan, a white race of tall people who also left their mummies in the Chinese Tarim Basin. This Valdivia culture was able to smelt platinum at the astounding temperature of 3,200 degrees Fahrenheit. Jomon pottery is the oldest in the world. One piece is estimated at 14500 BC. These ancients were cultivating rice as early as 10000 BC.

Kennewick Man (1996) on the Columbia River in Washington State, Ainuidal-Jomon type dated from 7300 BC. Another such Jomon type had been found several years earlier and dated at 8675 BC. These finds reminded researchers of the *Spirit Cave Mummy* (1940) in a rock shelter east of Carson City, Nevada, now redated by U.C. Riverside to 7400 BC. In 1926 E.W. Gilford produced photographs of bearded white California Indians of the Jomon type.

CHAPTER 8.2

American and Canadian Medicine Wheels

Another proof toward the extreme antiquity of America is the dating of native astronomical knowledge, which is of a very refined order dating back to 3200 BC. While the actual sites are primitive in construction, their alignments are of a high order of precision. The term "medicine" is here used in the Native American sense of sacred cosmic power assisting the possibility of healing.

The medicine wheels are found predominately in unusually far-north positions into the heart of Canada, such as Alberta, but also in Saskatchewan, Montana, and Wyoming, with others reported as far south as New Mexico and Arizona. In fact, more medicine wheels are being discovered every year. At the moment there are about 134 reported wheels. These ritual places of the Earth-Sky religion are also noteworthy because of their situations at extremely high altitudes. These high altitude and northerly sites make one wonder if these locations belong to a previous time when climatic conditions were much warmer or a time when native populations were much larger. The Mesoamerican and South American positions of Mexico City, Teotihuacán, the Kogi of Columbia, the Inca of Ecuador and Peru, and Tiwanaku in Bolivia are all around and above one mile high in altitude.

Milone and Kelley say that the layout of the medicine wheels is by the use of piled-up rocks and boulders, rather than standing stones. It has been suggested that poles were stuck into the tops of these cairns and alignments to have facilitated better precision. The size of the medicine wheels varies from 10m to over 100m. Ideally there is a central stone cairn, a surrounding circle or oval, a series of spokes, and some outlying cairns. Some of the medicine wheels are geoglyphs in the shape of a turtle or, as some say, a badger. Modern natives claim that the medicine wheels are burials or memorials to dead chiefs, but only two are known to have had burials in their central cairns.

Vogt (1993) says that these sacred sites on very high mountains are sometimes associated with caches and offerings. Some of these treasure receptacles have been in use over several thousands of years, as is the case at Majorville. Fifteen of the studied sites show orientation to true north. Not all the alignments can be explained by luni-solar or planetary alignments and must therefore be directed at individual stars or asterisms. Vogt says that the alignments were, "scientific elements of what probably were largely religious knowledge systems."

Furthermore, Vogt discusses the way in which Plains Natives symbolize the cosmos in their dwelling places and ceremonies. He emphasizes the importance of the central pole of the Sun Dance lodge as representing both the "World Pole" (the axis of the Earth) and the center of the cosmos. The Sun Dance takes place on the full moon after the summer solstice. Each family group has its own assigned place in a circle of tents around the Sun Lodge and in their permanent camps as well. The Sioux affirm that each clan is associated with a particular star or asterism as its special totem.

Three widely separated sites demonstrate a similar structural layout. These are Majorville in Alberta, Moose Mountain in Saskatchewan, and the Big Horn site in Wyoming. The Majorville site is badly damaged and disturbed, but it seems likely that there were originally 28 spokes around a central cairn, with several outlying cairns. Extensive excavations were carried out at the site by Richard Forbis and James Calder, showing that the cairn was increased from about 3200 BC until 1800 AD. Alignments to the heliacal risings of the stars Sirius, Aldebaran, and Rigel are evident, as well as the summer solstice sunrise and equinoctial markers. The value of the site is its demonstrated antiquity and its structural similarity to smaller, younger, and less-complicated sites.

The Moose Mountain site has five major outliers connected by long spokes to an egg-shaped ring of small stones surrounding a central cairn. Alignments indicate summer solstice sunrise, Sirius, Aldebaran, and Rigel. The Big Horn medicine wheel in Wyoming is at an elevation of 3,000m and inaccessible in the winter months. The number of spokes is 28, suggestive of a sidereal-month calendar device and of the Native Sun Lodges with their 28 rafters. Again, there are alignments to the summer sunset, Aldebaran, Sirius, and Rigel, and perhaps Fomalhaut. Tribal elders say that the site has always been considered sacred and neutral even in times of warfare.

Other medicine wheels of interest are Fort Smith, Montana, and the Minton Turtle effigy in south-central Saskatchewan, whose principle alignment is Sirius during the summer solstice sunrise at about 2300 BC. Cree and Assiniboine informants say that the shape is not that of a turtle but rather a badger.

CHAPTER 8.3

The Origin of Culture—Morocco and the Forgotten Context of History on the Atlantic

Apollodorus, Hesiod, and the Phoenician Sanchoniathon tell us about an ancient historical cycle called the "generations of the gods." The Phoenician history of Sanchoniathon comes to us from Eusebius Pamphilus (264 AD), who received it from Philo of Byblus (64–141 AD) in Phoenicia.

This mythic history begins with the most ancient gods, like Air (Chaos) and Night, whose histories are even scant in the mythic realm. Following these early gods, the lists of the gods becomes more exact and clear with an agreed sequence, such as Uranus (Scorpio), Helios and Titans (Sagittarius), Agathodaemon and Cyclopes (Capricorn), Saturn and Atlas (Aquarius), Zeus, Poseidon, and Pluto (Pisces). These gods reflect the epochal ages of the grand cycle of the rotation of the Milky Way.

Apollodorus and Hesiod agree that the episodes regarding Zeus happened primarily in Greece and the Mediterranean regions and that the adventures of Atlas and Saturn occurred further west in Italy and Morocco. The famous statue of Atlas holding the celestial globe was made around 300 BC by the nautical culture of the Tyrrhenian (Etruscans of Tuscany) in Italy. It is significant that this exquisite creation honoring one of the greatest scientists comes from the master artisans of Tyrrhenian, whose totem is the composite creature, the Chimaera. This mythical beast was descended from the ancient races of the Atlantic, a child of Typhon and Echidna according to Greek genealogy. This parentage makes the Chimaera come from an incredibly far-removed period of time. The Tyrrhenian truly fit their pedigree from an Atlantic culture because they were exceptional navigators.

Diodorus Siculus

Siculus (49 BC) starts his history with the Egyptians, who claim that the birth of the gods took place in the Land of the Nile. But Apollodorus and other mythographers and genealogists show that the Egyptians descended from Atlantian colonists on the coastlands of Morocco.

Diodorus Siculus has preserved the very ancient history of Skytobrachion, who lived before the Trojan War (c. 1192–1183 BC). Siculus (III.56) begins the history of Skytobrachion by making a very telling statement in saying that the accounts of the Greeks concur with those of the Atlantians. But Greek accounts could only resemble those of the Atlantians if certain tribes of the Greeks or their rulers originally came from the Atlantic. There could be no other possible reason for them to possess matching traditions. According to Skytobrachion:

> But since we have made mention of the Atlantians, we believe that it will not be inappropriate in this place to recount what their myths relate about the genesis of the gods, in view of the fact that it does not differ greatly from the myths of the Greeks. Now the Atlantians, dwelling as they do in the regions on the edge of the ocean and inhabiting a fertile territory, are reputed far to excel their neighbors in reverence toward the gods and the humanity they showed in their dealings with strangers, and the gods whom they say were born among them. And their account, they maintain, is in agreement with that of the most renowned of the Greek poets when he represents Hera as saying:
>
> > For I go to see the ends of the bountiful earth, the realm of Oceanus and mother Tethys, source of the gods.

Siculus continues the account of Skytobrachion, saying that Uranus was their first king, and he subdued the west and regions to the north while he gathered the people into walled cities and taught them laws and to cultivate, conserve, and store fruits. Uranus was an astronomer and cosmologer who introduced the calendar based upon the movements of the sun and moon. He also foretold many things that would take place throughout the world. The people marveled at his predictions and his knowledge of the stars and thought that he partook of the intelligence of the gods; and they used his name as their appellation of the heavens.

One of Uranus' wives was Titaea, mother of the Titians, who was later called Ge. Other children of Uranus were Pandora and Basileia, later called the "Great Mother." Basileia united with Hyperion, and they had two children called Helius and Selene, who was also called Mene. Helius was slain by the Titians. These are the stories shared by both the Phrygians and Atlantians.

Siculus records that the brother of Atlas named Cronus married Rhea, with whom he begat Zeus (Jupiter), the god of Olympus. It should be noted that there had been a previous Zeus, a brother to Uranus (epoch Scorpio), who was king of Crete and father of the Curetes. As Atlas (epoch Aquarius) ruled over the regions of Fez and Morocco, his brother Cronus was the king of Italy, Sicily, and Libya. Cronus and the Titians later attacked Zeus, who overcame his father in battle. Afterward Zeus visited and conquered the whole world, conferring benefactions upon humanity. Thus ends the accounts that Siculus retold from Skytobrachion—accounts that match the corpus of Greek traditions. These accounts confirm the histories of Atlantis, which the Egyptians of the city of Sais told to Solon and were later transcribed by the philosopher Plato.

The West was the homeland of Pluto, ruler of the underworld, as well as Pan, the creator of the music and dancing of the Satyrs. Also, it is an irrefutable fact that some of the adventures of Odysseus, Jason and the Argonauts, Perseus, Dionysius, Orpheus, Persephone, Linus, the Amazons, Gorgons, Aphrodite, Demeter, Hades, Pallas Athena, Cadmus, Hercules, Antaeus, Pleiades, the Golden Apples of the Hesperides, and the Isles of the Blessed all contain episodes that are originally located in the West and on the Atlantic coastlands of Europe and Africa.

The Parthenon on the Acropolis of Athens and the Temple at Delphi both feature tympanum carvings of the battles of the Amazons and also the battles of the children of the goddess Ge, mother of the Giants. Among the Amazons were Medusa, the Gorgons, and most probably the warrior goddesses Athena and Artemis, the huntress. Athens, Arcadia, Crete, and Libya all have a River Triton in memory of the original river in Fez and Morocco, which was called by the name of Triton.

Battle of the Amazons from the tympanum of the temple at Delphi. This theme was also found on the important tympanum upon the Acropolis in Athens. It is strange that the Amazons should be such an important and recurring theme among the Greeks. But, of course the ancient Amazons and Gorgon-Amazons lived in Morocco where the warrior goddess Athena was also born. The conflict between the Moroccan culture of Athena and the Libyan culture of Poseidon is well documented in Greek myth. Author photo.

Atlas, the Heaven Holder

Atlas was discussed above regarding his similarities to Adam. The Egyptian Hercules, during his travels to the West, had adventures in Spain and Morocco, where he studied under Atlas. This episode is told in the sense that Hercules takes the heavy burden of holding the celestial sphere from Atlas while Atlas goes to his daughters, the Pleiades, to collect the Golden Apples for Hercules. The Golden Apples, of course, refers to the planets, which circle the sun and, having no light of their own, reflect the golden sunlight from their orbs. It was Atlas who transmitted astronomy to the Egyptians through their god Hercules-Shu. Furthermore, Atlas had another brother named Prometheus, who lived in the region of the Caucasus Mountains. Prometheus could foresee the future. He was likewise an astronomer like his brother Atlas, and he founded the celebrated Vedic astronomy.

Atlas as the "Heaven-holder," a marble statue of Tyrrhenian origin in the Museum at Naples

Atlas made his observations from the Atlas Mountains near the Atlantic Ocean. His daughters, the Hesperides, were also called the Pleiades, and they guarded the Golden Apples on the Isles of the Blessed. It must be concluded that Atlas constructed the great Atlantic prime meridian from his astronomical knowledge. This prime meridian divides the geographic area of Capricorn from Aquarius. This prime meridian and the Islands of the Hesperides were still visited by Saints Marnoc (fourth century AD) and Brendon the Navigator (484–577 AD) from Ireland as places of unique interest.

The noted mapmaker Geraldus Mercator used the image of Atlas supporting the heavenly globe on his shoulders as the frontispiece of his new catalogue of ancient and modern maps. Since then the name *Atlas* has been applied to books of star maps, geographical charts, and many other types of catalogues.

Marinos of Tyre and the Phoenician Prime Meridian

Our modern global prime meridian is lined up with Greenwich, England, for no particular reason other than that Great Britain was the powerful and established world empire for a brief period of time.

The noted astronomer Hipparchus of Rhodes (160–125 BC) used the latitude of Rhodes as his baseline to establish increments of longitude with Rhodes as the prime meridian. However, ancient Phoenician maps copied by Marinos of Tyre (c. 120 AD) always respected the Atlantic prime meridian near La Palma. Marinos employed a grid of latitude and longitude with a 0° to 360° line upon the Canary Islands. This prime meridian was even upheld by Ptolemy of Alexandria, the famous astronomer and geographer, in preference to the views of Eratosthenes (276–195 BC), the librarian who had lobbied for a new prime meridian at the pyramids of Giza.

This Atlantic prime meridian, a special sacred and scientific phenomenon that demarcated the line between Capricorn-Aquarius was accepted through the ages by scientists from many nations, such as Marinos of Tyre (Phoenician), Ptolemy (Greek-Egyptian), Mercator (European), Abraham Ortelius (European), and Hadji Ahmed (Turkish). Hadji Ahmed, a Turkish subject, was originally from Tunis, while his world map was engraved on wooden plates in Venice. The map displays some interesting features.

The 1559 heart-shaped map of Hadji Ahmed beautifully demonstrates the ancient Atlantic prime meridian. Charles Hapgood discusses this chart, which he considers one of the most remarkable maps that he has ever seen. His reasons for this assertion are quite stunning. Hapgood says that the eastern hemisphere is quite ordinary and that the Mediterranean is based upon Ptolemy, instead of the more sophisticated superportolano of the earlier date of 1513. The story of the western hemisphere is entirely different and based upon some extraordinary source maps. Hapgood writes,

> The shapes of North and South America have a surprisingly modern look, the western coasts are especially interesting. They seem to be about two centuries *ahead* of the cartography of the time. Furthermore, they appear to have been drawn on a highly sophisticated spherical projection. The shape of what is now the United States is about perfect. This remarkable accuracy of the Pacific Coasts of the Americas, and the difficulty of imagining how they could have been drawn in the middle of the 16th Century [1559]...

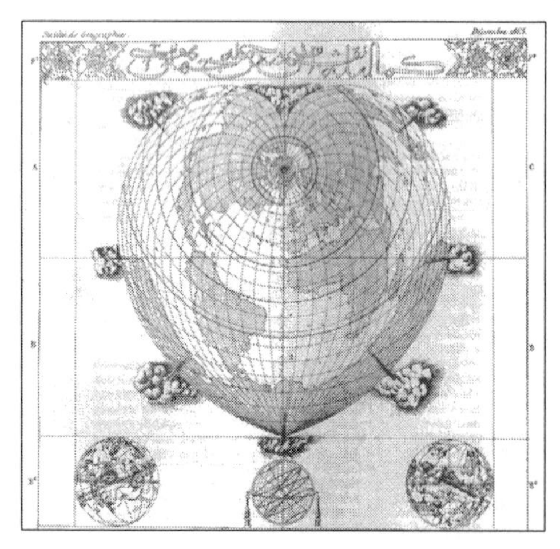

The 1559 heart-shaped map of Hadji Ahmed. A.E. Nordenskiold, *The Early History of Cartography*, Courtesy of University of San Francisco Library.

The Renaissance of Cartography—Ortelius and Mercator

The Age of Discovery brought about the renaissance of mapmaking. Abraham Ortelius (1527–1598 AD) and Mercator (c. 1569) collected antique maps all over Europe. Many of the maps that they collected were from the remarkable Jewish mapmakers of La Palma and other Atlantic islands mentioned above. Binding also says that explorations on the Atlantic changed the focus of science, commerce, and mapmaking from its traditional

Mediterranean home in Venice to its new home in Antwerp, located upon the new Atlantic trading zone.

It was the era of the fruits of the printing press and the Frankfort Book Fair, a meeting place of intellectuals, revolutionary thinkers, authors, and publishers. Also, the new and more exact copper-plate etchings replaced the less-defined woodcut forms, which now allowed for higher standards of precision in mapmaking and the incorporation of many more place names. There was also a need to design deep-ocean-going vessels to cross the Atlantic. The traditional Portuguese *falua* had evolved into the *caravel* and then into the *carrack*, with its several decks and square rigging. Yet only 1,500 years earlier, the Veneti of Brittany had constructed and sailed these types of advanced ocean-crossing vessels.

Abraham Ortelius belonged to a very influential family of Augsberg, Germany, and was introduced to the remarkable Gerardus Mercator, who formulated the "Mercator projection." Ortelius, sometimes accompanied by Mercator, traveled throughout Europe from 1550–1576 on his business of collecting ancient maps. He was a yearly attendee of the Frankfort Book Fair. Ortelius was also a collector of books and coins as well as a student of classical history. It will be remembered that Mercator was the one who placed the image of Atlas on the frontispiece of his masterwork of maps. Both men were responsible for the renaissance of European mapmaking. Abraham Ortelius, as a responsible scholar, credited 87 original authors of maps that he used in the creation of his own masterpiece collection of maps. Later editions of his atlas credited up to 183 map authors. It may be noted that Ortelius, a true scientist and scholar, defended the ancient Atlantic prime meridian in each of the maps that he copied and reproduced. His long studies of old maps prompted the idea of the possibility of "continental drift" and the theory of the supercontinent of Pangaea. He has been justly called "the father of modern cartography." While the achievement of Mercator and Ortelius is called an "advance in knowledge," it is obvious from the story of these two pioneers that their genius was founded upon their research and selections of excellent old examples of scientific mapmaking.

It was upon these ancient maps that they rebuilt the modern science of cartography by "organizing, reformulating, and reintroducing" advanced projections from the neglected works of the past. Indeed, this is another instance of the renaissance, the "rediscovery of the arts and sciences of the past." The best proof that Mercator discovered truly ancient and sophisticated maps is born out in his 1538 map of South America, which is more accurate than his later rendition of his 1569 map with the large bulge on the Chile coast. The later was truly the more ancient map prior to the default of this coastline, which raised the Andes to such heights as we now know them. In 1575 Ortelius became geographer to Philip II of Spain.

The *organization* of ancient knowledge by Ortelius and Mercator led to a scientific revolution in cartography. From their tradition, the Swedish scholar A.E. Nordenskiold collected and organized antique maps (1889), which led to Charles Hapgood's *Maps of the Ancient Sea Kings* (1966), which resulted in his stunning conclusions of an advanced scientific culture that had mapped the world in the far-distant past. It may be imagined that there are three types of antique maps that Mercator and Ortelius compared:

One type of map is very amateurish and not based upon any reasonable global projection. This map calculates distances from one port to another by means of compass and compass-rose geometry. The keyword here is that the map does not come from a fragment of a larger global projection. The maps created from the information of Ptolemy fall into this category, even though they were later graduated in longitude and latitude.

Another type of map, such as the mysterious Dulcert super-portolano (c. 1339 AD) of the Mediterranean discussed by Hapgood, clearly shows that it was derived from a genuine global projection. Nordenskiold and Brehmer conclude that the Dulcert-Portolano is of Phoenician origin and designed like the Phoenician maps of Marinos of Tyre (c.120 AD). All of the super-portolanos come from this one source which was copied over and over again. While Angelino Dulcert (fl.1339 AD) was a Venetian cartographer from Majorca inside the Mediterranean, his famous map was actually produced in the La Palma school in the Canary Islands just a few degrees away from the Atlantic Prime Meridian.

A third type of map is founded upon a global projection; but the shape and position of the landmasses does not match its present shape. These maps must be extremely ancient showing landmasses as they appeared before ages of plate-displacement, continental-drift and re-shaping of Pangaea. The Pangaea theory was originated by Abraham Ortelius out of necessity to account for the many differences and irregularities on the maps that he had collected.

The story of Mercator and Ortelius is a perfect example for every student of antiquity, because it shows that true knowledge is the product of ancient data combined with current science. This deep research into the past has spawned the ideas of Pangaea deformations, continental drift, and global warming.

On a final note to the genius of Ortelius is his publication of his own personally researched map of Fez and Morocco. Unbelievably, his map portrays an enormous sheltered ocean bay with islands and peninsula in the exact position where history, myth, and genealogy record the location of the Tritonian Marsh, the Island of Hespera, and the peninsula of Chersoneses.

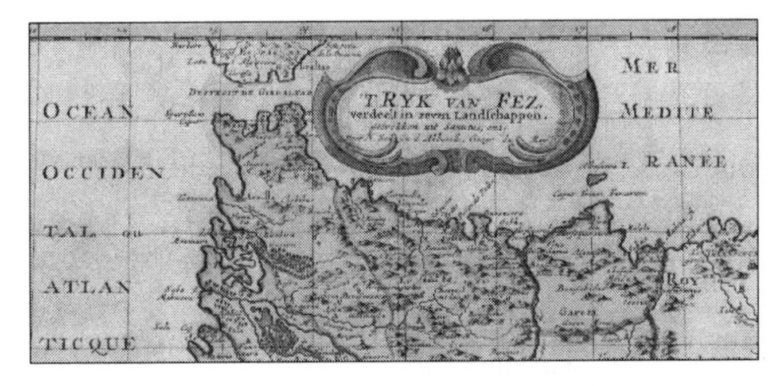

Map by Sanson after Abraham Ortelius showing the salt-water bay and islands upon which the Greek-Atlantic gods of antiquity were born. Author's map

Charles Hapgood (p. 224) gives Blundeville's directions (1594 AD) for constructing a map, "First draw a cross for the four principle winds: north, south, east, and west. Then divide these quarters into equal parts, and then divide them again so that a great circle is divided into 16 equal sections. Wherever these section lines cross the circle, draw a little circle and divide those into 16 parts whose lines lead to all the other little circles. The main compass in the middle is the "mother compass," and all the other compass roses show by what wind the ship has to sail by to get to a certain other place."

The layout of the Hadji Ahmed World Map is quite different from Blundeville's description. The cordiform (heart-shaped) projection uses the Earth's pole as the center line of all the evenly spaced circles of latitude drawn from one compass point on the pole. The circles of longitude are bent and only conform to an equal latitude at the equator. The map demonstrates two main features: The *horizontal* center of the map is marked by the Atlantic prime meridian off the coast of Africa. The *vertical* center is 30 degrees North latitude (not upon the equator). The lines that connect the eight winds at the edges of the map cross exactly at this point of the intersection of the prime meridian and the 30-degree-north line. This is the location of the point of the mother compass.

Blundeville's map certainly sounds practical. What secret is the Hadji Ahmed World Map trying to tell us? If the vertical center of the map is 30°N latitude of the equator, perhaps this represents one of the points of a vertically disposed hexagram whose points are the North and South Poles and 30°N and 30°S of the equator on both sides of the globe. The Hadji Ahmed map therefore discloses the double secret of the golden hexagram, not only of longitude but that there is a hexagon of latitude as well.

The total height of the cordiform map multiplied by the inverse of phi (1.-.618 =.382) = the distance of the North Pole to the equator. This means that the heart-shaped projection is also founded upon the golden-mean proportion.

The complex projection of the 1559 AD heart-shaped map (and its double-hexagram design) of Hadji Ahmed demonstrates a desire to adapt great astronomical cycles to their current position of influence upon the geography of the world. This synthesis of history, astronomy, and geography creates a global grid where the myth of the generations of the gods becomes a guideline to chronology and location of the ancient history of this planet.

Anyone who would question the validity of Greek myth should ask themselves, "Does anyone think that the Greeks, Romans, Phoenicians, Libyans, and Egyptians spent the wealth of their nations and the production of their artisans building massive temples to Zeus, Jupiter, and Saturn on the basis of the whimsical musings of their poets, folklore, mythographers, and genealogists?" Ancient people have transmitted these accounts at their full historical value as the root foundation of their culture and heritage. It would be inaccurate to decide that the background of prior people on this planet was based upon delusion and fantasy.

PART 9

Archaeoastronomy in Asia, Africa, and Europe

This part covers a review of the current understanding of archaeoastronomy in Asia, Africa, and Europe. It will be noted that discussions of local folk tradition, ancient mythology, ancient genealogy, and classical astrology are not included in these conventional reports of the *culture of astronomy.* "Culture" should include the abovementioned disciplines and categories.

"Ancient earthworks and megalithic sites are almost universally connected with *astronomy*—to a degree that one might say that the purpose of their construction was to record, study, celebrate, and pass-down vital astronomical data (Kelley and Milone, *Encyclopedia of the Ancient Skies*)." Archaeoastronomy concerns itself only with the cold and hard facts presented at each ancient megalithic site regarding astronomical markings, sight lines, and orientations that actually exist. Dating is based upon carbon-based materials that are found in place at these ancient sites. Therefore the Great Pyramid may be determined to be less old than a site where carbon-based materials have been found in place. Unless otherwise stated, this entire part is a brief summary taken from Kelley and Milone in their excellent *Encyclopedia of the Ancient Skies.*

CHAPTER 9.1

Astronomy of China and Japan

The history of the sophisticated astronomy of China and Japan goes back through many ages. Their ideas include large astronomical cycles and a cosmology formed of heaven-earth-man. China and Japan make use of numerology, male and female dichotomy, and the idea of heaven influencing political changes and events upon the Earth. Because of these reasons, Chinese astronomy must be included as a member of a worldwide *cosmological philosophy* that we have been speaking about.

Chinese astronomy is a very ancient and uniquely separate system from other cosmologies. In 130 AD there were star maps with 783 stars in 283 asterisms. In 310 AD there were 1,465 stars in 283 asterisms. In the writings of the second century AD, Chang Heng mentioned 2,500 bright stars and 11,520 very small stars. That Chinese astronomers have been looking at the skies for a very long time is apparent when 10 stars from ancient star maps showed a north-south movement relative to the ecliptic. They have also noticed sunspot cycles, comets, and meteors since the beginning of their records.

Schlegel (1875) surmised from internal structural elements and the equinoctial and solstical positions that the Chinese maps of the heavens dated back to 15000 BC. In 1984 Julius Staal supported Schlegel's ideas.

Fortunately, a wealth of astronomical material was discovered at the burial site of the son of the first Marquis of Yi in 168 BC. Among the burial goods of the son of the Marquis of Yi were discovered 20 silk books on astronomy and astrology. These included the movements of Jupiter from 246 BC to 178 BC and a catalogue of the shapes of comets.

General agreement in Chinese sources starts with the expulsion of the Western Zhou emperor Li in 841 BC. His father, named I came to the throne apparently during a sunrise eclipse placed at various dates between 966–899 BC. Just like in Mexica-Maya traditions, imperial changes took place at times of eclipses that were observed in that location.

Milone and Kelley write, "Astronomy in China was driven to provide precision in the timing of events because the political realm had to be in rhythm with the natural one. This is clear from many inscriptions and records, such as the "instructions" for future emperors draw up during the Sung Dynasty."

China used the system of equal double hours: 12 to the day, 12 to the night. The Chinese name for the Metonic cycle was *chang*. In the west the Callippic cycle was four Metonic cycles (76 yrs.) called *pu* in China. 27 x 19 = 513, called a *hui*, and also an eclipse interval. 3 *hui* = *thung* = 1,539 years. 3 *thung* = 4,617 (also used to coordinate with a 60 day sexgenary cycle, but off by half a day). Also, 20 *pu* = 1,520 years = 1 *chi*. 3 *chi* = 1 *shou*. And, 7 *shou* = 31,920 years when all things will end and return to their original state (equal to four Julian cycles of 7,980 years, independently invented by Joseph Scaliger in the west in the 16th century).

Milone and Kelley write, "The concept of a grand cycle of ages was widely held throughout the world." Liu Hsin (46 BC–23 AD) used an era base of 143,231 BC (Chang, 1980). In the Han Dynasty, it was supposed that the planetary cycles repeated every 138,240 years. When this was combined with the three-thung cycle of 4,617 years, the result was a "world cycle" of 23,639,040 years (Needham, 1959).

Needham (1959, p. 392) asserts that that the synodic month had been determined in the 14th century BC to be 29.53 days. In 237 AD, Yuang Wei got a value of 29.530591 compared to the modern vale of 29.530588. The departure of the moon from the ecliptic and the variation of the moon's orbital speed were recognized by Shih Shen (fl. 371–340 BC). The effect of the advance of the moon's line of apsides was first mentioned by Liu Xiang around 11 BC.

Chinese astronomy gave significance to the fact that Jupiter's sidereal period is close to one year in each sign, 12 years around the zodiac, and 5 x 12 = 60 year cycle. Triple conjunctions of Jupiter, Saturn, and Mars were especially significant.

The planets are described as the "essences" of the five elements. "The planets are said to assist the sun and moon to regulate the five 'emanations': rain, sunshine, wind, heat, and cold." The Chinese cosmologers thought that, as the sun, moon, and planets were the directors of the heavenly realm, and that the political world down below was a reflection of the celestial. "During the period of good government all human affairs are well regulated, and at those times, the Seven Directors move with regular constancy. But, if it happens that the Emperor interferes with the office of the ministers, or the latter usurps the Imperial power, the political administration falls into confusion and error, morals and precepts become perverted, also the malign influences change strangely and behave irregularly" (K&M, p. 328).

Chinese philosophers associated colors, directions, elements, musical notes, numbers, and, in fact, everything in nature with the four cardinal directions, using the Earth as the center and the fifth category. Mesopotamian and Mesoamerican culture also divided nature into such divisions, but there was no cosmology so dedicated to this compartmentalization as China. Even today these traditions are a strong part of their culture. The four directional animals are divided into seven mansions each (4 x 7 = 28 houses of the moon): Blue dragon is Jupiter, the year star, the east, and wood; the Red Bird is Mars, "the glitterer," the south, and fire; Saturn is "the filler," the center; the White Tiger is Venus, "the Great White," the west, and metal; and the Black Warrior is Mercury, "the hour star," the north, and water (according to Needham).

The turtle is a major figure in the astronomy and cosmology of China, as it is among the Maya. It is depicted with an intertwining serpent and associated with a magic square of 3 x 3 boxes. The eight trigrams are supposed to have originated during the Chou Dynasty (1050 BC). The *Book of Changes* is based upon eight combinations of the possibilities of three lines, the trigrams. The broken lines represent the female nature, while the unbroken are the male. They represent heaven, earth, water, fire, and so on in a combination of 64 possibilities. The even numbers are yin, while the odd are yang. The number *1* is masculine and associated with the sun and the heavens. The number *2* is feminine and associated with the earth. The number *3* is associated with man, who is between heaven and earth.

Astronomical calculators called the "diviner's plate" have been found in several tombs. These are made up of a square plate representing the Earth and its four directions, with a rotating disc superimposed upon it showing the 28 unequal divisions of the moon's circuit. This movable rotating disc could be adjusted to show the current influence of the moon and the heavens upon the earth. These divining boards also became game boards of chance and amusement. Another diviner's plate (c. 581 AD) shows a division of the outermost circle into 36 animal pictures.

Buddhist missionaries came from India bringing major cosmological beliefs from the fourth century onward. They settled in China, where they established families that maintained a connection with India. The traditions of the lotus flower, Gemini shown as a male and female pair, and Mount Meru—the navel of the world—stem from Buddhist influence.

It is apparent from the lengthy instructions (c. 1193 AD) that the new emperor needed to have extensive knowledge of astronomy to have a successful reign. The text, cited by Rufus and Tien (1945), begins:

> Before the Great Absolute had unfolded itself the three primal essences, Heaven, Earth, and Man...original chaos...the light and pure formed Heaven, the heavy and impure Earth, and the mingled pure and impure formed Man. The light and pure constitute spirit, the heavy and impure constitute body, and the union of spirit and body, constitute man. Hence, all manifestations of spirit emanate from Heaven...this evolves into the sun and moon, and divides into the five planets, arranges in order as the twenty-eight mansions, and meets to form the directors and the circumpolar stars. All of these, being involved in the immutable reason, are also in harmony with the

> rational principle in man, hence they may be interpreted by reason... the body of Heaven is round, and the body of Earth is square...The Red Road is the celestial equator...the Yellow Road is the course of the Sun, the ecliptic...the White Road is the Moon's path...the River of Heaven, the Milky Way...the Moon...rules with stern authority, to punish and chastise, and thus symbolizes the Prime Minister.

The Chinese were noted recorders of "guest stars," comets, supernova, and sunspot cycles and maxima. One of their observatories contains 365 stones and 28 rows starting from the lower base. Curiously, these observatories strongly resemble Irish towers. The Chinese also made long voyages to East Africa. Captain Cheng Ho (1405–1435 AD) actually created maps south of the Horn of Africa (Binding, p. 213, 246). Their maps were of the highest cartographic excellence compared to Europe. In 1541–1555 AD, the Ming Atlas was printed in China, recalling at least seven voyages to East Africa made more than 100 years earlier over a distance somewhat longer than that of Columbus' voyage across the Atlantic.

The Astronomy of Japan

Noted for its relative isolation, Japan was inhabited by the Jomon Neolithic culture (c. 11000 BC). The Jomon-type are very tall white people who are also found in North America, such as Kennewick Man in Washington, and identical types in Nevada and Minnesota. Jomon were deep-sea fishers, like the natives of Washington State, and probably whale hunters who lived in pit houses. Jomon, Yayoi, and Ainu cultures built many stone circles that act as sundials, and massive stone tombs with banks up to 82 meters in diameter. Sadly, none of the structures have been vetted for astronomical alignments. Later Japan was influenced by Korean, Chinese, and Buddhist cosmology.

Junko Habu, in his *Ancient Jomon of Japan* (pp. 150–5), presents drawings of numerous phallic stones, some of which were found in ceremonial places in pit dwellings. These stones are from 5 to 20 centimeters in diameter and up to one meter long. Habu does not comment on the fact that these phallic stones have knobs on the top, suggesting that they are circumcised. Jomon culture is dated conservatively about 14000 BC to 300 BC. Noted for their extravagant pottery design, some of the female forms that Habu shows share the exaggerated billowy forms of similar clay figures from the island of Malta in the Mediterranean. Stone circles and earthen mounds also abound in this culture.

Wayne Herschel, in *The Hidden Records* (p. 112), shows a photo of the Kitora Kofun Pyramid in Japan. This pyramid features a star map using gold dots joined by red lines to depict some of the brightest constellations in the sky.

CHAPTER 9.2

Astronomy of Brittany, Ireland, England, Scotland, and Europe

The Seven Saints, also known as the *Merec*, are the founders of Brittany:

St. Malo—ship .... Mercury? (Dioscuri)

St. Herve—wolf .... Saturn?

St. Ninnok—bitch .... Moon? (Artemis)

St. Eloi (Helios?)—horse .... Sun (Helios)

St. Corneli—bull .... Venus (Taurus)

St. Patern (Vannes .... Jupiter? (Pater)

St. Cado (Belz)—bridge and devil .... Mars?

Kelley and Milone describe primitive calendar sticks of antler bone with notches in France, Nicobar, and North America. They also mention that the cave paintings at Lascaux may represent the Pleiades and the constellation of Leo when it was seen to be in the shape of a horse.

William R. Corliss, in his *Ancient Infrastructure* (pp. 51–54) gives this excellent synopsis of the subject:

> Menhirs enter into archaeoastronomy because they are sharply defined vertical markers which, when combined with horizon features—hill tops, horizon notches, etc.—can serve as permanent recorders of extreme positions (called "standstills") of celestial objects. The menhirs (backsights) were placed so that they lined up visually with certain

> horizon features (foresights) when the moon reached these standstills. Over hundreds of years, such crude observations led to the recognition of the 18.5 year lunar cycle.

Corliss then expands upon the research of Alexander Thom, "renowned for his meticulous measurements," who surmised that the giant 67-foot-tall *Er Grah* menhir by Quiberon Bay was the universal foresight for at least eight sight lines, some as far away as 9.5 miles. If Thom's theory were true, this would imply that the ancient megalithic inhabitants had conceived and built *a huge astronomical instrument* to refine their observations of lunar "standstill nuances" in order to facilitate their prediction of solar eclipses.

Alexander Thom was one of the fathers of archaeoastronomy in mapping sites using his own version of *the megalithic yard* and studying their geometric layouts using Pythagorean triangles and their connection with astronomy. Thom was an avid sailor who understood stellar navigation and procedures in sighting directions, sun, moon, and stars. His avocation as a professor of engineering gave him the precise skills to develop this new field of study. Alexander Thom also maintained that many sites included alignments focused upon distant natural and artificial features, such as notches in mountains and cairns and standing stones on horizons or elevations.

Archaeoastronomers say that the megalithic monuments themselves are records in stone. O'Kelly (1982) suggested that, in the case of Newgrange, mythology was the vehicle for the transmission of astronomical knowledge. Most ancient scientific cultures had specific individuals who remembered data from generation to generation, sometimes assisted by devices such as Inca quipu bundles.

All aspects of farming are connected with the movements of the moon. Navigation has, in all cases, been tied to stellar observation and alignments. The moon's light and gravity had a pronounced effect on ancient societies who needed knowledge of the tides and who navigated by nocturnal light. Strongest tides occur at new and full moon. The moon contributes two-thirds, while the sun contributes one-third of the tide's rising force. Also, the tides are 17% greater when the moon is at perigee and the opposite percentage is at apogee. In harbors with strong riptides, these factors become of deadly importance for sailors.

Controversy surrounding alignments comes about because of historical records that sighting stones have been moved, restored, reset, realigned, and straightened. The growth of modern forests and vegetation interfere with the vantage points of older foresights and backsights. The best evidence is that an artificial knoll or a natural notch in the surrounding mountains corresponds to positions of moon or sun standstills. At Newgrange, the kerb stones are decorated on all sides, even those that face into the wall of the mound and cannot be seen.

Some questions about sites may be resolved by reference to Pythagorean triangles, which were used in laying out the site, such as the 30 MY-40 MY-50 Megalithic Yard triangle used at the Breton site of Crucuno. This little 3-4-5 dance is a common feature of megalithic sites, as it was also used in Egypt by the priest-surveyors in determining right angles.

There is also a rectangular basis for laying out megalithic sites at the 47.5-degree-latitude line on the globe where the long sides of this 3 x 4 rectangle are focused upon the rising and setting sun at the time of the solstices. Most commonly the dimensions are based upon solar alignments at a specific latitude. Also, the Earth's atmosphere both refracts and scatters light. Therefore, for accurate results, corrections to the altitude for elevation, dip (causes a flat horizon to be further depressed), and refraction must be made to determine the true azimuth and hour angle of the object (K&M, p. 165). Refraction is equal to about ½ a degree lift appearance prior to actual sunrise above the horizon, with variations due to atmospheric temperature and air pressure. Definition of true north may be accomplished by the bisection of the angle between the azimuths of sunrise and sunset.

Thom finds that such megalithic fan-shaped configurations of stones as at Mid Clyth in Caithness in Northern Scotland indicate evidence of stone grids used for lunar calculations.

Brittany

Brittany has early passage graves, oriented to the southeast (the region of the midwinter solstice sunrise), constructed out of gigantic rocks afterward covered with earth. At Dissignac in Brittany there are two passage graves, one of which has a precision alignment to the winter sunrise solstice that illuminates the burial chamber at the end of a 7m passage. The entrance capstone has representations of shepherds' crooks and axes. Mohen (1990) dates this site at 4500 BC.

Near Loc Mariaquer, there once stood the largest *menhir* at 20.3m, Le Grand Menhir Brise. This and other giant stones fell and broke in a great earthquake in that region (Thom and Thom). Thom hypothesized that this giant stone served as a foresight for movements of the moon.

Most interesting is the extensively decorated passage grave at Gavr'inis, dated about 3500 BC. Some of the carvings show long-horned cattle similar to Egyptian representations. The alignments here are extraordinary because the winter solstice sunrise intersects with the major southern moonrise halfway down the passage at stone 7, which is an undecorated white quartz slab illuminated by the rising sun and moon (Burl, 1985).

Regarding the passage grave at Le Table des Merchands, Muller notes that there is a representation of 56 shepherds' crooks, divided into 29 on the left and 27 on the right, and 19 accompanying curved elements, suggestive of the nearest whole number of synodic and sidereal months and of the Metonic cycle (18.6 x 3 = 55.8 (56) years of three Metonic cycles (Though the triple Saros cycles appears to be 54 years). In general, the motifs and style of the Breton passage graves are closely paralleled at Newgrange and Knowth in the Boyne Valley of Ireland. It is generally accepted that there is a close historical connection, and also both Newgrange and Gavr'inis are aligned to winter solstice sunrise.

Stone Rows at Karnak

The largest concentration of megaliths in the world is in Karnak in Brittany. Thom said that he had difficulty in finding a stone that had not been moved. Yet, Underwood says that the avenues of stones are placed upon wavy underground water phenomena. Kelley noticed that the stones are well founded beneath the ground level and that it would take an extraordinary amount of force to shift them. The actual date of these stone rows is unclear, while the nearby cromlechs are dated at about 3000 BC. Some of the stone rows and circles disappear into the sea as a testament to their great age. One of the stone rows is an astonishing 1km in length.

Burl writes that the short axis of the Menec West cromlech, an inverted egg, is in line with midwinter sunrise and that the long axis of its eastern counterpart points in the direction of the midsummer sunset. He goes on to suggest festivals that occurred on the cross-quarter days of Beltane in early May and Samhain in early November. He further points out that there is clear evidence of bonfires on these occasions and that the summer solstice was commemorated in this fashion as late as the 19th century.

Ireland, the Valley of the Boyne

The correct name for the remarkable complex at Newgrange is Brú Na Bóinne, the Mound on the Boyne River. Guy Underwood remarks that Brú Na Bóinne is very rare because it is a barrow enclosed by a ring of standing stones known as peristalith. Milone and Kelley write (p. 168) that, "It provides the best evidence of a complex context for existence and precise interest in astronomy. The three great mounds at Newgrange, Knowth, Dowth, and associated monuments are for the most part inter-visible, and together, they form a kind of massive record, which we only now are starting to understand." N.L. Thomas writes (p. 18) that Knowth is aligned to a minor lunar standstill (N56°W) as well as sunrise and sunset at equinox. The complimentary Dowth is also on a minor lunar standstill (N59°E) as well as midwinter sunset at solstice, complementing the sunrise passage on the same day at Newgrange. A larger passage blocked by modern-day archaeologists at Dowth appears to be aligned to the quarter days in November and February. Newgrange, Knowth, Dowth, and "a number of other standing stones and earthworks within the bend of the river provided a series of solar and lunar alignments, the totality of which shows the area was constructed according to a precise astronomical plan," which together created a sacred calendrical site.

Eogan's work at Knowth has revealed two massive passage graves, one aligned to the rising equinox sun, in which the sunlight directly penetrates the main burial chamber. The other passage is aligned to the setting equinox sun, with sunlight penetrating far down the passage, but prevented from actually entering the chamber by a bend (Was there a bronze mirror placed here?). This bent-shaft feature is similar to the second passage at Gavr'inis. Winter solstice sunsets are a feature of Dowth. "Slight changes in the direction of the sun cause different portions of the passageways and the burial chambers to be illuminated, giving high precision to the astronomical alignment" (Kelley and Milone, p. 170).

At Newgrange, Michael J. O'Kelly meticulously reset stones and cleaned and reconstructed the mound during the period from 1982–1989. The mound stands 45 feet high and 300 feet across, with its quartz-crystal face glistening in the sun, making this megalithic monument one of the most visually impressive of many sites. The global use of crystal and granite crystal is remarkable. O'Kelly discovered a "roof box," a 62-foot-long window shaft over the top of the entrance passage that still lets the rays of the rising winter solstice sun illuminate the great corbel-vaulted chamber. This particular discovery has convinced doubting archaeologists of the deliberate astronomical alignments of megalithic monuments. This feature was first demonstrated by Patrick (1974) and refined by Rea (1988), who showed that in Neolithic times the sun illuminated a three-leafed spiral on the back wall. This certainly reminds of the Anasazi light-and-shadow arrangements in Chaco Canyon and the same light-and-shadow displays at Giza and Chichen Itza.

The main curbstone at Newgrange is bisected with clockwise spirals to the left and counterclockwise spirals on the right of these stones. Newgrange is also surrounded by a ring of standing stones that may predate the mound. The diameter of the stone circle is 125 MY (megalithic yards), the same as at Brogar and the inner rings of Avebury. These stones cast shadows on some of the three-leafed spirals on the curbstones during equinox and solstice. Their ring was formed as a half ellipse and half circular arcs, with the arcs of circles centered upon on the corners of two opposed right-angled Pythagorean triangles.

At Knowth, spirals seem to be connected with calendrical concerns, while radiating lines and two depressions on the top of one of the stones resemble those seen on a flat Egyptian sundial found at Luxor. The marking on the Knowth sundial include eight major points and eight minor points, exactly the 26 divisions postulated by Thom. One of the stones has 22 crescents and seven circles, possibly mimicking the cycle and phases of the moon. At Dowth, there is a markedly different use of motifs, such as sunbursts.

Milone and Kelley write (pp. 174–176) that Brú Na Bóinne complex "is also the only set of megalithic monuments in Europe that is directly relatable to pre-Christian myths that clearly incorporate astronomical myths…nowhere else do we seem to have the degree of mythic relevance that appears with Newgrange and the Boyne complex." However, Michael J. O'Kelly (the archaeologist) warns that the myths are set in the time of the chariot-driving Celtic warriors of an age closer to us than to the builders of the mounds. Yet, their myths may contain older beliefs set into their contemporary surroundings and time. Some of the names in the myths are the *Dagda* = sun; and his wife, *Boand, Boine, Buvinda*, the White Cow = the moon; and their son, *Oengus Mac n Og* = the Ocean. Some of the other gods associated with this complex have associations with the roving planets whose movements are much more complex than those of the sun and moon (yet, in classical astrology, the sun and moon are marshals of every prediction—and therefore the precise placement is paramount—while the planetary positions can be located relative to constellations, asterisms, and the ecliptic). Langley (1986) relates the repeated symbols of Newgrange and Knowth in similar contexts to the art of Teotihuacán.

Forty kilometers west of the Boyne complex is the Loughcrew complex and the Hill of the Witch, with somewhat cruder art that may predate other Irish megalithic structures. The cairn features a determination of the equinoxes. In addition to summer solstice markers, there seem to be alignments to the cross-quarter points of the horizon (such as Halloween) and other alignments that are not deciphered as yet. (These cairns function as calendars to observe feast days connected with their cosmological religion.)

<u>*Stonehenge*</u>

Archaeologists agree that Stonehenge was built in three stages: Stonehenge I and II between 3000–2500 BC and Stonehenge III at 1500 BC. Originally the 125 MY-diameter ditch was constructed with 56 chalk-filled holes called the "Aubrey Holes" within this bank. This arrangement facilitated the observation of the midwinter sunrise and the northern risings of the moon. This construction preceded the erection of the Heel Stone, a sarsen sandstone. Brinckerhoff (1976) noted that between the causeway posts that the moon could be observed to rise one-quarter, one-third, and one-half the length of time between the midpoint and major standstill of the lunar cycle. The Heel Stone marked the lunar midpoint rise. The cardinal points of the solar stations are constructed upon a rectangle of two Pythagorean triangles of 5 x 12 x 13, which work precisely for the latitude of Stonehenge at 51°11'.

The Aubrey Holes are 56 in number. Hawkins (1965) and others have seen Stonehenge as an abacus-like computer, where stones could be advanced one hole every year in the circle of the Aubrey Holes to achieve predictions of eclipse and tallies of the Saros cycle (54 years, 33 days, nearly identical conditions for an eclipse) and the triple Metonic (18.618 x 3 = 55.854 or 56 years even), which reconciles lunar and solar calendars. Hawkins used dates in the mid-16th century BC, which showed that Stonehenge worked even 1,000 years after it was constructed.

Stonehenge II consists of a double ring of 82 "bluestones" of dolerite and rhyolite, which seem to come from the Prescelly Mountains in Wales. Stonehenge III involved the 80 sarsen stones of about 30 tons each. Carvings on these stones show about 30 axe heads and a hilted dagger that strongly resembles ones found at Mycenae in Greece. Axe cults are found in Minoan Crete, and similar carvings are found in Brittany and also resemble Bronze Age axes manufactured in Ireland. Milone and Kelley say, "It seems impossible that precision alignments could have been made with the massive, irregular stones of the monument as either backsights, or not so distant foresights…because a movement of 1 inch would change the date by 200 years, and that by using, say, the right eye instead of the left would shift it by 500 years!" Although Brinckerhoff (1976) has suggested that the pits on the lintels of the great stones of the Sarsen Circle could have held small wands as precise foresights. And also, Thom has proposed far-distant foresights on a distant horizon as a means of achieving high accuracy, as is evident from the many Scottish sites.

Anthony Johnson, in *Solving Stonehenge*, gives a thorough examination of the geometric layout of the site based upon square and circle designs carried out by simple rope-and-peg surveys. He has found that the flattened inside faces of the Sarsen Circle are founded upon a circle inscribed in a square. This length of the side of this central square is one-half of the side of a greater square based upon the station stones located on the inner circle of the circular mound enclosing Stonehenge. The Sarsen square (a circle inscribed in a square) is exactly one-quarter of the station stone square (p. 231). The positioning of the remarkable five pairs of trilithons is based upon a rectangle of two joined squares whose corners are circumscribed by great circles whose bisections determine the position of the trilithons. The abovementioned circle on the inside faces of the Sarsen Circle is the same size as circles inscribed in the two abovementioned squares that form the rectangle. The focus of this circle is the line between the two boxes, and its perimeter goes through the centers of the two circles inscribed in the boxes. Johnson substantiates the truth of the myth that Stonehenge was a carefully cut, prefabricated structure (p. 231) that had been set up in Africa, then Ireland, and finally Brittan.

Mount Pleasant in England

Thomas, in *Irish Symbols of 3500 BC* (p. 95), uses the Mount Pleasant calendar site to demonstrate his thesis. However, his own architectural survey shows 178 timber postholes and two major avenues crossing one another, forming four major entrances to the center of the ring. These features add up to a circle of 360° (178 + 178 + 4 =360). The outer ring of postholes equals 54, which culminate in the sexagesimal fractal (54 + 54 =108 + 108 = 216). The first ring around the stone-slab enclosure is composed of 16 timbers, the second of 24 (16 + 8 =24), the third of 36 (24 + 12 = 36), the forth of 48 (36 + 12 =

48), and the fifth of 54 (48 + 6 = 54). These increases by 8, 12, 12, and 6 are common to the geometry of the 360° circle.

Cumbria in England

There are over 50 stone circles in the Cumbrian region of England. Long Meg is a flattened circle 361 x 305 feet, the largest of the Cumbrian sites. The Long Meg stone has several engraved spirals associated with the winter solstice. At Ballynoe, there stands a circle of 72 stones (5 x 72 = 360). At Lochmaben, Dumfries is the remains of a great circle mentioned by the late Roman geographer of Ravenna as the *Locus Maponi*, and also associated with the Irish Mac nOg.

Outer Hebrides

Most famous of the sites of the Outer Hebrides on the Isle of Lewis is the stone circle at Callanish, called the White Cow. It consists of a ring of stones that (on the east side of the avenue) are consistently three-quarters as high as those on the west side. This feature is characteristic of Northern Irish avenues and double rows and of those on the Crozon peninsula in Brittany. All of these sites are accessible by water.

Callanish is constructed to observe a major standstill position of the moon against the distant Mt. Clisham in the Harris region, where the moon might appear to dance upon the undulating horizon. Also, alignments to the stars are claimed for Capella and the Pleiades.

The account of the Hyperborean Temple of Apollo by Diodorus Sicilus via Hecataeus of Abdera (500 BC) is often applied to Stonehenge, yet the appearance of the *dancing moon* and the *big moon* effect are better seen at Callanish, which is at a more northerly latitude. Abaris, a disciple of Apollo, is said to have been a teacher of Pythagoras. During a famine, a Gaelic-speaking white cow arrived from the sea to give the inhabitants a bucket of milk each. Another legend says that the stones were brought to Callanish on ships by black men and priests in feathered cloaks accompanied by golden-crested wrens, said to be the king of all birds. Black men are also celebrated at Baltimore in Ireland. Geoffrey of Monmouth says that the stones of Stonehenge were brought first to Ireland from Africa.

Another important bird is the raven or crow, called King Bran, and the white crow who is the sister of King Bran. Apollo's totem bird was also the crow. It is said that Bran's head was buried at Tower Hill in London to guard the city from invasion. Decapitation is associated with eclipses in many other cultures. We are familiar with the giant ravens that parade around the grounds of the Tower of London and the post-Conquest story that these ravens guard and protect the city of London.

Brogar, Stenness, and Maes Howe

These monuments lie at the latitude of about 59 degrees. The Brogar stone circle has a diameter of 125 MY, the same as Avebury and the stone circle around Newgrange. Thom and Thom argue that the site was used for high-precision lunar observation. The circle of Stenness originally had 12 standing stones. Seventeenth-century tales ascribe sun worship to Brogar and moon worship to Stenness. The Maes Howe passage grave is so carefully constructed with fine stone workmanship that it is ranked among Europe's finest works. Light from the midwinter sunset illuminates the tomb. There are other significant passage graves and circles in the area as well as the famous stone village of Skara Brae.

At Ballochroy in Argyll, Scotland, sight lines across the sea to the Paps of Jura are clearly discernable from the wide, flat faces of the slabs, which are also angled to other stones across the row to establish almost perfect 90-degree sight lines, because at this unique latitude (55:42'44") the summer and winter solstices occur almost 90 degrees apart.

Merrivale Stone Rows on Dartmoor in Devonshire boast 60 single, double, and triple rows of stones that show major moon standstills and may mark grids for computing other anomalies of the lunar movements.

The site at Temple Wood at Argylle has been called a lunar observatory by Thom. At Mid-Clyth in Caithness in Scotland, Thom derived several components of the moon's motion from the site called "the Hill o' Many Stanes" where about 250 stones establish grids upon a gently sloping hillside.

Thom carefully described exactly how observation and placing stakes in relation to positioned stones could produce a geometry and spherical trigonometry background for calculating the most complicated extremes of the moon's arcane motions with a scientific accuracy.

Megalithic Sites in Europe

In Oldenburg are seven pairs of long parallel stone rows known locally as *Hunenbetten*, "the Beds of the Huns." The equinox and midsummer major moon standstill is designated at this site. Two of the outside pillars have pointed tops, whereas the two interior pillars have flattened tops, paralleling a situation described by Burl regarding some British sites.

At Boitin in Mecklenburg are four stone circles called "Stone Dance." Lines between the centers of these circles form an isosceles triangle, one side of which is only ½ a degree shy of true north. At Klopzow, a double ellipse designates the summer solstice sunset.

The stone circles of Odry, West Prussia, function for equinoxes, solstices, and major moon standstills.

CHAPTER 9.3

Astronomy of Malta, Spain, Balearic Islands, and Sardinia

Milone and Kelley credit Michael Hoskin with the archaeoastronomy analysis of Spanish and Mediterranean islands sites. The megalithic sites and temples at Malta are supposed to have been built around 3600 BC. Most important of all, alignments here are not traditional soli-lunar but seem to be directed at asterisms and single stars. Milone and Kelley say that this aspect is markedly different from other megalithic sites. Yet they say that Mnajdra I is aligned to equinox sunrise and the heliacally rising Pleiades. They also mention a possible directional shift by way of a precessional shift deduced from Ggantija I. At Filotosa in Corsica, there were statue stones depicting the planets placed at specific sighting places relative to the central site. An ignorant archaeologist removed these from their places and assembled them in a childish and meaningless ring near the center of the site. Therefore, Malta declinations could have been focused upon planetary studies as is evident at Filotosa. Also, there are photographs of solar alignments at the Malta temples.

Los Millares (c. 3000 BC) is one of the most important megalithic sites in Spain and is recognized as the most southern manifestation of the European megalithic. The "tholos" tombs have elaborate corbelled domes and large stone-faced entrances that are in the same style as those of Crete and Mycenae in Greece. Orientations were somewhat south of midwinter sunrise. Hoskins (1994) says that Iberian tombs do not seem to be aligned to stars or to the moon. He suggests that many of them seem to be aligned to the sun at various times of the year, illuminating the interiors of the tombs, a pattern suggestive of alignments of medieval churches, many of which were set so that the sun illuminated the high altar on the day of the patron saint.

Elsewhere in Andalusia, there are several kinds of burial mounds that strongly resemble those of Brittany and the Northern Isles. The most remarkable single monument is that of the gigantic Dolmen de Menga at Antequera. The burial chamber is 18.5m long, 6m wide, narrowing to a passage 5m long and 3.5m wide. The entire structure is roofed by only five slabs.

Milone and Kelley report that the island of Menorca contains four megalithic sepulchers, and the neighboring islands of Mallorca and Formentera each contain one. There are also communal burial tombs of large stone blocks that are in the shape of overturned boats, called *nevetas* by the natives. These structures, say the authors, may stem from an earlier tradition. There are also the Menorca towers, called *talayots*, which dominate the local landscape of a village. Within the precincts of these towers are *taula*, massive tables composed of limestone slabs in the form of a *tau*-shaped object. These sacred precinct areas usually face southward. Hoskin (1991) suggested that they were aligned to face the rising of the constellation Chiron. One of these precincts contained a statue of the renowned Egyptian architect Imhotep, who was later deified and associated with medicine. He was also linked to the Greek Asklepios, a pupil of Chiron.

The towers of Sardinia resemble the talayots of Menorca. The Sardinian Tombs of the Giants are like the Menorcan nevetas. Many scholars have supposed a close cultural relationship between them.

CHAPTER 9.4

Astronomy of Egypt, Morocco, Senegambia, and the Dogon

Regarding the prehistoric city of Hurghada on the Red Sea, it is said (*Egypt Tourist Guide*) that it was originally called "Hor Djet" or "the Land of Hor." Similarly, the whole Red Sea was known in ancient times as "the Sea of Hor." According to legend, the followers of the god Horus first came into Egypt by this route. In fact, the whole of the region of the Red Sea coast is littered with sites and remains dating back to prehistoric times.

According to *The Perfect Discourse* by Asclepius/Imhotep, it is reported that Egypt was "the image of heaven" and the world's temple (K&M, pp. 259–61). But modern scholars have found nothing to justify that Egyptian astronomy was in any way superior to Greek, Roman, and Mesopotamian astronomy.

Parker (1950) suggested that the Osiris myth is lunar and based upon astronomy. The new crescent moon is a symbol of the Osiris reborn. Dying Horus is the waning moon. The night-by-night diminution of the moon is symbolized by the enemies of Osiris cutting up the moon. Eclipse is the killing of Osiris. The full moon is the complete Osiris.

The authors of *Ancient Skies* go on to say that the alignment of the pyramids to the cardinal points is good but hardly miraculous. They "are unconvinced that the shadow produced by the sun's disc did not provide sufficient precision to accomplish this alignment." The authors also criticize the invention of Bauval and Gilbert (1994) that the Giza pyramids are a geographic reflection of the stars in Orion's belt, because that would require an inversion as well as a reversal in their positions.

Sellers (1992) suggested that dynastic changes in Egypt followed total eclipses as on 4867 BC, 4849 BC, and 4787 BC. A text from the time of Ramses VI refers to Mercury as Seth in the evening twilight. Venus is sometimes equated with Osiris. Venus depicted with a human head and an animal head may refer to the dichotomy of the evening star and the morning star.

The Egyptian civil year was 365 days divided into three seasons of inundation, cultivation, and harvest. These were seasons of three, four, and five months each and of 30 days organized into three weeks of 10 decades, plus five holy days added to the end of the year. There was a 25-year luni/solar cycle, where 25 years = 309 lunations. Every five years, a half-day was added to the last two months of the year.

Lockyer was the first to rigorously study the alignments of the Egyptian temples. Egyptologists immediately dismissed all his works. However, the inscriptions at the Dendera complex indicated that the temples were aligned to stars. An inscription on the Temple of Hathor actually states: "Looking to the sky at the course of the rising stars and recognizing the *ak* of the Bull's Thigh constellation, I established the corners of the temple of Her Majesty."

Hawkins acted upon and confirmed many of Lockyer's findings, whose astronomical alignment dates, such as 3700 BC, pushed Egypt too far into the past relative to current anthropological dogma.

The earliest example of a sky map as the ceiling of a tomb is that of Senmut, the adviser of Hatshepsut, at Thebes, shown in Neugebauer and Parker (1969). Pogo suggests that the sky represents a time period in the past and not current with the time of Senmut. This is also one of the conclusions regarding the Circular Zodiac of Dendera, which represents a most ancient sky.

The crocodile god Sobek is called the "Lord of the Shifting Waterway," which is regarded to be the name of the Milky Way, regarded as the Heavenly Nile. The Egyptians represented a boatman upon Orion's belt and another boat halfway around the sky near Sagittarius, where the Milky Way crosses the ecliptic of the sun's path around the zodiac.

Mavor (1977) describes Mzorah, "Holy Place", south of Tangiers in Morocco. This is a major megalithic monument of about 60m in diameter, a great ellipse of 168 (originally possibly 175) *menhirs* surrounding a tumulus.

Mavor suggested that the ellipse was laid out on the basis of a 37-35-12 Pythagorean triangle, which Thom claimed was the second-most-common pattern in the British Isles. Mavor found that all solar and lunar standstills were represented in the alignments of the stones. The coincidence of the eastward thrust of the major axis with the direction of the rise of the moon at minor standstill coincides also with the summit of Mt. Jbel Si Habib.

Mavor cites anthropological and archaeological evidence to connect the cultures of Neolithic and early Bronze Age Europe to those of Morocco. The poet Pindar (518–438 BC) mentions this particular monument as the burial place of Antaeus, King of Libya. All of North Africa was called Libya in those days. Antaeus was a son of Poseidon and Mother Earth (Ge), who was killed by Hercules during his tour of the west.

The Dogon live in Mali, formerly French West Sudan below Egypt, at a place which lies across the trade route from the Mediterranean to the Gold Coast (K&M, pp. 273–277). In 1931 the French scholar Marcel Griaule— supported by his colleague, Germaine Dieterlen— compiled an account of Dogon cosmology.

The authors of *Ancient Skies* write, "At the heart of the Dogon cosmology appear a series of astronomical statements that are unexpected and remarkable. They have accounts of very sophisticated astronomical phenomena such as: the four moons of Jupiter, the rings around Saturn, of the revolutions of the planets around the sun and their elliptical orbits, and of the orbit of the binary star system involving Sirius."

Diodorus Sicilus and other historians report a highly developed science and astronomy in Africa, especially by Atlas, yet anthropologists and modern researchers have trouble believing the authenticity of Dogon accounts of their traditions.

Elaborate theories have been concocted to account for the presence of such advanced scientific notions among a seemingly technologically deficient people. These include: extraterrestrial visits, information imparted by a wandering Jesuit scholar, faked data by Marcel Griaule and Dieterlin, and that this information was actually introduced by them.

The authors of *Ancient Skies* argue that it seems difficult to believe that beliefs so central to the belief system of the Dogon could have been introduced to them in recent times. Also, quite humorously, they aver that Jupiter has more than 60 moons, not just four moons, which would implicate the Extraterrestrials as being *very badly* informed.

The Dogon mandala, or cosmological scheme, holds that the universe has the form of an 8 x 8 unit square platform erected upon a circular base of 20 units in diameter with a height of 10 units. Four stairways, each 10 steps high, climb the structure. The diagram is somewhat similar to the *Chellambaram* and the Chinese *Shih.* 20 x 10 units certainly reminds of Egyptian measurement specifically their stone sarcophagi burial caskets.

The widespread Polynesian myth of lifting up the sky is associated with Sirius, also called "the balance pole used across the shoulders to bear heavy weight." The pole is also associated with Orion's belt. Temple draws attention to the identification of parts of the diagrams of the Sirius system with a knife and the circumcision ritual among the Dogon. Polynesians do not equate Sirius with such rituals, but circumcision was an important element of some Polynesian cultures.

When one thinks of megaliths, one's thoughts usually turn to Britain and Brittany, forgetting that North Africa is covered with them. M.H. Hill sketches out the full extent of the great tract of megalithic remains on the Atlantic coast of Africa near Cape Verde, which he calls the Senegambian Monument Complex because it sits astride both Senegal and Gambia. An archaeological inventory of the region discloses 212 pillar-circle sites and 251 *tombelles*, which are stone cairns or heaps often surrounded by ringlike stone walls. Hundreds of sites with tumuli also dot the area. One of the pillar-circle sites boasts all of 50 individual pillar circles. Some of the pillars are topped with cupolas, raised discs, or balls. The fanciest pillars are *V*- or *Y*-shaped with crossbars. Archaeological exploration of these impressive sites is incomplete. Preliminary dating makes the Senegambian Complex over 1,000 years old (Hill, Matthew H.; "The Senegambian Monument Complex: Current Status and Prospects for Research," in *Megaliths to Medicine Wheels: Boulder Structures in Archaeology*, Michael Wilson, Calgary, 1981, p. 419).

Part 10

At Home in the Universe

It is important to have examined what ancient people have discovered about the universe. It is apparent that their investigations have been going on for a very long time and that they have come up with ingenious solutions for dealing with such opposing forces as harmony and disorder, matter and spirit, and logic and anomaly. These opposing forces are part of the condition of life as we see it and experience it. This dichotomy comes about because of movement which makes it difficult for us to determine if a thing is advancing or regressing, or moving with or opposing other cosmic cycles. Knowledge of astronomy helps us to define our perceptions and to craft our speech that it may be revealing to others. Astronomy assists philosophy, logic, science, and religion. Astronomy helps us to be more comfortable and at home in our universe.

CHAPTER 10.1

The Synchronic Mnemonic Universe

This chapter is a review of the concepts and numbers revealed in this work. Hopefully the reader has appreciated the simplicity and synchronism of ancient cosmological systems whose terms unfold like a blossoming flower. This is a system so simple and harmonious that a child could remember every bit of it (beginning with 5 + 8 = 13) and yet so deep as to fathom all of creation.

According to ancient cosmology, our spiral galaxy, the Milky Way, is moving around the universe. The Vedic cosmologers say that the universe pulsates like a heart, breathes like the lungs, wakes and sleeps, and functions like the human body. All these "so-called" modern notions like "intelligent design" and "big bang" have been appropriated from ancient cosmology.

The universe transfers spirit and energy to our galaxy, which communicates this energy to our Sun, which passes it on to the planets and our own Earth. Ancient people believed that this spirit and energy brought life to humans and that, upon death, this energy returned back to the Milky Way to be recycled and reborn back into the world again. This cosmology was the foundation of the theories of "resurrection" and the "transmigration of the soul."

There is a basic dichotomy in the universe of night and day, darkness and light, matter and spirit. Matter is symbolized by the square (= the number 4). Spirit is symbolized by the circle (= the number 6). When 4 is divided by 6 the result is .666, a matrix number used by creation to combine matter and spirit. This combination engenders life which is then developed by the golden mean proportion, .618 where every particle of spirit-matter is subdivided by the relationship: .382 + .618 = 1.

The circle of 360 degrees is based upon the 12 year sidereal period of Jupiter and the 30 year sidereal period of Saturn whose combination results in a number divisible by both (12 x 30 =360). The 360 degree circle is also reasonably close to the length of the year, or the synodic and sidereal period of the Earth. Jupiter and Saturn come into conjunction every 20, 40, 60 years and so on with amazing regularity. The number 360 ÷ 20 = 18, while 360 ÷ 40 = 9, and 360 ÷ 60 = 6. These numbers: 6, 9, and 18 have become very sacred numbers around the world.

Venus-Earth Relationship

Image by Martineau

In eight Earth years Venus traces a five-pointed pentagram star in the sky, during 13 of her own Venusian years. This relationship produces the numbers 5 + 8 = 13 and the Fibonacci series of numbers, 1, 1, 2, 3, 5, 8, 13, and so on by always adding the last two numbers together.

The numbers 5 x 8 = 40. The number 40 represents the intellectual maturity of a human, two conjunctions of Jupiter and Saturn, and 40 conjunctions in 800 years once around the complete circle of the zodiac.

In Hebrew tradition, the number 13 is highly esteemed: the 13-petaled rose is a Talmudic symbol for the Torah, 12 tribes of Israel plus the priestly tribe of Levi, and 12 sons of Jacob plus a daughter. In Greek tradition, the pentagram was the sacred sign of Pythagoras. In Egypt, the five-pointed star is the most common decorative device. And of course Venus was held in the highest esteem in the world of the Maya who use the 5 + 8 = 13 formula to unfold an entire system of astronomical numbers:

13 + 13 = 26 (260 day human gestation cycle = 9 moons)
(260 days x 3 = 780-day synodic period of Mars)
260 years ÷ 20-year conjunctions of Jupiter
and Saturn = 13)
(26,000-year return of the Pleiades cycle,

or equinox precession)

The cycle of eclipses also originates from these numbers: 260 ÷ 9 (months) = 28.888 days x 12 (months) = 346.666 (the eclipse year—actual 346.62).

26 +26 = 52 (5 x 8 x 13 = 520)

Every 52 years, or 18,980 days (52 x 365 = 18,980 = 260 x 73), the 260-day cycle and the 365-day cycle coincided on the identical month and day. This was called the Calendar Round and the festival of the New Fire. It was symbolized by a bundle of 52 sticks tied together. Another amazing factor of 18,980 days is that it equals the beloved Mayan number 13 x 1,460 days = 18,980 days, not years (1,460 are the *years* in the Egyptian Sothic cycle of the star Sirius).

The Maya Long Count cycle was completed every 5,200 years, which is one-fifth of their precessional cycle called "Return of the Pleiades" (26,000 ÷ 5 = 5,200). 520 years account for 26 conjunctions of Jupiter and Saturn.

52 + 52 = 104 years (Double Calendar Round when both the 260- and 365-day cycles coincided with the Venus Round: 8 x 13 = 104 years)

Return to the Sexagesimal System

This intrusion of the number 18 occurs at 360 days in the Maya astronomical system. This of course is significant as the period of 360 divided by the conjunction cycle of Jupiter and Saturn (360 ÷ 20 = 18) equals the number eighteen. The number 18 is of course 6 + 6 + 6, leading to 6 x 6 x 6 = 216, the prime matrix of the sexagesimal system.

1 day	= 1 kin	
1 unial	= 20 kins	
1 tun	= 18 unials	= 360 kins (18 x 20 = 360)
1 katun	= 20 tuns	= 7,200 kins (20 x 360)
1 baktun	= 20 katuns	=144,000 kins (400 x 360)

Therefore the Jupiter-Saturn system is expressed as cell-duplication numbers similar to the Earth-Venus–relationship numbers which the Maya used:

6 + 6 + 6 = 18
18 + 18 = 36
36 + 36 = 72 also, 36 + 72 = 108, and 108 + 108 = 216 (6 x 6 x 6)
72 + 72 = 144

Thus the Maya have entered into the sexagesimal through the doorway of the interior angles (36°, 72°, 108°) of the Venus pentagram and the 360 factor of the Jupiter-Saturn relationship:

6 x 6 x 6 = 216, and also 6 x 36 = 216, 3 x 72 = 216, 2 x 108 = 216
216 (a fractal of 2,160 years of precession in one house of the zodiac)
2,160 x 12 signs of the zodiac = 25,920 years for the Vedic precession of the equinoxes (Mayan cycle of the Pleiades = 5 x 5,200 = 26,000 years)

Ancient geographers measured the equatorial circumference of the globe as 21,600 nautical miles (stems from the 216 fractal). The geographers and astronomers of Egypt designed the Great Pyramid at Giza as a scale model of the Earth on the ratio of 1:43,200 (2 x 21,600). Irrespective of feet, cubits, stadia, or meters, the Great Pyramid is 1:43,200 the size of the Earth.

Use of the Number 13 in Mexica-Maya-Andean Astronomy

The Maya zodiac was divided into 13 star groups (Milbrath, p. 250–254), with Sagittarius divided into two constellations. This division creates 13 months (moons) of 28 days (28.426 is halfway between the *sidereal* 27.321 and *synodic* 29.530 periods of the moon). This almost creates a concord between the solar cycle of 365 days and the lunar cycle of 364 days (13 x 28 = 364).

Taube and Miller (p. 53) speak of the 13 levels of heaven and the 13 bird patrons of the daytime hours. Susan Milbrath cites (p. 254) the Postclassic Paris Codex, "long recognized as a form of zodiac representing thirteen star groups." Thirteen star groups also appear on the Madrid Codex, although not in a formal zodiac sequence. Milbrath cites (p. 257) Bruce Love, who concludes that there was a division of the stars into 13 constellations representing 13 months of 28 days. Milbrath also speaks (p. 14, 20) about the 13 hours of daylight, a ritual year equivalent to 13 months, and the 13 levels of the sky. Andean cosmology shows a special cross, called the *Chakana,* with 13 fields surrounded by the condor (symbol of heaven) at the top, the pumas at the side (symbols of this world), and the snake (symbol of the underworld) at the bottom.

The Long Count is completed after 13 Baktuns of 400 years (13 x 400 = 5,200 x 5 = 26,000 years of Mayan precession). This figure for Mayan precession divided by the 13 zodiac houses of the Maya would equal a period of 2,000 years per each zodiac house (26,000 ÷ 13 = 2,000 years), a nice round figure that the Maya preferred. Another chronological cycle that the Maya preferred was 819, which is the product of 7 x 9 x 13. Again the number 13 appears in the "trecena," the 13 day numbers that are multiplied by the 20 day names to achieve the all-important "gestation and agricultural cycle" of 260 days. The agricultural cycle is based upon the maturity of the ancient "mountain maize" whose cycle corresponds to the human gestation period (Milbrath, p. 30).

From the numbers 13, 26, and 52 the Maya developed an elegant synchronic system that intermeshed 13 hours of the day and 13 hours of the night (26 total hours), 13 signs of the zodiac, Venus, Moon, Earth, the 260-day calendar, human gestation, maturity of mountain maize, Long Count, and the precession of the vernal equinoxes. Tompkins, in *Mexican Pyramids*, writes (p. 289) that 13 days were added to the calendar (of 365 days) every 52 years to accomplish our leap-year correction. Aveni writes (p. 310) that the Andean culture portrayed the Pleiades as 13 stars, which can all be seen at the altitude of Cuzco. On the Asian zodiac, the sign of Cancer sometimes appears as a tortoise that has 13 raised areas on its shell. Thirteen is some kind of a code that has even come down to medieval times when the secret execution of the Knights Templar was scheduled for Friday (the day of Venus) the 13th.

The Human Element

The Greeks say that, "Man is the measure of all things" because humans are a seed, a microcosm, or a small model of the universe. The Mayan 260-day gestation cycle absolutely confirms the human element in cosmic chronology. The human element also appears in Egyptian measurement of the cubit:

The cubit is equal to 1½ feet (6"+6"+6") = 18".
6 x 6 x 6 = 216, the prime Vedic fractal for astronomical measurement.
The cubit is a measurement that fits into astronomy.

The Vedic-Hindu also believe that "Man is the measure of all things," and therefore human breathing reflects the cadence of the cosmos. Vedic cosmic cycles are based upon the numbers 6, 60, and 216 (6 x 6 x 6):

10 long syllables (gurvakshara) = 1 respiration (prana) = 4 seconds
6 respirations = 1 vinadi = 24 seconds
60 vinadis = 1 nadi = 1,440 seconds
60 nadis = 1 day = 86,400 seconds = 24 hours
86,400 seconds ÷ 4 seconds = 21,600 human breaths over 24 hours

There is a time clock within humans that reflects the movements and pulse of the universe. Humans also have rhythmic fluctuations in their circulatory system in what has been found to be a 10-second cycle, or six times per minute:

6 x 60 minutes = 360 per hour
6 x 360 = 2,160 every 6 hours
12 x 360 = 4,320 per day
24 x 360 = 8,640 per day and night, 24 hours

These again are the sexagesimal numbers of the Great Pyramid and the cycle of precession of the vernal equinoxes (2160, 4320, 6480, 8640…).

Lounsbury's Discovery:

Forstemann's and Lounsbury's examination of the Dresden Codex probes deep into Maya synchronicity, a journey that shows that the Mayan worldview attempts to relate everything in the universe to everything else in the universe. Floyd Lounsbury found that three times Venus' synodic period times the synodic period of Mars' = 1,366,560 days. This number is called the "super-number" of the Dresden Codex because it synchronizes so many different cycles:

1,366,560 days = Ω (used as a symbol for this number throughout below)

780 x 1,752 = Ω

(780-day synodic Mars = 3 x 260 gestation period)
(1,752 = 3 x 584-day average synodic Venus period)
(Therefore 3 x 584 synodic Venus x 780 synodic Mars =Ω)
This synchronizes moon, gestation, Venus, and Mars.

584 x 2,340 = Ω

(Venus 584-day average synodic period)
(2,340 = 3 x 780 Mars synodic. Also 9 x 260 gestation period)
This again synchronizes moon, gestation, Venus, and Mars.

468 x 2,920 = Ω

(5 x 584 Venus synodic = 2,920 = 8 x 365 Earth synodic)
(468 = 13 x 36, or 26 x 18, or 52 x 9. The numbers 13, 26, 52 come from the Venus-Earth relation. The numbers 9, 18, 36 are sexagesimal. This confirms the synchronism between the Venus-Earth numbers with the sexagesimal (.6 +.6 +.6 =1.8 x 260 = 468. ÷ 216 = 2.166).

365 x 3,744 = Ω

(365 = the vague Solar year)
(3,744 = 8 x 468) 3,744 ÷ 3 = 1,248, and ÷ 6 = 624, while ÷ 18 = 208

260 x 5,526 = Ω

(260 is 9-month human gestation and agricultural cycle)
(5,526 ÷ 6 = 921)

72 x 18,980 = Ω

(365 x 52 = 18,980 = 260 x 73: the 52-year cycle of the Calendar Round, which reconciles the 260-day Sacred Round and the 365-day Solar year. The 360° in a circle ÷ 5 pentagram = 72).

36 x 37,960 = Ω

(Double Calendar Round of 18,980 days = 2 x 52 years = 104 years)

(36 is a fractal of 360, which synchronizes Jupiter and Saturn)

Because of fluctuations in the speed, orbit, and axis of all heavenly bodies there is a mean number around which their movements hover above and below –as they continually adjust to the combined movements of the universe. It is possible that the Mexica-Maya-Andean cosmologers discovered these mean numbers in the movements of Earth and Venus, and the amazing concord of these numbers with humans, agriculture, other planets and the cosmos. Celestial patterns and synchronic relationships inspired human reason, logic, morals, law, science, and religion. These interrelationships became the paradigm of the ancient cosmic worldview.

CHAPTER 10.2

Harmony in the Solar System

There is nothing alien in the cosmos. Everything in the universe must come from the universe and therefore contain the genetics of the universe within itself. Every part seems to be a microcosm intertwined, interrelated, and interwoven within the pattern of existence. There is variety and difference because everything is born of different parents, in a different place, and in different cycles of time. Albert Einstein wittily remarked, "God made time so that everything did not happen at once."

If the Earth could possibly be located at the center of the solar system, then every species would have only one type and no individuals. But as the third rock from the sun, the Earth is in an offset position from the central sun and is therefore barraged with an incredible number of abstract perspectives of energy from the other planets as well as subject to variations in its own tilt of axis, obliquity of its orbit, and so on and so on. The Earth is a veritable cosmic blender initiating a garden of varying life forms.

Harmonic Relationships of Earth, Moon, and Sun

John Martineau, in *A Little Book of Coincidence, Pattern in the Solar System* (p. 30), writes that from the surface of the Earth, the sun and the moon appear to be the same size. This permits total solar and lunar eclipses. It also puts the moon on an equal footing with the sun in order to balance the sun's great size, gravity, and power. According to modern cosmology, this is nothing but a coincidence.

The size of the moon compared to the Earth is 3-to-11. The closest- and farthest-distance ratio between the orbits of Mars and Venus is also 3-to-11, which equals 27.3%. The moon orbits the Earth every 27.3 days, which is also the average rotational period of a sunspot.

Using information gleaned by Robin Heath, John Martineau suggests that there may be fundamental relationships between space, time, and life that have not yet been understood. Martineau laments that while we are engaged in listening for alien radio signals from the universe; our own planets are creating exquisite patterns in the skies and, in a sense, trying to teach us wonderful and elegant cosmic relationships.

The Croll-Milankovitch climate cycles show us that slight changes in the geometric mechanics of inclinations and eccentricities of the members of the solar system produce exceptional results here on Earth. Geometry, proportions, balance, and harmony are still important. Interestingly, the plane of our solar system is tilted at 30 degrees to the plane of our galaxy so that our solar system actually proceeds in a corkscrew pattern around the center of the Milky Way.

Music of the Spheres of the Solar System

Martineau (p. 14) says that in ancient times, the seven musical notes were assigned to the seven heavenly bodies (see Pythagoras regarding gravity). Kepler noticed that the ratios between planets' extreme angular velocities were all harmonic intervals. In 1968 A.M. Molchanov revealed that the entire solar system is a tuned quantum resonant structure, with Jupiter as the conductor.

There is a harmony to the positions of the planets from the sun, according to the Titius-Bode Law of Planetary Distances:

- Mercury 4 + 0 = 4 (actual distance is 3.86)
- Venus 4 + 3 = 7 (actual distance is 7.21)
- Earth 4 + 6 = 10 (actual distance is 9.97)
- Mars 4 + 12 = 16 (actual distance is 15.19)
- Asteroids 4 + 24 = 28 (actual distance is between 22–35)

- Jupiter 4 + 48 = 52 (actual distance is 51.89)
- Saturn 4 + 96 = 100 (actual distance is 95.13)
- Uranus 4 + 192 = 196 (actual distance is 191.27)
- Neptune 4 + 384 = 388 (this is wrong. Actual distance is 299.87)
- Pluto 4 + 384 = 388 (Pluto seems to occupy the correct position for Neptune. Pluto's actual distance is 393.33)

Pluto is at the correct harmonious distance. Neptune will possibly break up into pieces like the asteroid belt. But when final harmony is achieved, will our solar system collapse? Perhaps perfection and harmony are the final act of creation before destruction. The universe works because everything was set into motion at once, allowing everything to adjust, conform, and coordinate with everything else. The universe is still adjusting, and the lack of symmetry of Neptune is still correcting.

The universe is traveling toward perfect numbers and perfect harmony. As yet, the universe has not achieved perfection in numbers. Though as the Mexica-Maya-Andean cycles demonstrate, perfection is very close. Perhaps this is what causes momentum. Imperfection is movement. Perfection is lack of movement.

Below are some examples of geometry, number, harmony, music, and proportion that come from our own solar system, according to John Martineau in *A Little Book of Coincidence, Pattern in the Solar System*:

- The centers of four touching circles describe the mean orbit of Jupiter. A circle inscribed in the vacant area of their meeting describes the mean orbit of Mars. In the same diagram, if the orbit of Mars is a circle around the outside of the four circles, then the centers of the four circles form the orbit of the Earth.
- Jupiter and Saturn come into conjunction every 20 years, forming an equilateral triangle upon the ecliptic of the

zodiac. Another triangle of their oppositions every 20 years complements to form a Hexagram upon the zodiac.

- If a circle is inscribed in an equilateral triangle, the circle can represent the orbit of Saturn, while a circle described around the equilateral triangle would represent the orbit of Uranus. On the same diagram, an octagram star placed in Saturn's orbit creates another circle upon the rays of the octagram that is in proportion to the orbit of Jupiter. Saturn's and Jupiter's orbits are in proportion to 6:11, the octave, or double, of the 3:11 moon-to-Earth ratio. Saturn's orbit invokes pi twice. Saturn's orbit circumference is the diameter of Neptune's orbit.
- From our perspective here on Earth, Neptune and Uranus dance around each other, creating a beautiful pattern that divides the zodiac into 25 perfect kisses every 4,300 years.

John Martineau discusses the musical relationships and draws the amazing variety of convoluted dances of all the other planets in his book, which is well worth reading. One becomes convinced that the special harmony of music, number, and geometry is the reason for the possibility of life upon our planet. It is also the mechanism that allows the formation and exercise of our thought processes, logic, and reason.

The universe and our solar system teach us geometry. A circle can be perfectly surrounded by six circles of similar size. This gives us the sexagesimal system and the 12 divisions of the circle of the sky. Many significant astronomical relationships are built upon the relationship of these circles and the great triangles that can be drawn between their centers and tangents, such as the two equilateral triangles that form the sacred hexagon. The two giant asteroid clusters, called the Trojans, travel upon Jupiter's orbit and are exactly stationed 120 degrees apart. These travel 60 degrees in front of Jupiter, and another group travels 60 degrees behind Jupiter. The speeds of these two heavenly bodies are relative to each other in terms of the golden mean proportion, .618 phi. The star Sirius and the Pleiades are also separated by 60 degrees.

Martineau claims (p. 14) that circles inscribed and circumscribed around nested pentagons show relations between the relative mean orbits of the planets. Martineau reveals (p. 20) that the orbits of Mercury and Venus are based upon three triangularly placed touching circles, where the orbit of Mercury passes through the centers of these circles while the orbit of Venus passes around a circle that encloses these three circles.

Venus has the most perfectly circular orbit in the solar system. In the course of eight Earth years and 13 Venus years, Venus and Earth join together five times around the zodiac, creating a perfect pentagram, or five-pointed star. The periods of Earth and Venus, 8 and 13, as well as the pentagram 5, are the Fibonacci series, which attempts to become the phi proportion. In addition, if a circle is drawn around the interior angles of the pentagon at the heart of the five-pointed star, then the star points extending beyond that pentagon have isosceles sides that equal phi, 1.618 in relation to the pentagon.

Martineau then compares (p. 28) the orbits of planets with their physical size. If a pentagram is inscribed upon the Earth, then a circle drawn upon the pentagon within the five-pointed star perfectly describes the size of the planet Mercury in relation to the size of the Earth. This pentagram-pentagon size relationship is exactly the same relationship that exists between the orbits of Mercury and Earth. Martineau then claims that a 15-pointed star drawn upon the orbit of Saturn produces the orbit of the Earth within the 15-sided polygon at the center. Martineau uses the mean central obit of the planets and claims about 99.5% accuracy.

There is a geometric relationship between the orbits of Mars and Jupiter. If a square is drawn inside the orbit of Jupiter, then the corners of the square may serve as the centers of four circles that touch one another. A circle can be drawn at the center of the square that is tangent to the four great circles. This circle is the orbit of Mars. The circumference of Mars' orbit just happens to be the radius of Saturn's orbit (p. 48), while the circumference of Saturn's orbit is the diameter of Neptune's orbit.

The arabesques of Islam art certainly look as if they derive from the "dances of the planets" drawn by Martineau:

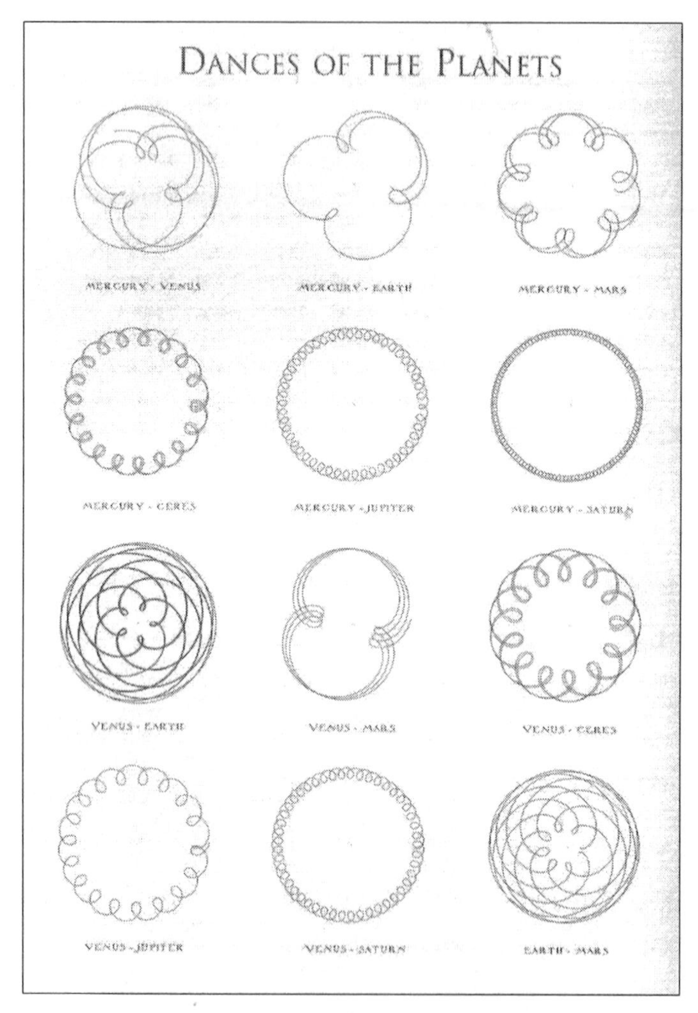

Dances of the planets by permission from John Martineau, *A Little Book of Coincidence, Pattern in the Solar System.*

CONCLUSION OF

The Culture of Astronomy

In his conclusion to *Skywatchers,* Anthony Aveni (p. 320) says, "Anthropologists shall ever debate whether a universal view of the natural order composed of archetypes was built into our minds long before we became civilized. Or do the similarities we find among different and distant cultures result from the diffusion of ideas among them? Or neither?"

Professor Aveni's questions point at the very heart of the subject of *The Culture of Astronomy.* How was it possible that so many ancient advanced civilizations shared a common cosmic worldview?

Today's worldview does not correspond to the ancient perspective of the universe. The ancient cosmic worldview shows that everything is very old and that origins are so old that they seem impossible to determine. The examination of the Venus pentagram; the numbers 5, 8, and 13; creation through speech and *logos*; ideal *Platonic* forms in the heavens; divine milk, soma, and manna from the galaxy; and the soul's journey to the underworld and heaven, rebirth, resurrection, and metempsychosis are not ideas solely from Greek and Middle Eastern culture but ideas that were part of Mexica-Maya-Andean culture long, long ago.

We are the seed of the universe; we are cosmic creatures who live in a cosmic context founded upon a cosmological hierarchy of a Creator God, a dualistic universe energizing our dualistic Earth. Between God and Earth stands the Milky Way Galaxy, spawning many themes and heroes to be born into the drama of life and subject to the convoluted eternal cycles of moist-hot-dry-cold, where humans are free to choose and follow their base cravings or their divinely sanctioned will to achieve whatever they can imagine.

Human advancement is continually checked by wars, plagues, stupidity, climate change, overpopulation, and natural disasters. Astronomy has ever provided the foundation, the base rock, and the stepping stones for humanity to rise up again to the attainment of culture, science, and religion. It is hoped that the study of astronomy will always open up new and fresh perspectives that in turn will make humans stronger and wiser by realizing their roots in the cosmos.

Finally, this book brings forward questions which are difficult to answer:

1. If myth is based upon an astronomic and cosmic foundation, then myth contains scientific data from extremely ancient times. This would make myths –that are properly interpreted –very valuable pieces of information regarding past history, climate, natural disasters, and events.

2. The diagram of the north-polar view of the globe sectioned into the 12 houses of the zodiac shows the extraordinary extension of the North and South American continents from Scorpio/Sagittarius to Taurus/Gemini –that is precisely under the band of the Milky Way Galaxy. This is as if the Milky Way has pulled these continents in this non-conforming direction to the spin of the Earth. Since the discovery of phenomenally accurate global maps, the question may be asked if this precision mapping brought forward and defined the astronomic influence of the Milky Way upon the planet Earth? Was this where the ideas of astronomic and astrologic cause came from?

3. In *Fingerprints of the Gods* Graham Hancock (p.183) says that "mathematical code along astronomic and geodetic lines" are the permanent records and common language that antiquity has passed down to us. Many great scholars and astronomers have agreed that mathematics, geometry, and astronomy are

the common language of humankind. The Tower of Babel certainly has a meaning in the world of civilization and politics where World Empires force the globe to accept one language. The Tower of Babel also has a cultural meaning that when the scientific and common language of mathematics, geometry, and astronomy breakdown –then indeed there is a dispersion of knowledge and a diminution of human potentiality. Graham Hancock (p.193) writes, "Early Jesuit scholars who were among the first Europeans to visit China had the opportunity in the Imperial Library to study a vast work, consisting of 4320 volumes, said to have been handed down from ancient times and to contain 'all knowledge'." Anyone who has read this book will immediately recognize "4320" as one of the great and important cosmological numbers.

APPENDIX:

Cosmo-Geo-Symbol Dating

This author's first book, *Origin of Culture and Civilization*, uncovered an ancient context in Fez-Morocco on the North African shore of the Atlantic Ocean. Here was the place of the origin of the ancient gods, the Greek myths and the heroes and characters of the Greek, Egyptian, and Middle Eastern genealogies. Here was the ancient location of heaven as well as the portals to the underworld. Those who are interested in myth will be very interested in pursuing these accounts.

In the Middle Ages, Herbort von Fritzlar (*On Troye*, V831.2) connects astronomy with history when he writes that the enchantress Medea declared, "On the heavens I have seen—what in olden times has been." Again, the cycle of precession is only for brief reflections of the past. This cycle does not originate events and cannot show the pattern of the generations of the gods, the Legend of the Five Suns,

The Zodiac	*The Generations of the Gods*	
Virgo	The Virgin, exaltation of Mercury, Agathodaemon	**dry** *The Womb & Bowels*
Leo	The House of the Sun	**hot** *The Heart*
Cancer	The House of the Moon The Great World Fire	**moist** *The Chest*
Gemini	Adam & Eve Tree of Life, Garden of Eden	**cold** *The Shoulders*
Taurus	The Exaltation of the Moon Mene, Selene, Jana, Diana	**dry** *The Neck*
Aries	Jesus Christ Horus Athena Mohamed, Huitzilopochtli	**hot** *The Head*
Pisces	Zeus & Hera Osiris & Isis Poseidon Pluto, Seth & Nephtys, Coyolauxqui	**moist** *The Feet*
Aquarius	Atlas & Pleion, Cronus& Rhea, Iapetus & Asia Geb & Nut, Lesser Titians	**cold** *The Legs*
Capricorn	The Great Flood, Thoth, Noah Shu & Tefnut, Sosis, Cyclopes	**dry** *TheKnees*
Sagittarius	Helios, Hundred-handed, Titea & Idea The Great Titians, Ra-Atum	**hot** *The Thighs*
Scorpio	Uranus & Ge Ptah, Hephaestus	**moist** *The Genetials*
Libra	The Goddess Night The God Ocean	**cold** *The Forearms*

the true cosmic times of Adam, or the world fire and flood. Only the Milky Way exhibits the duration of time necessary to influence culture here upon the Earth. Below is a general chart of the relationship of the cycle of the Milky Way and the history and geography of the world:

Many Myths from Many Cycles

Ancient myth from around the world exhibits curious common characteristics. We hear about Athena, the intelligent warrior goddess of the Greeks, being born fully armed from the head of Zeus. We read about Zeus changing his form into that of a bull in order to abduct Europa. We see images of the Mexican goddess Coyolxauhqui, with pendant breasts, tied up with snake ropes, dismembered at the foot of her own former temple.

The common thread that unites these pictures is that they are deities in action in some sort of mysterious drama where "heads," "bulls," and "breasts" convey a very important meaning. One need only examine the 10-foot diameter, eight-ton, round megalithic icon to Coyolxauhqui to appreciate that the people who executed this work were deadly serious in their respect for this goddess and the importance of the correct representation of her person, symbols, and accoutrements.

The unifying key to these myths is that they all come from an astronomical context. Athena the warrior goddess relates to the zodiac sign of the god of war, Mars, whose solar house is Aries. Europa and the bull are connected to the bull sign of Taurus. Coyolxauhqui is a major deity of Pisces of the Milky Way cycle, which had recently moved into Aries, the home of her stepbrother, Huitzilopochtli.

Correspondence of History, Astronomy, and Geography

Ancient cosmologers equated the human body with the body of the universe. More precisely, they equated man with the Milky Way Galaxy; and, in turn, with the houses of the zodiac –as an expression of the total cosmos.

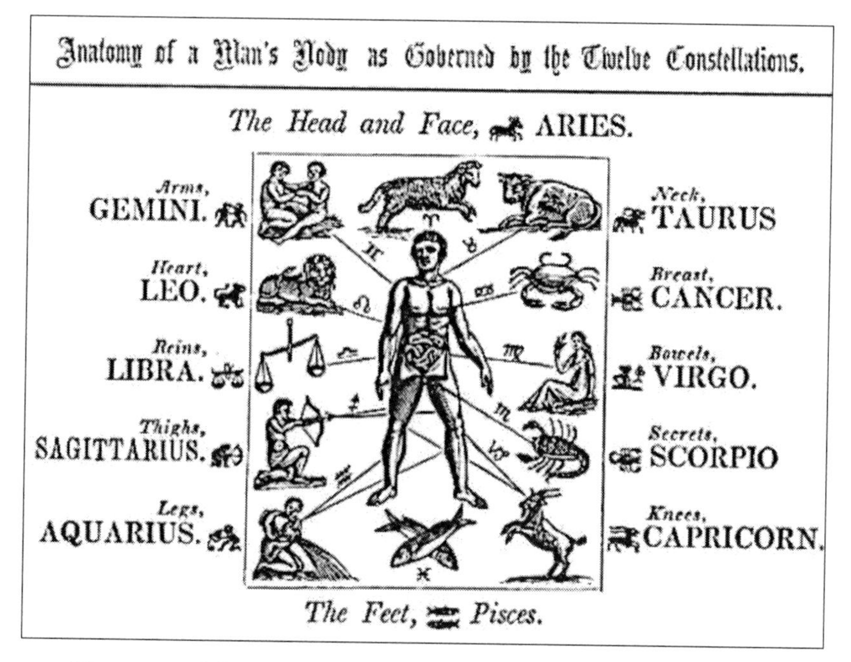

The signs of the zodiac compared to the human body. Bing free images: adequatebird.com/2009/zodiac symbols. This idea is very ancient and is expressed by the Hathor image on the zodiac of Dendera and images of the sky goddess Hathor painted inside coffin lids.

PISCES (the feet of the cosmic body) (*ancient zodiac:* crocodile) lunar house of Jupiter, exaltation of Venus, triangle: *Cancer, Scorpio, Pisces* ruled by Mars, Venus, and Moon by night.

Geography: Eastern Europe, Greece, and Egypt. Pisces is in the triangle of Cancer (Japan), and Scorpio (Mexico and Yucatan). Dichotomy: world's greatest deserts: Sahara, the Kalahari, the Great American Desert, the Great Sandy Desert, and the Gibson Desert of Australia.

Pisces is the Epoch of: Greek Zeus, Hera, Poseidon, and Pluto; EgyptianIsis, Osiris, Seth, and Nephtys; Mexican Coyolxauhqui, India Indra wins the cosmic tug-of-war over the churning of the Milky Way with the assistance of his Devas, who are benevolent gods. Indra is seated upon an elephant.

Traditions: exaltation of Venus and triangle of Venus, Mars, and moon. This accounts for the wealth of traditions of matriarchal societies and warrior women. In Central American tradition, Venus as a morning star foreboded the chance of war. Warrior women lived along the Amazon River in Brazil, in ancient Morocco, Libya, and Asia Minor, where they ruled empires that were controlled by women who had conquered the world.

The City of Troy—gateway to the Black Sea, Europe, and Russia—stands in the middle of Pisces. Troy was one of the great colonies from the Atlantic. One of the great events marking the epoch of Pisces was the judgment of Paris at Troy: Paris awards the golden apple to Aphrodite/Venus as her prize for being the most beautiful. This is because Pisces is the exaltation of Venus, goddess of love and beauty. Athena is a goddess of war as well as wisdom. She is a contestant because Pisces is a triangle of Mars (war) and of the moon (wisdom). Hera is in the contest because she is the wife of Zeus, the god of the epoch of Pisces (the lunar house of Jupiter/Zeus). She is also in the contest because Pisces is a triangle of the moon (the mother of the universe). She is bare-breasted, and she supplies the milk for the Milky Way.

Bayer, in his *Uranometria* (1603), describes Pisces as producing the theme and influence of the *Veneris Mater*, the Venerable Mother. Pisces was the image and the prototype of the Divine Feminine and all aspects of womanhood—from the Divine Virgin to the Earth-Mother, from chaste to promiscuous, from peaceful to the dreaded warrior Amazon.

Pisces is responsible for the appearance of the "fish men" as teachers of culture. Berosus tells us that, in the time of Ammenon the Chaldaean, Musarus Oannes (Ozanes) appeared from the Persian Gulf. His whole body was like that of a fish, and under his fish's head was another head. He taught men every manner of science (Cory and Hodges, *Ancient Fragments*, Babylonia). After the tremendous battle with the lords of the underworld, the Hero Twins of the Maya emerged as fish men (Schele, *Maya Cosmos* p. 109). In Taube (p. 44) there is an image of Tlaloc letting the blood of a fish man.

ARIES (the head of the cosmic body) (*ancient zodiac:* cat) the lunar house of Mars, exaltation of the sun, triangle: *Aries, Leo, Sagittarius* ruled by Sun and Jupiter.

***Geography**:* Dichotomy: The hemisphere directly opposite Jerusalem on the other side of the globe is entirely composed of the Pacific Ocean.

Aries is the Epoch of: Jesus Christ, the Messiah, Mohamed, and Huitzilopochtli. Ancient goddesses include Athena, Minerva (born of the head of Zeus during epochal Pisces).

Traditions: The region beginning at Bethlehem until the tip of Arabia is rich in the lore about the ram, most notably the sacrificial substitution of the ram for Isaac, the son of Abraham. The tradition of ancient Iran is monotheistic, disallows all images and idols, and only holds fire as a sacred sign of adoration and contemplation (Aries is a fire sign). This region is well known as the ancient home of the sun worshippers, Heliolatry, under the name of Mithra, the Iranian sun god worshipped by the Maga.

Aries is the time period of the building of the Temple of Solomon. Hebrews take the destruction of the temple very seriously, not only as an act against themselves as participants in the cosmic drama but as a direct assault against their connection and covenant with God. Jerusalem in the region of Aries is at the center of the greatest landmass upon the globe. Bauval, in *Egypt Code* (pp. 158–61), mentions D. Redford, who writes that Akhenaten believed that the gods had ceased to be operative and that there was soon to be a new messiah, a unique god in the heavens. Akhenaten symbolized the new god by a simple solar-disc, disenfranchising Ra-Horakhti, solar god of the north, the falcon-headed man with the solar disc, as well as Amun-Ra, solar god of the south, the human-headed man crowned with two divine plumes. The Amarna heresy represents the anticipation of the change of the Milky Way cycle from Pisces into Aries.

In a mind that is totally fixated upon cosmic symbol, it is possible to account for the prevalence of human skulls and decapitation since Aries is the head of the cosmic body. Aztec sacrifices are said to have ceremonially ripped out the still-beating human heart. This could relate to the fact that Aries is a member of the triangle of Aries-Leo-Sagittarius, where Leo represents the cosmic heart.

The crucifixion of Christ is said to have occurred during the crossing of the cycles of precession and the rotation of the Milky Way cycle over the point of the division between Aries and Pisces. The Aries/Pisces point is again celebrated upon the stone Zodiac of Dendera, a Ptolemaic copy of a very ancient work.

TAURUS (the neck of the cosmic body) (*ancient zodiac:* dog) house of Venus, exaltation of the Moon, triangle: *Taurus, Virgo, Capricorn* ruled by Venus and the Moon.

Geography: India, as far as Burma, is noted for its reverence for the sacred cow, which enjoys unusual rituals and protection. Dichotomy: Indian Ocean. Creation of life within the swirling elements of the universe takes place in Taurus, the exaltation of the moon. Life is formed from the generative moisture of the oceans as the most ancient cosmologies have told us—an idea that modern science has explicitly adopted as the best paradigm.

Taurus is the Epoch of: The moon is also known as Jana, Diana, Selene, and Artemis. Moses, the author of *Genesis*, is portrayed as having horns on his head by Renaissance artists like Michelangelo. This may refer to the precessional period of Taurus. The sacred Apis bull of Egypt belongs to the time of the precessional cycle of Taurus. Moses brings the Commandments down from the mountain and catches the Israelites dancing around the golden calf.

Traditions: Zeus, the Shepherd of the Universe (Nonnos, p. 31), turns himself into a bull on the shores of Sidon to steal away Europa upon his back. Twins were born from this union, which Zeus gave to Asterion, King of Crete. Io, daughter of Inachus, was turned into a heifer. Hera, wife of Zeus, is always called *bo-opis*, or cow-eyed. In Nonnos (Ch. 9) Hera is asked to protect Dionysos, the young bull god and son of her sister Semele, daughter of Cadmos and Harmonia.

GEMINI (the arms of the cosmic body) (*ancient zodiac:* snake) lunar house of Mercury, triangle: *Gemini, Libra, Aquarius* ruled by Saturn and Mercury.

Geography: The celestial region of Gemini covers the geography of Thailand, Philippines, to eastern China. The border regions of Gemini/Taurus intersect the powerful Milky Way. Here are the tallest mountains in the world, many glaciers and water sources for this side of the planet. Sagittarius/Scorpio on the other side of the planet also has some of the highest mountains on the globe as well as the most significant water resources for this hemisphere of the planet.

Gemini is the Epoch of: Adam and Eve stand under the tree of life in the Garden of Eden. This is said to be an Egyptian tradition (K&M, p. 498). Adam's rib was used to create Eve (= Cancer, the chest, and house of the moon, patron of women. Taken from Adam, its neighbor = Gemini, the tree of life, which is the home of the Serpent of Knowledge, ancient constellation of the snake). Josephus, in his *Jewish Antiquities*, says that Adam was the first cosmologer who recognized the orderly arrangement of the heavens.

Traditions: Atlas belongs to the era and geography of Aquarius. Yet he is always portrayed carrying the celestial globe on his shoulders (Gemini). Gemini, Libra, and Aquarius form the triangle governed by Saturn and Mercury. Atlas is often called "dark-minded and aloof" because of Saturn.

The people of Vietnam are noted mathematicians. These regions celebrate the many birthplaces of the Buddha (the wise philosopher like the god Mercury), and the multiarmed Hindu god Vishnu and the god Shiva. There is an aspect of hermaphrodite Shiva called *Shiva Ardhanarishvara*, male with breasts called "the lord is half-woman" because the universe is feminine and masculine. Shiva is also the lord of the dance. This version of Shiva is the creator of the sacred food of the milk of the Milky Way. In Chiang Mai, Thailand, there is a 2,500-year-old marble relief of Buddha and a 1,800-year-old crystal Buddha. In Bangkok there is the Emerald Buddha. In Ayuthaya,

Thailand, is an ancient Buddhist temple reconstructed in the 13th century with a solid-gold spire. Vientiane, Laos, is the residence of the Supreme Patriarch of Lao Buddhism. The Buddah has 32 marks and signs by which he is recognized. One is that he has a large torso and his arms (Gemini) are long that his hands can cover his knees without bending. Also, his private parts are hidden by a sheath of skin (Sagittarius and Scorpio are opposite to Gemini).

The islands of Java and Bali may be the original site of the island of Paradise, where the first man and woman were created. On Java there is a veritable cluster of important sacred sites: Mendut; Gedung Songo Temples and Hot Springs; the Abode of the Gods at Arjuna; Mount Merapi, residence of the god Indera/Indra, who resolves conflicts between heaven and earth; Candi Sukuh; the Great Prambanan Temple; Karang Tretes Cave (dedicated to the Virgin Queen of the Southern Ocean); and many more. But the most famous site of this major cluster at Java is the imposing Borobudur. This may originally have been a Hindu site built in emulation of Mount Meru. It became a center for pilgrimage, a Mecca for Buddhists. Colin Wilson writes (p. 103),

> Hindus regard the square as the perfect shape, the ultimate symbol of order, and claim that the circle is derived from it. Borobudur is built in square terraces leading to a circular summit—five large square terraces and three smaller circular ones, symbolizing the eightfold path (the ninth base was later built to stabilize the entire structure). In several religions, mandalas symbolize the harmony of the universe, usually on the form of circle in a square.

Bali is another cluster of many ancient sacred sites dedicated to Vishnu and the water goddesses Dewi Danu, Shiva, and sacred places of eels and snakes who are messengers to the water god, and a stone throne for the demons of the underworld.

In the Buiriram Provence of Thailand is a Khmer temple complex with a phallic image of Shiva. Shiva has many arms, an important theme of the zodiac sign of Gemini. The Cambodian temple of Angkor Wat, built by the Khmer, was originally dedicated to the Hindu god Vishnu. The city was designed to represent the sacred mountain of Mount Meru surrounded by the great ocean.

The Chinese government is secretive about the enormous pyramid complex near their space center. It is rumored that these structures are orientated toward the constellation Gemini, or they are arranged on the ground in the shape of Gemini.

CANCER (the breast of the cosmic body) (*ancient zodiac:* dung beetle; turtle) House of the moon, exaltation of Jupiter, depression of Mars, and triangle: *Cancer, Scorpio, Pisces* ruled by Mars, Venus, and the moon.

Geography: Cancer covers the geography of Japan, New Guinea, and eastern Australia.

Cancer is the Epoch of: Eve as the original Moon and mother goddess. In Oriental symbols, Cancer becomes the sign of the tortoise. Pan or Hermes is said to have invented the tortoise-shell lyre. Music is said to exhibit cosmic harmony. The turtle shell is divided into 13 raised areas.

Traditions: The sign of the great universal fire (to dry-out the cosmic spring) caused by the depression of Mars and the exaltation of Jupiter.

The region of Japan exhibits the ancient Shinto belief, a religion of nature worship that venerates the spirits of mountains, springs, and trees. Colin Wilson, in the *Atlas of Holy Places*, reports that the wooden Royal Shinto Shrine at Ise is rebuilt every 20 years, as it has been for over 14 centuries. The sacred shrine is said to be dedicated to the sun goddess Amaterasu, yet her myth is connected with a sacred mirror, and the moon is the mirror of the sun's light. People born in this region have very moonlike faces.

In about 600 BC Solon of Athens (638–568 BC) heard the account of the island of Atlantis from the priests of the city of Sais in Egypt, who informed him that giant earthquakes destroyed Atlantis about 9,000 years ago (600 + 9,000 = 9600 BC). If we rewind the cycle of precession to 9600 BC, we find a position of 13.3 degrees in Cancer. This position is directly opposite to 13.3 degrees of Capricorn and the mid-Atlantic Ridge east of the mouth of the Amazon River—in other words, a very likely location for the original Island of Atlantis.

LEO (the heart of the cosmic body) (*ancient zodiac: donkey*) house of the Sun, triangle:

Aries, Leo, Sagittarius ruled by the Sun and Jupiter.

Geography: Leo commands the Bering Sea, North and South Pacific Ocean to New Zealand.

Leo is the Epoch of: The 12 labors of Hercules symbolize a cosmological odyssey. The lion skin is the talisman of Hercules.

Traditions: Leo is one of the houses of the triangle of solid signs, which are said to assist firm foundations and buildings that will last forever. All great megalithic structures possibly date from a period of Leo. Also, most renovations are possibly done during an era of the solid signs: Taurus, Leo, Scorpio, and Aquarius. Pyramids are said to be symbols of fire and possibly built during precessional periods of Leo, a solid and a fire sign, and the house of the sun.

VIRGO (*the belly, intestines, womb of the cosmic body*) (*ancient zodiac:* lion) solar house of Mercury, exaltation of Mercury, and triangle of *Taurus, Virgo, Capricorn* ruled by Venus and the moon

Geography: Virgo covers the region of the Pacific Ocean, Hawaii, and Alaska.

Virgo is the Epoch of: Virgo is the home of the Holy Virgin who holds the sheaf of wheat like the goddess Ceres. Virgo is the house of the Great Spirit and the Mother of the Universe. It is the residence of the avatars of Mercury, such as Agathodaemon (the Good Spirit), Thoth, and Hermes.

Traditions: Virgo may be the home of Air (Gr. Chaos) who combined with Darkness (Erebos) to create the children Light (Aither—the blue atmosphere) and Day (Hemera). Chaos is classed among the primordial deities. She is one of the "firstborn" (protogenoi) who are cosmological and elemental gods. Phoenicians symbolize the first creation by a serpent wrapped around an egg. Christian statues of the Blessed Virgin show her standing upon the globe with her foot upon a serpent's neck.

Images of the wise philosopher Buddha portray him as a person with large lower intestines. This is said to be a sign of fruitfulness and abundance. Yet, the astronomical sign of Virgo is related to the lower intestines of the cosmic figure. Therefore, a big lower belly is a code for intelligence, since Virgo is the exaltation of Mercury. Hermes-Mercury is the messenger of the gods. As Ganymede, he is also the cup-bearer of the gods.

LIBRA (*the reins, the forearms of the cosmic body*) (*ancient zodiac:* goat) house of Venus, exaltation of Saturn, the depression of the sun, the triangle: *Gemini, Libra, Aquarius* ruled by Saturn and Mercury.

Geography: Libra covers the geography of California, Baja, the western United States, and western Canada.

Libra is the Epoch of: the god Ocean as well as the home of the goddess Night (Gr. Nyx). This is the period of the fabled Golden Age of Libra when men, animals, and all of nature live in perfect balance and harmony. Possibly, a time of confrontation between heat and ice with a few select kingdoms surviving on the equator with a limited world population.

Traditions: Nonnos, in the *Dionysiaca* (I.493), tells that the giant monster Typhon, by a well-directed blow, cut out the sinews of Zeus. Typhon then steals the weapons and sinews of Zeus, which renders him ineffectual. Cadmus, in the character of Hermes-Cadmillos, tells Typhon that he needs sinews for the strings of his harp to play the beguiling music that Typhon likes to hear. Thus Cadmus tricks Typhon and recovers the sinews and lightning bolts of Zeus. On the image of the cosmic man, the sinews or reins are the forearms of the man, and they are associated with the sign of Libra.

One of the most horrifying images of a mythological deity must be "She of the Serpent Skirt," Coatlicue, the Earth-Mother goddess of Mexico. Libra is opposite to Aries, the sign of the head. Libra is therefore an anti-sign as "headless." The Earth goddess is represented as headless with two blood serpents springing from her severed neck, and these form a new face composed of these serpents facing one another and forming a wide-fanged mouth as each serpent forms one of her new eyes. Two other poorly preserved images of this goddess have also been found. If Coatlicue was adopted by the invading Aztec, who created this new cosmic mythology, it could be surmised that the Aztec came from the lands of western America and California, which lies under the auspices of Libra.

SCORPIO (*the secrets, the private parts of the cosmic body*) (*ancient zodiac:* bull) solar house of Mars, depression of the moon; triangle: *Cancer, Scorpio, Pisces* ruled by Mars, Venus, and the moon.

Geography: Central Canada, Middle America, Mexico, Yucatan, and Honduras.

The Epoch of Scorpio belongs to: Uranus, one of the first cosmologers and "Heaven-holders." Scorpio is the cosmic sign related to the genitalia, and therefore the myth about Uranus is that his son cuts off his genitals. In one of the legends of Noah, his sons had seen the "naked privates" of Noah who had fallen into a drunken sleep after inventing wine from grapes. Noah's wife is said to be Titea, who in Greek myth appears in Sagittarius, which follows the sign of Scorpio. This seems to reflect a cosmological pattern because Eve (Cancer) followed Adam (Gemini).

Traditions: Scorpio is connected with phallic worship, circumcision, and rites of ritual coition and sexual acts. Nowhere in the world have so many phallic images been found as in Mexico and the Yucatan, where they perform blood-letting and sacrifice by piercing their penis. Phallic stones are everywhere. These are universally carved into the stones as circumcised male organs. Many of these icons were broken and hidden by the Spanish. Here, too, circumcision has been practiced from the beginning of time.

Miller and Taube (p. 132) speak of the Mesoamerican "sky-holder" Pauahtun, who maintained the cosmic balance of the world upon his shoulders. Miller and Taube cannot understand why, "Ironically, although he bears the weighty office of supporting the sky, he is frequently portrayed as a drunken and lecherous old man, hardly a paragon of security and responsibility." Of course, Uranus was one of the first "heaven-holders" and his wife, Ge, the mother of Giants (Ge-gantes = Earth-born). Scorpio is most probably also the home of the ithyphallic Ptah and Hephaestus.

The Egyptian Seth cuts the body of Osiris into 72 parts, which he makes his co-conspirators eat to share in his guilt. However, Seth throws the male organ of Osiris into the delta waters of the Nile, the symbol for the Milky Way. Later on, Horus, the son of Osiris, avenges his father by cutting off Seth's genitals. There is a saying in Egypt that there are some events so ancient that they precede the history of the time when Seth lost his testicles and Horus lost his eye in the fight between them.

This land of Scorpio spawns the infamous monster hurricanes of the Caribbean and tornadoes of Tornado Alley in North America. The largest and most powerful caldera on the planet is located in Yellowstone National Park, located under Scorpio.

SAGITTARIUS (*the thighs of the cosmic body*) (*ancient zodiac:* falcon) solar house of Jupiter, triangle: *Aries, Leo, Sagittarius* ruled by the sun and Jupiter

Geography: The East Coast of North America and the greater part of South America minus the Atlantic tip of Brazil. Half of Costa Rica and Panama are on the borders of Scorpio and Sagittarius upon the line of the black hole at the center of the Milky Way Galaxy. Costa Rica is noted for its gigantic precision-milled granite spheres said to demarcate important places on the globe and to have been part of an ancient nautical school and observatory.

The Epoch of Sagittarius belongs to: Sagittarius is the home of Ra-Atum (the Ennead of Heliopolis), the home of Helios and the Hundred-Handed, and the home of Titea and his wife Idea, who produce the Great Titians. It is also the home of Dionysos, Bacchus, the vine and the grapes. It is also the place of Chiron, who is said to be the original image of Sagittarius.

The Andean people say that Jupiter is the guardian of the empire and provinces of Peru (K&M, p. 464). Zeus cuts open his thigh (cosmic symbol of Sagittarius) to incubate Bacchus-Dionysius. This Dionysius destroyed the "serpent-headed or serpent-haired" Typhon.

Tradition: Sagittarius is *the Black Hole, the Gran or Grieta Oscura,* the matrix and center of the Milky Way Galaxy. The region of Sagittarius intersects the powerful Milky Way. Here are the second-tallest mountains in the world, glaciers and water sources for this side of the planet. The Milky Way also intersects with Gemini (which lies directly opposite to Sagittarius) and has the highest mountains on the planet as well as the most significant water resources and an abundance of glaciers for this side of the planet.

At the Coricancha, temple of the sun at Cusco, the daily ritual revolved around an image of the sun in the form of a solid-gold year-old baby whose description "sounded suspiciously like that of the Catholic Christ Child" (Hemming and Ranney, p. 79). Cusco is triangular to Jerusalem in Aries.

CAPRICORN (*the knees of the cosmic body*) (*ancient zodiac:* ape) solar house of Saturn, exaltation of Mars, depression of Jupiter, triangle: *Taurus, Virgo, Capricorn* ruled by Venus and the Moon. The goat-fish, Capricorn, was replaced in India by *makara,* the crocodile (K&M, p. 498).

Geography: Capricorn covers the region of the mid-Atlantic Ocean, the eastern regions of Brazil, Greenland, and western Iceland. This is the ancient territory of the mythical Island of Atlantis.

The Epoch of Capricorn belongs to: Agathodaemon, Cyclopes, Shu and Tefnut.

Traditions: Capricorn is the sign of the great world flood, the deluge (after the drought of the cosmic autumn caused by the exaltation of Mars and the depression of Jupiter.) After the great flood, Agathodaemon (the second Hermes-Mercury) translated the sacred works of Thoth (the first Hermes-Mercury) who had written his works on stone that they might be recovered after the deluge.

Dupuis says (p. 134) that the destruction of the Giants (of Scorpio) and the Titians (of Sagittarius) were avenged by Jupiter (Capricorn is the depression of Jupiter) through the destruction of the ancient world by the deluge. There are images as Chalchiutlicue, the water goddess of the Age of the Deluge (Taube, p. 35, *Codex Borbonicus*). It appears that the flood is generated from the "G images" (symbols of the Milky Way Galaxy), which generate the massive flow of water that carries the people along with it. This is another validation that the Legend of the Five Suns concerns the cycle of the rotation of the Milky Way Galaxy.

AQUARIUS (*the legs of the cosmic body*) (*ancient zodiac:* ibis) lunar house of Saturn, triangle: *Gemini, Libra, Aquarius* ruled by Saturn and Mercury. The water-carrier was depicted as a simple pot by the Egyptians (K&M, p. 498).

Geography: The Atlantic Ocean, Ireland, Iceland, England, Western Europe and Africa

The Epoch of Aquarius belongs to: The home of Geb and Nut of the Ennead of Heliopolis. The home of Cronus and Rhea, Iapetus and Asia, Atlas and Pleione, and also the Lesser Titians

Traditions: Diodorus Siculus tells us that Atlas was born in Morocco and that Saturn was his brother, who became lord of Italy. The authors of *Ancient Skies* (K&M, p. 273) tell us that the native populations of North Africa—the Berbers, Moors, Mycenaean Greeks, Phoenicians at Carthage, Romans, and all people who settled in northwestern Africa—identified Saturn as their principal deity. Cronus/Saturn is lord of the house of Aquarius. Kelley and Milone (p. 486) report that Middle Eastern astrologers associated Saturn with the Jewish people. Jews have lived in Portugal, Spain, and North Africa since ancient times and have associated with the Phoenicians especially during the reign of King Solomon.

CONCLUSION Cosmo-geo-symbol dating attempts to connect astronomical and astrological symbols, history, and myth with the cultures in specific regions of the globe according to a synthesis of the cycle of the Milky Way related to and imposed upon the geography of the world.

BIBLIOGRAPHY

———. *The Holy Bible, King James Version*. New York: The American Bible Society, Est. 1816.

———. *The New Testament, Greek-English edition*. London: Samuel Bagster & Sons, 1862.

Allen, J.H. *Judah's Sceptre and Joseph's Birthright*. Merrimac, Massachusetts: Destiny Publishers, 1902.

Alouf, Michel M. *History of Baalbek*. Escondido, California: The Book Tree, 1999.

Apollodorus. *The Library*. Translated by Sir J.G. Frazer. Harvard, MA: Loeb Classical Library, 1963.

Asimov, Isaac. *Biographical Encyclopedia of Science and Technology*. London: Pan Books, 1975.

Aston, W.G. *Nihongi, Chronicles of Japan from the Earliest Times to A.D. 697*. Tokyo, Japan: Tuttle Company, 1975.

Aveni, Anthony F. *Skywatchers*. Austin, Texas: University of Texas Press, 2001.

Awe, Jaime. *Maya Cities and Sacred Caves*. Belize: Cubola Productions, 2006.

Babcock, William H. *Legendary Islands of the Atlantic*. Glen Arm, MD: The Sourcebook Project, 1922.

Bauval, Robert. *The Egypt Code.* New York, New York: The Disinformation Co., 2008.

Bermann, Marc. *Lukurmata, Household Archaeology in Prehispanic Bolivia.* Princeton, N.J: Princeton University Press, 1994.

Bierhorst, John. *History and Mythology of the Aztecs, the Codex Chimalpopoca.* Tucson: Universtiy of Arizona Press, 1992.

Binding, Paul. *Imagined Corners, Exploring the World's First Atlas.* London: Headline Books, 2003.

Boll, Franz. *Sphaera, Neue Griechische Texte und Untersuchungen zur Geschichte der Sternbilder.* Leipzig, Germany: B.G. Teubner, 1903.

Cassinelli, Dennis. *Gathering Traces of the Great Basin Indians.* Reno, Nevada: Western Book/Journal Press, 1996.

Carew, Mairead. *Tara and the Ark of the Covenant.* Dublin, Ireland: The Discovery Programme/Royal Irish Academy, 2003.

Coe, William R. *Tikal, A Handbook of the Ancient Maya Ruins.* Philadelphia: University of Pennsylvania Press, 1967.

Conty, Patrick. *The Genesis and Geometry of the Labyrinth.* Rochester, VT: Inner Traditions, 2002.

Corliss, William R. *Ancient Infrastructure.* Glen Arm, MD: The Sourcebook Project, 1999.

Corliss, William R. *Ancient Structures.* Glen Arm, MD: The Sourcebook Project, 2001.

Corliss, William R. *Biological Anomalies: Humans I.* Glen Arm, MD: The Sourcebook Project, 1992.

Corliss, William R. *Earthquakes, Tides, Unidentified Sounds.* Glen Arm, MD: The Sourcebook Project, 1983.

Corliss, William R. publisher: *Science Frontiers* and *The Anomaly Register.* Bi-monthly newsletters. Glen Arm, MD: The Sourcebook Project, various years.

Corliss, William R. *Stars, Galaxies, Cosmos.* Glenn Arm, MD: The Sourcebook Project, 1987.

Cory, Preston and Hodges, E.R. *Phoenician, Carthaginian, Babylonian, and Egyptian Fragments.* Reeves & Turner. London 1876.

Cremo, Michael. *Forbidden Archaeology & the Hidden History of the Human Race.* Los Angeles: Bhaktivedanta Books, 1999.

de Landa, Diego. *Yucatan, before and after the Conquest.* Trans. W. Gates. New York: Dover Publications, 1978.

De Roo, Peter. *History of America before Columbus.* Philadelphia: J.B. Lippincott Co., 1900.

De Santillana, Giorgio and Hertha von Dechend. *Hamlet's Mill, An Essay Investigating the Origins of Human Knowledge and its Transmission through Myth.* Boston: Godine, 1977.

Dietrich, Thomas Karl. *The Origin of Culture and Civilization.* Austin, TX: Turnkey Press, 2005.

Diodorus Sicilus. *History.* Trans. C.H. Oldfather. Harvard, MA: Loeb Classical Library, 1968.

Dupuis, Charles Francois. *The Origin of All Religious Worship—Memoires sur l'Origine des Constellations et sur l'Explication de la Fable par l' Astronomie. 1781. On the Origin of the Constellations and the Explanation of Fable through Astronomy.* The Scholarly Publishing Office. The University of Michigan, Ann Arbor. 1872.

Duran, Fray Diego and Heyden Doris. *El Templo Mayor de Tenochtitlan en la Obra de Fray Diego Duran.* Mexico City: Instituto Nacional de Antropología e Historia, 2000.

Dunn, Christopher. *Giza Power Plant, Technologies of Ancient Egypt.* Rochester, VT: Bear & Company, 1998.

Dunn, Christopher. *Lost Technologies of Ancient Egypt.* Rochester, VT: Bear & Company, 2010.

Elst, Koenraad. *Update on the Aryan Invasion Debate.* New Delhi, India: Aditya Prakashan, 1999.

Erikson, George & Ivar Zapp. *Atlantis in America.* Kempton, IL: Adventures Unlimited Press, 1998.

Erlich, Avi. *Ancient Zionism: The Biblical Origins of the National Idea.* No city: Free Press. 1994.

Finn, James. *Sephardim, History of the Jews in Spain and Portugal.* London: Rivington, 1841.

Fix, William. *Pyramid Odyssey.* New York: Mayflower Books, 1978.

Frawley, Dr. David. *The Milky Way and the Cosmic Soma.* Scriptu.com. 2009

Freidel, David, Linda Schele, and Joy Parker. *Maya Cosmos.* New York: William Morrow & Co., 1993.

Frisbee, Jerome Bernard. *King Solomon's Temple.* Phoenixmasonry.org 2009.

Gardner, Laurence. *Bloodline of the Holy Grail.* Shaftesbury, Dorset, UK: Element, 1996.

Godwin, Joscelyn, *Robert Fludd, the Hermetic Philosopher and Surveyor of Two Worlds.*

Grand Rapids, MI: Phanes Press, 1991.

Grant, Edward. *God and Reason in the Middle Ages.* Cambridge, MA: Cambridge UP, 2001.

Grant, John. *Discarded Science, Ideas That Seemed Good at the Time.* Turnaround Publishers: Wisley, Surrey. 2006.

Grey, Martin—website: sacredsites.com. *Sacred Earth, Places of Peace and Power.* Sterling Publishers: 2007. Noted photographer.

Habu, Junko. *Ancient Jomon of Japan.* Cambridge, UK: Cambridge University Press, 2004.

Hadingham, Evan. *Early Man and the Cosmos.* Norman, OK: University of Oklahoma Press, 1984.

Hagan, Helene E. *The Shining Ones: An Etymological Essay on the Amazing Roots of Egyptian Civilization.* No city: Xlibris Corporation, 2000.

Hancock, Graham. *Fingerprints of the Gods.* New York: Three Rivers Press, 1995.

Hancock, Graham. *Underworld, the Mysterious Origins of Civilization.* New York: Three Rivers Press, 2002.

Hapgood, Charles H. *Maps of the Ancient Sea Kings: Evidence of Advanced Civilization in the Ice Age.* Kempton, IL: Adventures Unlimited Press, 1996.

Harbison, Peter. *Irish Art and Architecture.* London: Thames and Hudson, 1978.

Harrison, Peter D. *The Lords of Tikal.* London: Thames and Hudson, 1999.

Heath, Richard. *Matrix of Creation.* Rochester, VT: Inner Traditions, 2002.

Heath, Robin and John Michell. *The Lost Science of Measuring the Earth.* Kempton, IL: Adventures Unlimited Press, 2006.

Hemming, John and Edward Ranney. *Monuments of the Incas.* Albuquerque: University of New Mexico Press, 1982.

Hesiod. *Theogony.* Trans. H.G. Evelyn-White. Harvard, MA: Loeb Classical Library, 1977.

Hoyle, Sir Fred. *The Origin of the Universe and the Origin of Religion.* London: The Frick Collection, 1993.

INAH productions. Instituto Nacional de Antropologia e Historia. *Archaeological Mexico.* Mexico City: Monclem Ediciones, no date.

INAH productions. Instituto Nacional de Antropologia e Historia. *Great Temple of Tenochititlan.* Mexico City: Monclem Ediciones, 2003.

INAH productions. Instituto Nacional de Antropologia e Historia. *Mexico City.* Mexico City: Monclem Ediciones, 1999.

INAH productions. Instituto Nacional de Antropologia e Historia. *Museum of the Great Temple.* Mexico City: Monclem Ediciones, 2003.

INAH productions. Instituto Nacional de Antropologia e Historia. *Teotihuacan, History, Art and Monuments.* Mexico City: Monclem Ediciones, 1995.

INAH productions. Instituto Nacional de Antropologia e Historia. *Yucatan and Its Archaeogical Sites.* Mexico City: Monclem Ediciones, no date.Irwin, Constance. *Fair Gods and Stone Faces.* New York: St. Martin's Press, 1963.

Johnson, Anthony. *Solving Stonehenge, the New Key to and Ancient Enigma.* London: Thames & Hudson, 2008.

Johnson, Charles William. *The Aztec Calendar, Math and Design.* Chicago: Gyldan Edge Publishing, 2004.

Johnson, Charles William. *Hindu-Vedic Astronomy.* Earthmatrix.com. 2006

Joseph, Frank. *Discovering the Mysteries of Ancient America.* Franklin Lakes, NJ: New Page/Career Press, Inc., 2006.

Joseph, Frank. *The Lost Treasure of King Juba.* Rochester, VT: Bear & Company, 2003.

Josephus. *Jewish Antiquities.* London: Harvard Press (Loeb Classical Library), 1978.

Keating, Rev. Jeoffry. *General History of Ireland.* Dublin, Ireland: James Duffy, 1861.

Kelley, David H. and Eugene F. Milone. *Exploring Ancient Skies, An Encyclopedic Survey of Archaeoastronomy.* New York: Springer Science & Business Media, 2005.

Kelly, D.H., Trans. *Book of Fenagh.* Dublin, Ireland: Stationary Office, 1939.

Kilian or Caillin, Saint. *The Book of Fenagh.* Dublin, Ireland: Alexander Thom, 1875.

Kurlansky, Mark. *The Basque History of the World.* Middlesex, England: Penguin Books, 1999.

LaViolette, Paul A. *Genesis of the Cosmos.* Rochester, VT: Bear & Company, 1995.

Livio, Mario. *The Golden Ratio, the Story of Phi.* New York: Broadway Books, 2002.

Lockyer, J. Norman. *The Dawn of Astronomy.* Cambridge, MA: The M.I.T. Press, 1960.

Lougheed, Vivien. *Adventure Guide Belize.* Edison, NJ: Hunter Publishing, 2007.

Manetho. *Aegyptiaca.* Translated by W. G. Waddell. London: William Heinemann Ltd., 1971.

Mann, Charles C. *1491, New Revelations of the Americas before Columbus.* New York: Alfred Knopf, 2005.

Mannikka, Eleanor. *Angkor Wat; Time, Space, and Kingship.* Honolulu: University of Hawaii Press, 2000.

Martineau, John. *A Little Book of Coincidence, Pattern in the Solar System.* New York: Wooden Books, Walker & Co., 2001.

Martineau, John. *Quadrivium, the Four Classical Liberal Arts of Number, Geometry, Music, and Cosmology.* New York: Walker & Co., 2010.

Mavor, James W. Jr. *Manitou, The Sacred Landscape of New England's Native Civilization.* Rochester, VT: Inner Traditions, 1989.

Men, Hunbatz, *Secrets of Mayan Science & Religion.* Santa Fe: Bear & Company, 1990.

Mercier, Alloa Patricia. *Los Secretos de Los Chamanes Mayas.* Barcelona, Spain: Ediciones Luciérnaga, 2009.

Milbrath, Susan. *Star Gods of the Maya.* Austin, TX: University of Texas Press, 1999.

Miller, Crichton E. M. *The Golden Thread of Time.* Rugby, UK: Pendulum Publishing, 2001.

Miller, Mary and Karl Taube. *An Illustrated Dictionary of the Gods and Symbols of Ancient Mexico and the Maya.* London: Thames & Hudson, 1993.

Miller, Mary, Simon Martin, and Kathleen Berrin. *Courtly Art of the Ancient Maya.* Fine Arts Museums of San Francisco. London: Thames & Hudson, 2004.

Miller, Mary. *Maya Art and Architecture.* London: Thames & Hudson, 1999.

Morton, Chris and Ceri Louise Thomas. *The Mystery of the Crystal Skulls.* Rochester, VT: Bear & Co., 1997.

Mustafa, Mohamed. *Egypt Tourist Guide,* Egyptian Media Center. 1998

Nienhuis, James. *Ice Age Civilizations.* Houston: GenesisVeracity, 2006.

Nonnos. *Dionysiaca.* Trans. W.H.D. Rouse. Harvard, MA: Loeb Classical Library, 1963.

Ogren, Thomas L. *Safe Sex in the Garden.* Berkeley, CA: Ten Speed Press, 2003.

Oommen, Anitha, Tom Mainker, and Aninash Mainker. *Study of significant correlation between hand length and foot length (p<0.0001).* Internet Sept. 2010.

Petrie, George. *The Rediscovery of Ireland's Past.* Kinsale, Ireland: Crawford Art Gallery (Cork & Gandon Editions), 2004.

Petrie, W.M. Flinders. *The Religion of Ancient Egypt.* London: Archibald Constable, 1908.

Pinkham, M.A. *Guardians of the Holy Grail.* Kempton, IL: Adventures Unlimited, 2004.

Ptolemy, *Tetrabiblos.* Translated by F.E. Robbins. London: William Heinemann Ltd., 1971.

Rowse, A.L. *The Tower of London in the History of the Nation.* London: Weidenfeld & Nicolson, 1972.

Saward, Jeff. *Labyrinths and Mazes, A Complete Guide to Magical Paths of the World.* New York: Lark Books, 2003.

Seneca. *Naturales Quaestiones* in ten volumes. Translated by T.H. Corcoran. Cambridge, MA: Harvard UP,1971.

Shugarts, David A. *Secrets of the Widow's Son.* London: Orion Books, 2006.

Schele, Linda, David Freidel, and Joy Parker. *Maya Cosmos.* New York: William Morrow & Co., 1993.

Schliemann, Heinrich. *Abenteuer Meines Lebens.* Leipzig, Germany: F.A. Brockhaus Verlag, 1958.

Schwaller de Lubicz, Isha. *Journey into the Light.* Rochester, VT: Inner Traditions, 1984.

Schwaller de Lubicz, R.A. *The Temple in Man, Sacred Architecture and the Perfect Man.* New York: Inner Traditions International, 1960.

Schwaller de Lubicz, R.A. *The Temples of Karnak.* Rochester, VT: Inner Traditions, 1999.

Snobelen, Stephen D. 'The mystery of this restitution of all things': Isaac Newton on the return of the Jews". In *The millenarian turn: millenarian contexts of science, politics, and everyday Anglo-American life in the seventeenth and eighteenth centuries,* ed. James E. Force and Richard H. Popkin. Dordrecht: Kluwer, 2001, 95-118.

Sora, Steven. *Secret Societies of America's Elite.* Rochester, VT: Destiny Books, 2003.

Taube, Karl. *Aztec and Maya Myths.* Austin, TX: University of Texas Press, 1997.

Thom, Alexander. *Megalithic Sites in Britain.* Oxford, England: Clarendon Press, 1967.

Thomas, N.L. *Irish Symbols of 3500 BC.* Dublin, Ireland: Mercier Press, 1988.

Tompkins, Peter. *Secrets of the Great Pyramid.* New York: Penguin, 1973.

Tompkins, Peter. *Mysteries of the Mexican Pyramids.* New York: Harper & Row, 1976.

Turk, Jon. *In the Wake of the Jomon, Stone Age Mariners and a Voyage across the Pacific.* Camden, Maine: International Marine/ McGraw-Hill, 2005.

Underwood, Guy. *The Pattern of the Past.* Surrey, England: Pitman Publishing, 1969.

Vance, Rob. *Secrets of the Stones: Decoding Ireland's Lost Past.* Dublin, Ireland: Ashfield Press, 2009.

Villena, Carlos Milla. *Genesis de La Cultura Andina.* Lima, Peru: Talleres Graficos Nelly, 2008.

Wasserman, James. *Art and Symbols of the Occult, Images of Power and Wisdom.* Rochester, VT: Destiny Books, 1993.

Westrem, Scott D. *The Hereford Map.* Turnhout, Belgium: Brepols, 2001.

Wiesenthal, Simon. *Sails of Hope, The Secret Mission of Christopher Columbus.* Translated by R & C Winston. New York: Macmilla1973.n Publishing,

Wilson, Colin and Rand Flem-Ath. *The Atlantis Blueprint.* New York: Delta Trade Paperbacks, 2000.

Wilson, J. *Our Israelitish Origin :Lectures on Ancient Israel, and the Modern Nations of Europe.* London: James Nisbet & Co., no year given.

Witkowski, Igor. *Axis of the World.* Kempton, IL: Adventures Unlimited, 2008.